Frames for Undergraduates

STUDENT MATHEMATICAL LIBRARY
Volume 40

Frames for Undergraduates

Deguang Han
Keri Kornelson
David Larson
Eric Weber

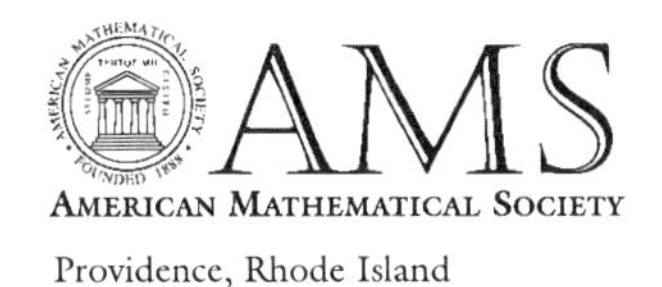

American Mathematical Society
Providence, Rhode Island

2000 *Mathematics Subject Classification*. Primary 47-01, 42-01, 15-01, 42C15, 15A60, 41-01, 47A05, 47A30.

For additional information and updates on this book, visit
www.ams.org/bookpages/stml-40

Library of Congress Cataloging-in-Publication Data

Frames for undergraduates / Deguang Han ... [et al.].
p. cm. — (Student mathematical library, ISSN 1520-9121 ; v. 40)
Includes bibliographical references and index
ISBN 978-0-8218-4212-6 (alk. paper)
1. Frames (Vector analysis) I. Han, Deguang, 1959–

QA433.F73 2007
515′.63–dc22 2007060796

∞ The paper used in this book is acid-free and falls within the guidelines established to ensure permanence and durability.
Visit the AMS home page at http://www.ams.org/

10 9 8 7 6 5 4 3 2 1 12 11 10 09 08 07

Contents

Preface for Instructors

This book is intended to provide an introduction to finite frames, presented at a level suitable for students in the later stages of their undergraduate studies. This book evolved from the results of Deguang Han and Dave Larson in [**42**], which formed the kernel for material about frames presented in an NSF-sponsored REU (Research Experience for Undergraduates) at Texas A&M University entitled *Matrix Analysis and Wavelets*. The REU was led by Dave Larson while Eric Weber and Keri Kornelson acted as mentors and co-instructors.

The REU students found frames particularly enticing because the questions can be approached using techniques from linear algebra and geometry. They were excited by the fact that there are interesting open questions regarding frames in finite dimensions, and even more enthusiastic once they realized that frames have widespread applications to a variety of mathematical, scientific, and industrial problems. We wished to develop a resource which would help undergraduate students gain access to this burgeoning area of mathematics.

The study of finite frames provides an excellent, highly motivating framework (pardon the pun) in which to introduce the essentials of matrix analysis and the rudiments of finite-dimensional operator theory. Students learn the mathematical theory while simultaneously seeing how operator theory is used to develop a body of results about frames. Many of the 50 or so students who have participated in our REU site over the past six years have found this pure/applied approach to matrix analysis exciting, especially when the applied feature led to publishable new results.

The prerequisites we would recommend for this book are a one-semester course in college level linear algebra, and a one-semester proof-oriented course in analysis. The analysis course is primarily a maturity requirement, in the sense that a student should be well acquainted with reading and creating mathematical proofs.

We have written this book with three sorts of usages in mind.

(1) This book can serve as the primary text for an undergraduate special-topics course on frames. An early draft was used very successfully at Grinnell College in such a course. Students who already have a second course in linear algebra might skim over Chapters 1 and 2 fairly quickly, while students having less linear algebra experience might need to spend more time in these chapters. In either case, such a course might start in Chapter 3, flipping back to the previous chapters as needed for review or to learn a necessary new topic. In this case, one could reasonably complete Chapters 3, 4, 5, 6, and selected sections from Chapters 7, 8, and 9 in a one-semester course.

(2) We realize that not every mathematics curriculum contains a special topics course for undergraduate students. This book would also serve very well for a second course in linear algebra, using frames as an application to demonstrate the new theory. The instructor could spend time carefully going through the topics in the first two chapters before introducing frames. This course might reasonably cover Chapters 1, 2, 3 (sections 3.1 through 3.5), 4, 5, and 6 with a few selected sections as time permits from the other chapters.

(3) Because this book was so heavily motivated by our REU experiences, we naturally intended it to be a resource for summer research students as they learn about frame theory and matrix analysis. The method used in the Texas A&M REU was to send the text to students before the start of the

> summer program, so that they could start reading and working out the exercises in the first three chapters. Once the program started up, the mentors gave lectures over the key ideas and topics in the material. Students used the text as a reference as they began working on research problems. We also found that the more advanced students in the program began volunteering to present lectures.

The chapter entitled *Student Presentations* is intended to give a tutorial on a selection of topics, in such a way that good students can learn and compose individual or small group presentations on the topics. For instance, one of these is a detailed exposition on the proof of the Polar Decomposition Theorem in finite dimensions. In this way, students can get involved in the class by actually giving lectures on important topics. The presenters gain valuable experience communicating a technical proof to their peers, while giving the other students a change of style and pace from the instructor's lectures.

The last chapter, *Anecdotes*, tells some stories about different types of students as they learn about frames. With these, we intend to offer snapshots of the various settings – classrooms, REU programs, independent studies – in which we find students excited by this subject. The authors welcome your feedback and suggestions. We'd also enjoy hearing your "anecdotes", since we were able to share ours with you.

Deguang Han
Keri Kornelson
David Larson
Eric Weber

Acknowledgements

Our decision to write this book arose from the success of a series of graduate seminars, VIGRE courses, and the NSF REU *Matrix Analysis and Wavelets* at Texas A&M University over the years 1997-2006. We wish to express our thanks to the National Science Foundation and to the Mathematics Department at Texas A&M University for the resources which enabled these seminars, courses, and REU programs to take place.

The students who took part in these activities at Texas A&M University helped to shape our vision and understanding about frame theory. As we lectured, mentored, and answered questions, the ideas which are present in this book were taking form. Students who gave presentations or worked on research projects related to this material helped us to adapt the material to be useful for undergraduate students. We heartily express our thanks to all of these students.

Preliminary versions of this book have been used in REU programs, seminars, and courses at Texas A&M University, the University of Central Florida, the University of Iowa, Iowa State University, and Grinnell College. Students in these programs have found errors and oversights, worked out the exercises, discovered duplications or inconsistencies, and given us valuable feedback on the book. We greatly appreciate their contributions. We particularly recognize the assistance of Nga Nguyen with the material in Chapter 4 and Section 10.5.

We are grateful to Troy Henderson, who lent his superior technical expertise to improve the figures in this book.

A number of postdoctoral fellows, visiting scholars, and regular faculty members helped the authors to mentor REU and VIGRE students at Texas A&M University during one or more years. We take this opportunity to thank Ken Dykema, Dan Jupiter, Robin Harte, Marc Ordower, David Redett, and Nico Spronk.

Thanks also to Julien Giol, Jimmy Dillies, David Kerr, and Thomas Schlumprecht, for participating in a working seminar on frames and operator algebras at Texas A&M University with Dave Larson during 2005–2007, and for their comments concerning the near-final version of this REU book. Thanks to Karen Shuman for her careful reading and editing of tricky passages.

Introduction

Consider two finite sequences of vectors in the plane $\mathbb{R}^2$,

$$A = \left\{ \begin{bmatrix} 1 \\ 0 \end{bmatrix}, \begin{bmatrix} 0 \\ 1 \end{bmatrix} \right\} \text{ and } B = \left\{ \sqrt{\frac{2}{3}} \begin{bmatrix} 1 \\ 0 \end{bmatrix}, \sqrt{\frac{2}{3}} \begin{bmatrix} -\frac{1}{2} \\ \frac{\sqrt{3}}{2} \end{bmatrix}, \sqrt{\frac{2}{3}} \begin{bmatrix} -\frac{1}{2} \\ -\frac{\sqrt{3}}{2} \end{bmatrix} \right\}$$

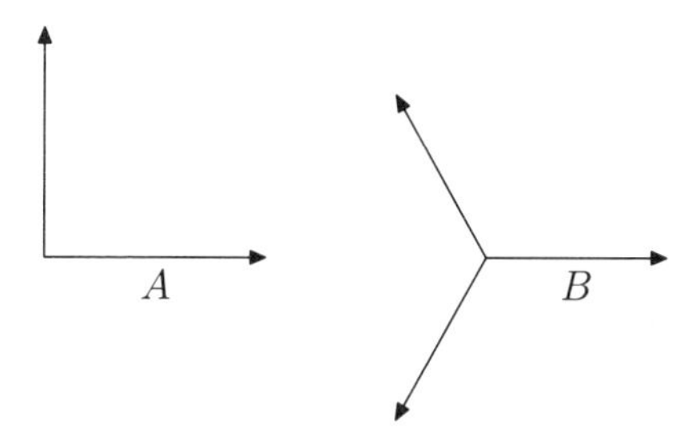

The sequence A is an orthonormal basis (ONB) for $\mathbb{R}^2$, and it has certain properties which we recall from calculus and linear algebra. The sequence B is a bit different. Let us compare the two.

- Both A and B are spanning sets for $\mathbb{R}^2$, so every $x \in \mathbb{R}^2$ can be written as a linear combination of the vectors in A, and similarly for the vectors in B.
- The vectors in A are linearly independent, so the coefficients in the linear expansion $x = c_1 \begin{bmatrix} 1 \\ 0 \end{bmatrix} + c_2 \begin{bmatrix} 0 \\ 1 \end{bmatrix}$, where $c_i \in \mathbb{R}$,

are unique. The vectors in B are not linearly independent, so a linear expansion would not be unique.

- The vectors in A all have length 1. The vectors in B all have length $\sqrt{\frac{2}{3}}$.
- The vectors in A are orthogonal (i.e., their dot product is zero). The vectors in B are not orthogonal.
- The coefficients $\{c_i\}_{i=1}^2$ for a linear expansion in the sequence A can be computed easily using the dot product. Specifically, let $x = c_1e_1 + c_2e_2$ where the vectors in A are denoted e_1 and e_2. The coefficients are computed by the dot products $c_i = x \cdot e_i$ for $i = 1, 2$. This is a property of orthonormal bases. If we check, however, we find that one way to write x as a linear combination of the vectors in B can be found using the coefficients formed by taking the same dot products. In other words, if we denote the vectors of B by f_1, f_2, f_3 and given some $x \in \mathbb{R}^2$ we take $d_i = x \cdot f_i$ for $i = 1, 2, 3$, then $x = d_1f_1 + d_2f_2 + d_3f_3$. Even without being orthogonal or linearly independent, the set B retains one of the extremely useful features of an orthonormal basis.
- Both A and B satisfy a property which is known as Parseval's identity for orthonormal bases. In the case of sequence A, this is a version of the Pythagorean Theorem. Let $\|x\|$ denote the length, or norm, of the vector x. Then,

  $$\|x\|^2 = \sum_{i=1}^{2} c_i^2 = \sum_{i=1}^{3} d_i^2.$$

  Again, we see that even though B is not even a basis, and certainly not an orthonormal basis for $\mathbb{R}^2$, it maintains an important characteristic of an ONB.

Both sequences A and B are examples of a particular type of *frame*, called a Parseval frame, for the vector space $\mathbb{R}^2$. Sequence B demonstrates that many of the properties of an orthonormal basis can be achieved by nonbases. This is exactly the motivation behind the study of frames. Frames are more general than orthonormal bases, but can often maintain some of the interesting and useful characteristics of ONBs.

The property that makes orthonormal bases desirable in many applications is that we can find the (unique) expansion coefficients for a vector by taking inner products (dot products in $\mathbb{R}^n$ or $\mathbb{C}^n$). This requires fewer computations than matrix inversion, and is numerically more stable. Let's say you want to send a signal across some kind of communication system, perhaps by talking on your wireless phone or sending a photo to your mom over the internet. We think of that signal as a vector in a vector space. The way it gets transmitted is as a sequence of coefficients which represent the signal in terms of a spanning set. If that spanning set is an ONB, then computing those coefficients just involves finding some dot products of vectors, which a computer can accomplish very quickly. As a result, there is not a significant time delay in sending your voice or the photograph. This is a good feature for a communication system to have, so orthonormal bases are used a lot in such situations.

Orthogonality is a very restrictive property, though. What if one of the coefficients representing a vector gets lost in transmission? That piece of information cannot be reconstructed. It is lost. Perhaps we'd like our system to have some redundancy, so that if one piece gets lost, the information can be pieced together from what does get through. This is where frames come in. Generally, a frame for a finite-dimensional vector space is just a spanning set for the vector space. In particular, it need not be a basis, which would require linear independence. Where frames get interesting is that we can find certain frames that retain that very handy ONB property – that we can find the coefficients for expanding vectors using the dot product instead of matrix inversion. We can retain the quick computation time found in ONBs while not restricting ourselves in number, norms, or linear independence.

By using a frame instead of an ONB, we do give up the uniqueness of the coefficients and the orthogonality of the vectors. In many circumstances, however, these properties are superfluous. If you are sending your side of a phone conversation or a photo, what matters is quickly computing a working set of expansion coefficients, not whether those coefficients are unique. In fact, in some settings the linear independence and orthogonality restrictions inhibit the use of ONBs. Frames can be constructed with a wider variety of characteristics, and can thus be tailored to match the needs of a particular system.

This book gives an introduction to the study of frames to undergraduate students who have had a course in linear algebra and a proof-based course in analysis. The first chapter is a review of some concepts from linear algebra, while the second chapter covers more advanced matrix and finite-dimensional operator theory. The discussion of frames begins in Chapter 3. A student can study the chapters in order, but may wish to jump right into Chapter 3 and flip back to the earlier chapters as needed.

We consider Chapters 7, 8, and 9 to be advanced topics. The first two of these describe more theoretical results in the theory of frames, while the last demonstrates how frames are applied to actual problems in sampling theory.

Chapter 1

Linear Algebra Review

The purpose of this chapter is to review some fundamental concepts and results from linear algebra and matrix theory that will be needed in the main chapters of this book. A wide variety of additional resources is available for students who want a more detailed or more advanced treatment of these topics. In particular, we refer the reader to [**4**] and [**45**]. The exercises at the end of this chapter are intended to remind the reader of some of the skills learned in their first semester of linear algebra. If a student can work his or her way through these exercises, with accuracy and understanding, then Chapter 1 can be skipped except for gaining familiarity with our notation.

1.1. Vector Spaces

We will consider vector spaces over the real numbers $\mathbb{R}$ or the complex numbers $\mathbb{C}$. We will use the notation $\mathbb{F}$ when the result being stated holds for both $\mathbb{R}$ and $\mathbb{C}$. Elements of $\mathbb{F}$ are called *scalars*.

Given $\alpha \in \mathbb{C}$, we will denote the complex conjugate of α by $\overline{\alpha}$ and the modulus of α by $|\alpha|$.

Definition 1.1. A *vector space* $\mathcal{V}$ is a nonempty set with two operations: addition " $+$ " and multiplication " $\cdot$ " by scalars such that the following conditions are satisfied for any $x, y, z \in \mathcal{V}$ and any α, β in $\mathbb{F}$.

(i) $x + y = y + x$.

(ii) $(x + y) + z = x + (y + z)$.

(iii) $x + z = y$ has a unique solution z for each pair (x, y).

(iv) $\alpha(\beta x) = (\alpha\beta)x$.

(v) $(\alpha + \beta)x = \alpha x + \beta x$.

(vi) $\alpha(x + y) = \alpha x + \alpha y$.

(vii) $1x = x$.

Elements of a vector space are called *vectors.* For any vector space $\mathcal{V}$, there exists a unique vector z such that $z + x = x$ for all $x \in \mathcal{V}$. This vector z is called the *zero vector* of $\mathcal{V}$ and will be denoted by 0. The *trivial* vector space is the space $\{0\}$ consisting of the zero vector alone. Another typical example of a vector space is Euclidean space

$$\mathbb{F}^n := \left\{ \begin{bmatrix} x_1 \\ \vdots \\ x_n \end{bmatrix} : x_i \in \mathbb{F} \right\}$$

with the usual addition and scalar multiplication.

Many natural examples of vector spaces are collections of functions under the usual operations of multiplication by scalars and addition of functions. That is, if f and g are functions on some specified domain D, and if $\alpha \in \mathbb{F}$, then αf and $f + g$ are defined to be the functions on D given by $(\alpha f)(x) = \alpha f(x)$ and $(f + g)(x) = f(x) + g(x)$, respectively, for all points $x \in D$. It is straightforward to show that any set of functions that is closed under this definition of scalar multiplication and addition satisfies all the vector space axioms, so such a set is indeed a vector space.

Definition 1.2. A *function space* is a set of functions on some specified domain that is closed under function addition and multiplication by scalars.

Example 1.3. Let $[a, b]$ be a closed bounded interval in $\mathbb{R}$. Define $C[a, b]$ to be the set of all continuous real-valued functions on $[a, b]$. Since the sum of two continuous functions is continuous, and a scalar times a continuous function is continuous, we have that $C[a, b]$ is a vector space over the scalar field $\mathbb{R}$.

By the same reasoning, the set of all complex-valued continuous functions on $[a, b]$ is a vector space over the complex scalar field $\mathbb{C}$. The same notation $C[a, b]$ is usually used to denote this complex function space, with the particular scalar field specified by the context in which the notation is used if there is no ambiguity.

This notation can be generalized to other domains. For instance, $C(\mathbb{R})$ will denote the set of all continuous functions on $\mathbb{R}$.

Example 1.4. A function space which we don't often talk about is the set $F(D)$ of all functions, continuous or not, from a specified domain D into the scalar field $\mathbb{F}$. The function space $F(D)$ has the mathematically interesting properties of being *maximal*, in the sense that it is not contained as a proper subset of any larger function space on the domain D, and also *universal*, in that it contains, as subsets, all other function spaces on D. These are particularly interesting features when we note that, among the more abstract spaces, there are no maximal vector spaces and no universal vector spaces.

Example 1.5. Another function space that we will frequently encounter is the set $\mathbb{P}_n[a, b]$ of all polynomials on the interval $[a, b]$ of degree less than or equal to n, for a specified positive integer n, with coefficients in $\mathbb{F}$. Similarly, $\mathbb{P}_n(\mathbb{R})$ denotes the set of all polynomials on $\mathbb{R}$ of degree n or less with coefficients in $\mathbb{F}$. As above, the scalar field is usually specified by context. It is clear that these sets are closed under addition and scalar multiplication, so they are indeed vector spaces.

From the above examples, the reader should not be surprised to find that, in general, the most attractive and useful function spaces are those that are *proper subsets* of the maximal function spaces $F(D)$. This is often true in other vector spaces as well. While there do not exist maximal vector spaces in general, many vector spaces are often best studied as proper subsets of larger vector spaces in which they are naturally contained, or embedded. The reader should look for this phenomenon as we describe more examples of vector spaces. This leads us to the definition of a subspace of a vector space.

Definition 1.6. A *subspace* of a vector space $\mathcal{V}$ is a nonempty subset E of $\mathcal{V}$ which is closed under the addition and scalar multiplication operations from $\mathcal{V}$. That is, it is required that $x + y$ and αx are contained in E whenever $x, y \in E$ and $\alpha \in \mathbb{F}$.

In other words, a subspace of $\mathcal{V}$ is just a nonempty subset of $\mathcal{V}$ which is a vector space in its own right under the addition and scalar multiplication operations it inherits as a subset of $\mathcal{V}$.

From this definition it is clear that $\mathbb{P}_n[a, b]$ sits naturally as a subspace of $C[a, b]$ by simple set-inclusion, and similarly $C[a, b]$ is a subspace of $F[a, b]$. In fact, every function space on the domain $[a, b]$ is a subspace of $F[a, b]$.

From the above definition, the entire space $\mathcal{V}$ is also a subspace of $\mathcal{V}$. The subset of $\mathcal{V}$ consisting of the zero vector alone is a subspace of $\mathcal{V}$ called the *zero* or trivial subspace, and it is written $\{0\}$. A subspace is called *proper*, or *nontrivial*, if it is neither the entire space nor the zero subspace. A *superspace* of a vector space $\mathcal{V}$ is a larger vector space $\mathcal{W}$ which contains $\mathcal{V}$ as a proper subspace.

1.2. Bases for Vector Spaces

A fundamental idea in the study of vector spaces is the practice of combining certain elements together to form others. There are a variety of interesting questions that arise:

- Which vectors "can be obtained from" a specific collection of vectors?
- How many vectors are needed to "create" all the vectors in the space?
- Is there more than one way to "get" a vector from a given set of vectors?

In this section we will make this notion of "combining elements to form other vectors" precise.

Definition 1.7. Let $x_1, x_2, \ldots, x_k$ be vectors in a vector space $\mathcal{V}$. A *linear combination* of vectors $x_1, x_2, \ldots, x_k$ is a sum of the form:

$$x = c_1 x_1 + c_2 x_2 + \cdots + c_k x_k,$$

where $c_1, c_2, \ldots, c_k$ are scalars.

Definition 1.8. A finite, nonempty set of vectors $\{x_i\}_{i=1}^k$ in $\mathcal{V}$ is called *linearly dependent* if there exist scalars $c_1, c_2, \ldots, c_k$, which are not all zero, such that $\sum_{i=1}^k c_i x_i = 0$. A finite nonempty set of vectors is defined to be *linearly independent* if it is not linearly dependent. In other words, $\{x_i\}_{i=1}^k$ is linearly independent if the only set of scalars $\{c_1, c_2, \ldots, c_k\}$ which gives $\sum_{i=1}^k c_i x_i = 0$ is the zero set $c_1 = c_2 = \cdots = c_k = 0$.

We remark that the empty set $\emptyset$ of vectors is defined to be neither linearly dependent nor linearly independent, and the trivial subset $\{0\}$ containing the zero vector alone is considered to be a linearly dependent set.

It follows from the definition that a nonempty set of at least two vectors is linearly dependent if and only if at least one of the vectors can be written as a linear combination of others in the set (Exercise 1).

We can now extend these definitions to *infinite* sets of vectors.

Definition 1.9. A nonempty infinite set of vectors in a vector space is defined to be *linearly dependent* if at least one of the vectors in the set can be written as a linear combination of a finite number of other vectors in the set, and it is called *linearly independent* otherwise.

It is easy to see that linear dependence is a hereditary property in the sense that if a given set has a linearly dependent subset, then it itself is linearly dependent. For instance, the set of polynomials $\{1, x, x^2, 2x + 1, x^3\}$ is easily seen to be linearly dependent simply because the fourth polynomial is clearly a linear combination of the first two. The other polynomials don't have to be checked. On the other hand, linear independence is a hereditary property in the exact opposite sense: if a given set is known to be linearly independent, then every nonempty subset of it is also linearly independent.

From the above discussions it should be clear that linearly independent sets are special, whereas linearly dependent sets are very common.

Definition 1.10. Let $\mathcal{S}$ be a subset of a vector space $\mathcal{V}$. We define the *linear span of* $\mathcal{S}$ to be the set of all the finite linear combinations of vectors from $\mathcal{S}$. That is:

$$\operatorname{span}(\mathcal{S}) = \{c_1x_1 + \cdots + c_kx_k : x_i \in \mathcal{S}, c_i \in \mathbb{F}\}.$$

A *spanning set* for a vector space $\mathcal{V}$ is a set $\mathcal{S}$ whose linear span is $\mathcal{V}$.

If $\mathcal{S}_1$ and $\mathcal{S}_2$ are subsets of $\mathcal{V}$, we use the notation $\operatorname{span}(\mathcal{S}_1, \mathcal{S}_2)$ to denote $\operatorname{span}(\mathcal{S}_1 \cup \mathcal{S}_2)$. We use analogous notation for the span of three or more sets.

Definition 1.11. A vector space is called *finite-dimensional* if it has a finite spanning set. Otherwise, it is called an *infinite-dimensional* vector space.

In the remainder of this section, $\mathcal{V}$ is assumed to be a finite-dimensional vector space. The results, however, are still valid in the infinite-dimensional setting.

Lemma 1.12. *Suppose that $\{x_i\}_{i=1}^k$ is a spanning set for the vector space $\mathcal{V}$, and let w be a vector in $\mathcal{V}$. Then the set $\{w, x_1, x_2, \ldots, x_k\}$ is linearly dependent.*

Proof. Exercise 2. □

The following lemma is most useful in constructing and working with subspaces.

Lemma 1.13. *The linear span of a finite set of vectors in a vector space $\mathcal{V}$ is a subspace of $\mathcal{V}$.*

Proof. Let $\mathcal{S} = \{x_1, x_2, \ldots, x_n\} \subset \mathcal{V}$ be a given set of vectors, and let $\mathcal{W} = \operatorname{span}(\mathcal{S})$. Let u and v be vectors in $\mathcal{W}$, and write $u = c_1x_1 + c_2x_2 + \cdots + c_nx_n$ and $v = d_1x_1 + d_2x_2 + \cdots + d_nx_n$. Then $u + v = \sum_{i=1}^n (c_i + d_i)x_i$, which is a linear combination of the vectors x_i, so $u + v$ is an element $\mathcal{W}$, thus proving that $\mathcal{W}$ is closed under addition. If a is a scalar, then $au = ac_1x_1 + ac_2x_2 + \cdots + ac_nx_n$ is again a linear combination of $\{x_1, x_2, \ldots, x_n\}$. Since $\mathcal{W}$ is closed under addition and scalar multiplication, it is a subspace of $\mathcal{V}$. □

Definition 1.14. A *basis* for a nontrivial finite-dimensional vector space $\mathcal{V}$ is a linearly independent spanning set for $\mathcal{V}$. (We note that for an infinite-dimensional vector space, a linearly independent spanning set is called a *Hamel basis*. We will not use the notion of a Hamel basis in this text; we simply include this fact for student interest.)

If $\{x_i\}_{i=1}^k$ is a basis for $\mathcal{V}$, then the coefficients $c_1, c_2, \ldots, c_k$ in the linear expansion of any vector x must be unique. If not, then there would be two ways of writing x as a linear combination of $x_1, x_2, \ldots, x_k$. But if $\sum_{i=1}^k c_i x_i = x = \sum_{i=1}^k d_i x_i$ with at least one index value i_0 for which $c_{i_0} \neq d_{i_0}$, then we would have $0 = x - x = \sum (c_i - d_i) x_i$ and not all coefficients would be zero. This would contradict the linear independence of $\{x_i\}_{i=1}^k$.

The following lemma gives a general principle which is useful in constructing and otherwise working with bases.

Lemma 1.15. *If $\{x_1, x_2, \ldots, x_k\}$ is a linearly independent subset of a vector space $\mathcal{V}$, and if x_{k+1} is a vector in $\mathcal{V}$ which is not contained in $\operatorname{span}\{x_1, x_2, \ldots, x_k\}$, then $\{x_1, x_2, \ldots, x_k, x_{k+1}\}$ is a linearly independent set.*

Proof. Suppose $c_1, c_2, \ldots, c_{k+1}$ are scalars such that $c_1 x_1 + c_2 x_2 + \cdots + c_{k+1} x_{k+1} = 0$. Suppose, by way of contradiction, that $c_{k+1} \neq 0$. Then

$$x_{k+1} = \sum_{i=1}^{k} [-(c_{k+1})^{-1} c_i] \, x_i$$

and so $x_{k+1} \in \operatorname{span}\{x_1, x_2, \ldots, x_k\}$, a contradiction to the hypothesis. Hence we must conclude that $c_{k+1} = 0$, which then implies $c_1 x_1 + c_2 x_2 + \cdots + c_k x_k = 0$. Since $\{x_1, x_2, \ldots, x_k\}$ is linearly independent, this implies that $c_1 = c_2 = \cdots = c_k = 0$. Hence $\{x_1, x_2, \ldots, x_{k+1}\}$ must be linearly independent. □

Proposition 1.16. *Let $\mathcal{V}$ be a nontrivial vector space which has a spanning set $\{x_i\}_{i=1}^k$. Then there is a subset of $\{x_i\}_{i=1}^k$ which is a basis for $\mathcal{V}$.*

Proof. We will divide the set $\{x_i\}_{i=1}^k$ into two sets, which we will call *good* and *bad*. If $x_1 \neq 0$, then we label x_1 as *good* and if it is zero, we label it as *bad*. For each $i \geq 2$, if $x_i \notin \operatorname{span}\{x_1, \ldots, x_{i-1}\}$, then we label x_i as *good*, and otherwise we label it as *bad*. Let B be the set of all the *good* elements. We claim that B is a basis for $\mathcal{V}$.

B is nonempty because not all the x_i are zero and the first nonzero x_i will be *good*. We must first verify that B is a linearly independent set. Let $B = \{b_1, b_2, \ldots, b_\ell\}$ and assume we have scalars $c_1, c_2, \ldots, c_\ell$ such that $c_1b_1+c_2b_2+\cdots+c_\ell b_\ell = 0$. Then $c_1b_1+c_2b_2+\cdots+c_{\ell-1}b_{\ell-1} = -c_\ell b_\ell$, and by the construction of the set B, b_ℓ is not a linear combination of the previous elements, which therefore implies that c_ℓ must be zero. But we can repeat this argument. We now know that $c_1b_1+c_2b_2+\cdots+c_{\ell-1}b_{\ell-1} = 0$, so that $c_1b_1+c_2b_2+\cdots+c_{\ell-2}b_{\ell-2} = -c_{\ell-1}b_{\ell-1}$ and again this implies that $c_{\ell-1} = 0$. Repeating this will prove that all the coefficients must be zero. Therefore, B is a linearly independent set.

We leave it as Exercise 3 to show that the span of the elements of B is all of $\mathcal{V}$. □

Example 1.17. It is easy to see that the proof of the above proposition is actually an algorithm for choosing a subset that is a basis. Such a proof is called constructive. For a specific example, let S be the span of the polynomials $1+x, 1+2x, x, 1+x^2$ in $\mathbb{P}_2$. In the first step of the proof, we see $1+x$ is labelled *good*. Next, since $1+x, 1+2x$ is linearly independent, the element $1+2x$ is also labelled *good*. We see by inspection that x can be written as $x = (1+2x)-(1+x)$, so x is labelled *bad*. Lastly, $1+x^2$ cannot be written as a linear combination of the first three $1+x, 1+2x, x$, because it is of degree 2 and the first three are of degree 1, so it is labelled *good*. Thus $B = \{1+x, 1+2x, 1+x^2\}$ is our basis for S.

Note: It should also be noted that the algorithm in the proof does *not* yield the only subset that is a basis. In particular, $\{1+2x, x, 1+x^2\}$ is also readily seen to be a basis.

Proposition 1.18. *Every linearly independent set in $\mathcal{V}$ can be extended to a basis of $\mathcal{V}$.*

Proof. Let $\{x_1, x_2, \ldots, x_\ell\}$ be a linearly independent subset of $\mathcal{V}$. We must show that either $\{x_i\}_{i=1}^{\ell}$ is already a basis for $\mathcal{V}$, or else there exist additional vectors $\{x_{\ell+1}, \ldots, x_p\}$ in $\mathcal{V}$ such that $\{x_i\}_{i=1}^{p}$ is a basis for $\mathcal{V}$.

Since $\mathcal{V}$ is finite-dimensional, it has a spanning set $\{s_1, s_2, \ldots, s_r\}$. If we take the union with our linearly independent set, we still have a spanning set $\{x_1, \ldots, x_\ell, s_1, \ldots, s_r\}$. We apply the *good/bad* argument from the proof of Proposition 1.16 to this list, extracting a basis for $\mathcal{V}$. Since we considered the elements in order, we see that each of the elements x_i, $i = 1, 2, \ldots, \ell$ are *good*, and therefore are present in the new basis. Thus, the new basis extends $\{x_i\}_{i=1}^{\ell}$. □

Lemma 1.19. *Let E and F be subspaces of $\mathcal{V}$ with $E \cap F = \{0\}$ and $\operatorname{span}(E, F) = \mathcal{V}$. Suppose that $\mathcal{E} = \{e_1, \ldots, e_k\}$ is a basis for E and $\mathcal{F} = \{f_1, \ldots, f_m\}$ is a basis for F. Then $\mathcal{E} \cup \mathcal{F}$ is a basis for $\mathcal{V}$.*

Proof. Let

$$\mathcal{B} = \mathcal{E} \cup \mathcal{F} = \{e_1, e_2, \ldots, e_k, f_1, f_2, \ldots, f_m\}.$$

Then $\operatorname{span}(\mathcal{B})$ contains both the sets $E = \operatorname{span}\{e_1, e_2, \ldots, e_k\}$ and $F = \operatorname{span}\{f_1, f_2, \ldots, f_m\}$, so $\operatorname{span}(\mathcal{B}) \supseteq \operatorname{span}(E, F) = \mathcal{V}$. Thus $\operatorname{span}(\mathcal{B}) = \mathcal{V}$.

Thus we need only prove that $\mathcal{B}$ is linearly independent. For this, suppose $\{c_1, \ldots, c_k, d_1, \ldots, d_m\}$ are scalars such that

$$c_1 e_1 + \cdots + c_k e_k + d_1 f_1 + \cdots + d_m f_m = 0.$$

We have

$$c_1 e_1 + \cdots + c_k e_k = -(d_1 f_1 + \cdots + d_m f_m).$$

Let $z = c_1 e_1 + \cdots + c_k e_k$. Then $z \in E$ because E is closed under taking of linear combinations of its members. Similarly, $z = -(d_1 f_1 + \cdots + d_m f_m)$ and so $z \in F$. Therefore $z \in E \cap F$. But $E \cap F = \{0\}$ which implies that $z = c_1 e_1 + \cdots + c_k e_k = 0$. So, since $\{e_1, \ldots, e_k\}$ are linearly independent, we must have

$$c_1 = c_2 = \cdots = c_k = 0.$$

Similarly, by using the fact that $\{f_1, \ldots, f_m\}$ is a basis for F, we can show that $d_1 = d_2 = \cdots = d_m = 0$ as well. This proves that $\mathcal{B}$ is linearly independent. Since a linearly independent spanning set is a basis, we have proven that $\mathcal{B}$ is a basis for $\mathcal{V}$. □

Lemma 1.20. *Let $\mathcal{V}$ be a finite-dimensional vector space, and suppose $\{x_i\}_{i=1}^{n}$ is a basis for $\mathcal{V}$. Suppose z is any vector in $\mathcal{V}$ which* *is not a linear combination of the vectors* $\{x_1, x_2, \ldots, x_{n-1}\}$*. Then* $\{x_1, x_2, \ldots, x_{n-1}, z\}$ *is also a basis for* $\mathcal{V}$*.*

Proof. Since $\{x_i\}_{i=1}^n$ is a basis for $\mathcal{V}$ and $z \in \mathcal{V}$, we can write

$$z = c_1 x_1 + c_2 x_2 + \cdots + c_n x_n$$

for some set of scalars $c_1, c_2, \ldots, c_n$. Since $z \notin \operatorname{span}\{x_i\}_{i=1}^{n-1}$, the value of c_n cannot be zero. Hence,

$$x_n = c_n^{-1}(z - c_1 x_1 - c_2 x_2 - \cdots - c_{n-1} x_{n-1}).$$

This shows $x_n \in \operatorname{span}\{x_1, x_2, \ldots, x_{n-1}, z\}$. Therefore, any vector which is a linear combination of $\{x_i\}_{i=1}^n$ can be written as a linear combination of the vectors $\{x_1, x_2, \ldots, x_{n-1}, z\}$, which means that $\{x_1, x_2, \ldots, x_{n-1}, z\}$ is also a spanning set for $\mathcal{V}$.

Referencing Lemma 1.15, $z \notin \operatorname{span}\{x_i\}_{i=1}^{n-1}$ implies that the set $\{x_1, x_2, \ldots, x_{n-1}, z\}$ is linearly independent, and therefore a basis for $\mathcal{V}$. □

Theorem 1.21. *Let* $\mathcal{V}$ *be a finite-dimensional vector space. Suppose that* $\mathcal{V}$ *has a basis containing* n *elements.*

(i) *Any other basis of* $\mathcal{V}$ *also has* n *elements.*

(ii) *Any linearly independent set of* n *vectors in* $\mathcal{V}$ *is also a basis for* $\mathcal{V}$*.*

Proof. (i) Suppose $\{x_i\}_{i=1}^n$ and $\{y_i\}_{i=1}^k$ are both bases for $\mathcal{V}$. Without loss of generality, we can assume $n \le k$. By the definition of linear independence, $\{x_2, \ldots, x_n\}$ does not span all of $\mathcal{V}$. In particular, there exists at least one of the vectors, say y_{i_1}, in $\{y_1, y_2, \ldots, y_k\}$ such that $y_{i_1} \notin \operatorname{span}\{x_i\}_{i=2}^n$. By Lemma 1.20, $\{y_{i_1}, x_2, \ldots, x_n\}$ is also a basis for $\mathcal{V}$.

We repeat this argument for x_2. Since $\{y_{i_1}, x_3, \ldots, x_n\}$ does not span $\mathcal{V}$, we can select $y_{i_2} \notin \operatorname{span}\{y_{i_1}, x_3, \ldots, x_n\}$. Note that this certainly requires $i_2 \ne i_1$. Lemma 1.20 again proves $\{y_{i_2}, y_{i_1}, x_3, \ldots, x_n\}$ is a basis for $\mathcal{V}$.

We proceed inductively. Assume for some $p, 2 \le p < n$, we have selected distinct $\{i_1, i_2, \ldots, i_p\}$ from among $\{1, 2, \ldots, k\}$ so that the set $\{y_{i_1}, y_{i_2}, \ldots, y_{i_p}, x_{p+1}, \ldots, x_n\}$ is a basis for $\mathcal{V}$. At least one of the vectors y_i is not in the span of the set $\{y_{i_1}, y_{i_2}, \ldots, y_{i_p}, x_{p+2}, \ldots, x_n\}$, so we can select $i_{p+1} \in \{1, 2, \ldots, k\}$ such that

$$y_{i_{p+1}} \notin \operatorname{span}\{y_{i_1}, y_{i_2}, \ldots, y_{i_p}, x_{p+2}, \ldots, x_n\}.$$

In particular, we see that this requires $i_{p+1} \notin \{i_1, \ldots, i_p\}$. By Lemma 1.20, the set $\{y_{i_1}, y_{i_2}, \ldots, y_{i_{p+1}}, x_{p+2}, \ldots, x_n\}$ is a basis for $\mathcal{V}$.

We can repeat this algorithm until all the original x_i have been replaced, and we have a basis $\{y_{i_1}, y_{i_2}, \ldots, y_{i_n}\}$ for $\mathcal{V}$. If $k > n$, then there is a $j \in \{1, 2, \ldots, k\}$ such that $j \notin \{i_1, i_2, \ldots, i_n\}$. But for this j, $y_j \in \mathcal{V}$; hence it must be in the span of the basis elements $\{y_{i_1}, y_{i_2}, \ldots, y_{i_n}\}$. This contradicts the assumption that $\{y_i\}_{i-1}^k$ is linearly independent, so we must have $n = k$.

(ii) Repeat the above argument, replacing the basis $\{y_i\}_{i=1}^k$ with a linearly independent set of n elements $\{y_i\}_{i=1}^n$. The induction argument proves that $\{y_{i_1}, y_{i_2}, \ldots, y_{i_n}\}$ is a basis for $\mathcal{V}$. Since the set $\{i_1, i_2, \ldots, i_n\}$ is a permutation of $\{1, 2, \ldots, n\}$, we have $\{y_i\}_{i=1}^n$ is the same set, and thus is a basis for $\mathcal{V}$. $\square$

From the above theorem, every basis of a vector space $\mathcal{V}$ has the same cardinality (number of elements).

Definition 1.22. The *dimension* of a vector space $\mathcal{V}$ is the cardinality of a basis, which we denote by $\dim \mathcal{V}$.

Example 1.23. Let $\mathbb{F}$ be either $\mathbb{R}$ or $\mathbb{C}$. Then, as we have seen, $\mathbb{F}^n$ is a vector space under the usual addition and scalar multiplication. One basis for $\mathcal{V}$ is $\{e_1, e_2, \ldots, e_n\}$ with

$$e_1 = \begin{bmatrix} 1 \\ 0 \\ 0 \\ \vdots \\ 0 \end{bmatrix}, e_2 = \begin{bmatrix} 0 \\ 1 \\ 0 \\ \vdots \\ 0 \end{bmatrix}, \cdots, e_n = \begin{bmatrix} 0 \\ 0 \\ 0 \\ \vdots \\ 1 \end{bmatrix}.$$

This is usually called the standard basis for $\mathbb{F}^n$. We then see that the dimension of $\mathbb{F}^n$ is n.

Lemma 1.24. *Suppose $\mathcal{V}$ is a nontrivial vector space, let $\{x_i\}_{i=1}^l$ be any finite subset of $\mathcal{V}$, and let E be the linear span of $\{x_i\}_{i=1}^l$. Then $\dim E \leq l$.*

Proof. Exercise 4. □

Definition 1.25. If E and F are subsets of a vector space $\mathcal{V}$, we define the sum

$$E + F = \{x + y : x \in E, y \in F\}.$$

Proposition 1.26. *If E and F are subspaces of a vector space $\mathcal{V}$, then $E + F = \operatorname{span}\{E, F\}$, and therefore $E + F$ is a subspace of $\mathcal{V}$. Moreover, $\dim(E + F) \leq \dim E + \dim F$, with equality if and only if $E \cap F = \{0\}$.*

Proof. The proof that $E + F = \operatorname{span}\{E, F\}$ is left as Exercise 5.

To prove the second statement, let $\{e_i\}_{i=1}^{\ell}$ be a basis for E and let $\{f_i\}_{i=1}^{m}$ be a basis for F. Then the union $\{e_1, e_2, \dots, e_\ell, f_1, f_2, \dots, f_m\}$ spans $E+F$, which proves that $\dim(E+F) \leq \ell+m = \dim E+\dim F$.

From Lemma 1.19, we know that if $E \cap F = \{0\}$, then the vectors $\{e_1, e_2, \dots, e_\ell, f_1, f_2, \dots, f_m\}$ form a basis for $\operatorname{span}(E + F)$, and therefore we have $\dim(E + F) = l + m = \dim(E) + \dim(F)$. If $E \cap F$ contains a nonzero element x, then x can be written as a linear combination of the elements in each basis:

$$x = \sum_{i=1}^{\ell} c_i e_i = \sum_{i=1}^{k} d_i f_i.$$

But this equality implies that the union of the bases is a linearly dependent set, so $\ell + m$ is strictly greater than $\dim(E + F)$. This proves the last part of the proposition. □

If E and F are subspaces of $\mathcal{V}$ with $E \cap F = \{0\}$ and $E + F = \mathcal{V}$, then F is said to be a *subspace complement* of E in $\mathcal{V}$. Proposition 1.26 above shows that, in this case, $\dim \mathcal{V} = \dim E + \dim F$, and the union of any basis of E with any basis of F is a basis for $\mathcal{V}$.

Definition 1.27. If E and F are subspaces of $\mathcal{V}$ such that every $v \in \mathcal{V}$ can be written uniquely as a sum $v = x + y$ with $x \in E, y \in F$, then we say $\mathcal{V}$ is a *direct sum* of E and F. This will be denoted

$$V = E \dot{+} F.$$

Remark 1.28. There is a stronger notion of direct sums of inner product spaces, defined in Section 1.6, which additionally requires the component subspaces to be orthogonal. It is often called the *orthogonal direct sum* to differentiate it from the direct sum of vector spaces. We will use the notation $E \oplus F$ for the orthogonal direct sum of inner product spaces.

Lemma 1.29. *If $\mathcal{V} = E \dot{+} F$, then $E \cap F = \{0\}$, and therefore the direct sum is exactly the special case of the sum $E + F$ in which E and F are subspace complements.*

Proof. Exercise 6. □

See Exercise 36 for an extension of the notion of direct sum to finitely many direct summands.

1.3. Linear Operators and Matrices

In this section, we consider the mappings between vector spaces that preserve the linear operations of addition and scalar multiplication. In particular, we establish the connections between such mappings and matrices.

Definition 1.30. Let $\mathcal{V}$ and $\mathcal{W}$ be two vector spaces over the same field $\mathbb{F}$. A *linear operator* (or transformation) is a mapping T from $\mathcal{V}$ to W such that

$$T(\alpha x + \beta y) = \alpha Tx + \beta Ty$$

for all $x, y \in \mathcal{V}$ and all $\alpha, \beta \in \mathbb{F}$. A linear operator T is called *injective* (or one-to-one) if $x = 0$ whenever $Tx = 0$, and it is called *surjective* (or onto) if the range of T, defined by $\text{range}(T) = \{Tx : x \in \mathcal{V}\} = T\mathcal{V}$, is equal to the entire vector space $\mathcal{W}$. When T is both injective and surjective, we say that T is *bijective.*

Given a linear operator T from a vector space $\mathcal{V}$ to a vector space $\mathcal{W}$, the *kernel* of T is defined by

$$\ker(T) = \{x \in \mathcal{V} : Tx = 0\}.$$

Proposition 1.31. *Let T be a linear operator from $\mathcal{V}$ to $\mathcal{W}$.*

(i) *The set* $\ker(T)$ *is a subspace of* $\mathcal{V}$ *and the set* $\operatorname{range}(T)$ *is a subspace of* $\mathcal{W}$.

(ii) *The operator* T *is injective if and only if* $\ker(T) = \{0\}$.

Proof. Exercise 7. □

Given two linear operators $T_1 : \mathcal{V}_1 \to \mathcal{V}_2$ and $T_2 : \mathcal{V}_2 \to \mathcal{V}_3$, the composition of the operators will be written as a product T_2T_1. This composition will be a map from $\mathcal{V}_1$ to $\mathcal{V}_3$. The operator T_2T_1 will be linear, since for any $x, y \in \mathcal{V}_1$ and $a, b \in \mathbb{F}$, we have

$$\begin{aligned} T_2T_1(ax+by) &= T_2(aT_1x + bT_1y) && \text{by linearity of } T_1, \\ &= aT_2(T_1x) + bT_2(T_1y) && \text{by linearity of } T_2, \\ &= a(T_2T_1)x + b(T_2T_1)y. \end{aligned}$$

For any bijective linear operator $T : \mathcal{V} \to \mathcal{W}$, there exists a unique mapping $S : \mathcal{W} \to \mathcal{V}$ (which is also linear) such that $ST = I_{\mathcal{V}}$ and $TS = I_{\mathcal{W}}$, where $I_{\mathcal{V}}, I_{\mathcal{W}}$ denote the identity operator on $\mathcal{V}$ and $\mathcal{W}$ respectively. The operator S is called the *inverse* of T and is denoted by T^{-1}. If T has an inverse, it is called an *invertible* operator.

Proposition 1.32. *Suppose* T *and* S *are linear operators on a vector space* $\mathcal{V}$ *that are both invertible. Then* $(T^{-1})^{-1} = T$ *and* $(ST)^{-1} = T^{-1}S^{-1}$.

Proof. Exercise 8. □

Theorem 1.33. *Let* $T : \mathcal{V} \to \mathcal{V}$ *be a linear operator and assume that* $\dim \mathcal{V} = n$. *Then* T *is surjective if and only if* T *is injective.*

Proof. Exercise 9. □

Definition 1.34. Let $m, n \in \mathbb{N}$. An *$m \times n$ matrix* A over a field $\mathbb{F}$ is a rectangular array of the form

$$A = \begin{bmatrix} a_{11} & a_{12} & \cdots & a_{1n} \\ a_{21} & a_{22} & \cdots & a_{2n} \\ \vdots & \vdots & \ddots & \vdots \\ a_{m1} & a_{m2} & \cdots & a_{mn} \end{bmatrix},$$

where $a_{ij} \in \mathbb{F}$. We sometimes use $A = [a_{i,j}]$ when m, n are well understood.

Definition 1.35. An $n \times n$ matrix $D = [d_{i,j}]$ is called a *diagonal* matrix if $d_{i,j} = 0$ for $i \neq j$. We often denote an $n \times n$ diagonal matrix D, where $d_{i,i} = \lambda_i$, by $D = \operatorname{diag}(\lambda_1, \lambda_2, \dots, \lambda_n)$. The $m \times m$ identity matrix I is the matrix $[a_{ij}]$ such that $a_{ii} = 1$ for $i = 1, 2, \dots, m$ and $a_{ij} = 0$ if $i \neq j$.

Definition 1.36. (i) Suppose that $A = [a_{ij}]$ and $B = [b_{ij}]$ are two $m \times n$ matrices over the same field $\mathbb{F}$. Then $A + B$ is the $m \times n$ matrix $C = [c_{ij}]$ with $c_{ij} = a_{ij} + b_{ij}$.

(ii) For any $\alpha \in \mathbb{F}$, αA is defined to be the matrix $D = [d_{ij}]$ with $d_{ij} = \alpha a_{ij}$.

(iii) Suppose that $A = [a_{ij}]$ is an $m \times k$ matrix and $B = [b_{ij}]$ is a $k \times n$ matrix. Then the product AB is the $m \times n$ matrix $C = [c_{ij}]$ with entries

$$c_{ij} = \sum_{\ell=1}^{k} a_{i\ell} b_{\ell j}.$$

(iv) Suppose that $A = [a_{ij}]$ and $B = [b_{ij}]$ are two $m \times m$ matrices over the same field $\mathbb{F}$. If $AB = I$, then we say that A is *invertible*, and denote B by A^{-1}.

Matrix multiplication is distributive over addition and scalar multiplication. That is, if A is an $m \times n$ matrix and B, C are $n \times k$ matrices, then

$$A(B + C) = AB + AC.$$

If $\lambda \in \mathbb{F}$, then

$$A(\lambda B) = \lambda(AB).$$

We remark that the matrix multiplication is not commutative. A special case of matrix multiplication is the product of an $m \times n$ matrix A over $\mathbb{F}$ and $x \in \mathbb{F}^n$. The above formula gives $Ax = y \in \mathbb{F}^m$ of the form:

$$y_i = \sum_{j=1}^{n} a_{ij} x_j$$

for $i = 1, 2, \dots, m$.

The *transpose* of an $m \times n$ matrix $A = [a_{ij}]$ is defined to be the $n \times m$ matrix $A^T = [a_{ji}]$. In other words, the columns of A are the rows of A^T.

Proposition 1.37. *The following properties of the transpose hold:*

(i) *For a matrix A of any size, $(A^T)^T = A$.*

(ii) *For a matrix A of size $n \times m$ and a matrix B of size $m \times k$, $(AB)^T = B^T A^T$.*

(iii) *For an invertible matrix A of size $n \times n$, $(A^{-1})^T = (A^T)^{-1}$.*

Proof. Exercise 10. □

Proposition 1.38. *Let A be an $m \times n$ matrix over $\mathbb{F}$. Define a mapping $T : \mathbb{F}^n \to \mathbb{F}^m$ by*

$$Tx = Ax, \quad x \in \mathbb{F}^n.$$

Then T is a linear operator.

Proof. Let $x, y \in \mathbb{F}^n$ and let $\alpha, \beta \in \mathbb{F}$. We have that

$$\begin{aligned} T(\alpha x + \beta y) &= A(\alpha x + \beta y) \\ &= A(\alpha x) + A(\beta y) \\ &= \alpha A x + \beta A y \\ &= \alpha T x + \beta T y \end{aligned}$$

because A acts by matrix multiplication, which is distributive over addition and scalar multiplication. □

We will often not distinguish between a matrix A and the linear operator T_A given by $T_A x = Ax$.

Lemma 1.39. *Fix a basis $\{v_1, v_2, \ldots, v_n\}$ for an n-dimensional vector space $\mathcal{V}$. Define a linear operator $T : \mathcal{V} \to \mathbb{F}^n$ in the following way: For each $x = \sum_{i=1}^n c_i v_i \in \mathcal{V}$, define*

$$Tx = \begin{bmatrix} c_1 \\ c_2 \\ \vdots \\ c_n \end{bmatrix} \in \mathbb{F}^n.$$

Then T is a linear operator.

Proof. Exercise 11. □

Definition 1.40. We will call the vector

$$\begin{bmatrix} c_1 \\ c_2 \\ \vdots \\ c_n \end{bmatrix}$$

in Lemma 1.39 the *coordinate vector* of x with respect to the basis $\mathcal{B} = \{v_1, \ldots, v_n\}$ for $\mathcal{V}$, and we will use the notation

$$[x]_{\mathcal{B}} = \begin{bmatrix} c_1 \\ c_2 \\ \vdots \\ c_n \end{bmatrix}.$$

Lemma 1.39 simply states that the mapping from $\mathcal{V}$ to $\mathbb{F}^n$ that assigns to each vector $x \in \mathcal{V}$ the coordinate vector in $\mathbb{F}^n$ with respect to a fixed basis is a linear operator.

Lemma 1.41. *Fix a basis $\{w_1, w_2, \ldots, w_m\}$ for an m-dimensional vector space $\mathcal{W}$. Define $T : \mathbb{F}^m \to \mathcal{W}$ in the following way: For each*

$x = \begin{bmatrix} c_1 \\ c_2 \\ \vdots \\ c_m \end{bmatrix} \in \mathbb{F}^m$, *define*

$$Tx = \sum_{j=1}^{m} c_j w_j.$$

Then T is a linear operator.

Proof. Exercise 12. □

The connection between linear operators from an n-dimensional vector space $\mathcal{V}$ to an m-dimensional vector space $\mathcal{W}$ and matrices can be established as follows. Let $A = [a_{ij}]$ be an $m \times n$ matrix. Fix a basis $\{v_1, v_2, \ldots, v_n\}$ for $\mathcal{V}$ and a basis $\{w_1, w_2, \ldots, w_m\}$ for

$\mathcal{W}$. Define T_A in the following way: Let $x = \sum_{j=1}^{n} c_i v_i \in \mathcal{V}$ and $d_i = \sum_{j=1}^{n} a_{ij} c_j$, and then set

$$T_A x = \sum_{i=1}^{m} d_i w_i.$$

Proposition 1.42. *The mapping T_A defined above is a linear operator from $\mathcal{V}$ to $\mathcal{W}$.*

Proof. Observe that T_A is equal to the composition of the linear operators from Proposition 1.38, Lemma 1.39, and Lemma 1.41. Thus, T_A is a linear operator. □

On the other hand, we have the following:

Proposition 1.43. *Let T be a linear operator from $\mathcal{V}$ to $\mathcal{W}$. Suppose that $\{v_1, v_2, \ldots, v_n\}$ is a basis for $\mathcal{V}$ and $\{w_1, w_2, \ldots, w_m\}$ is a basis for $\mathcal{W}$. For each j with $1 \leq j \leq n$, there exists a unique set of scalars $a_{1j}, a_{2j}, \ldots, a_{mj}$ such that*

$$Tv_j = \sum_{i=1}^{m} a_{ij} w_i.$$

If we let $A = [a_{ij}]$, then $T_A = T$.

Proof. Exercise 13. □

The above two propositions tell us that once we fix a basis for $\mathcal{V}$ and a basis for $\mathcal{W}$, then there exists a one-to-one correspondence between all the linear operators from $\mathcal{V}$ to $\mathcal{W}$, and all the $m \times n$ matrices. Often we will not distinguish them from each other when no ambiguity will occur. We will say that the matrix A in Proposition 1.43 is the *matrix representation* of T with respect to these two bases.

Proposition 1.44.

(i) *Let $A = [a_{ij}]$ and $B = [b_{ij}]$ be two $m \times n$ matrices over the same field $\mathbb{F}$. Then $T_{\alpha A + \beta B} = \alpha T_A + \beta T_B$ for all $\alpha, \beta \in \mathbb{F}$.*

(ii) *Suppose that $A = [a_{ij}]$ is an $m \times k$ matrix and and $B = [b_{ij}]$ is a $k \times n$ matrix. Then $T_{AB} = T_A T_B$.*

(iii) *Suppose that A is an $n \times n$ matrix. Then A is invertible if and only if T_A is invertible. Moreover, $(T_A)^{-1} = T_{A^{-1}}$.*

Proof. Exercise 14. □

Definition 1.45. If $\mathcal{B}_1$ and $\mathcal{B}_2$ are two different bases for a vector space $\mathcal{V}$ of dimension n, then the *transition matrix* S for this pair of bases is the $n \times n$ matrix with the property that for every $x \in \mathcal{V}$,

$$S[x]_{\mathcal{B}_1} = [x]_{\mathcal{B}_2}.$$

That is, S is the matrix which converts vectors expressed in terms of one basis to vectors expressed in terms of the other basis. We will use the more complete notation $S_{\mathcal{B}_1}^{\mathcal{B}_2}$ for the transition matrix when there is any ambiguity on the particular ordered pair of bases for $\mathcal{V}$ used.

Given a linear operator on $\mathcal{V}$, the matrix representation of that operator described in this section depends on the choice of basis for $\mathcal{V}$. We can describe the relationship between two matrices which represent the same linear operator using the notion of similarity.

Definition 1.46. Let A and B be $n \times n$ matrices over $\mathbb{F}$. Then A and B are called *similar matrices* if there exists an invertible $n \times n$ matrix S such that $B = S^{-1}AS$.

Proposition 1.47. *Let A and B be the $n \times n$ matrices which represent the same linear operator T on $\mathbb{F}^n$ with respect to two bases $\mathcal{B}_1$ and $\mathcal{B}_2$ of $\mathcal{V}$, respectively. Then A and B are similar; indeed,*

$$B = S^{-1}AS$$

where

$$S = S_{\mathcal{B}_1}^{\mathcal{B}_2}.$$

Proof. Exercise 15. □

1.4. The Rank of a Linear Operator and a Matrix

Definition 1.48. Let T be a linear operator from $\mathcal{V}$ to $\mathcal{W}$. The *rank* of T is defined to be the dimension of the range space $T\mathcal{V}$, and we denote this by $\operatorname{rank}(T)$.

Theorem 1.49. *Let $\mathcal{V}$ and $\mathcal{W}$ be two finite-dimensional vector spaces and let T be a linear operator from $\mathcal{V}$ to $\mathcal{W}$. Then*

$$\dim \mathcal{V} = \dim \ker(T) + \operatorname{rank}(T).$$

Proof. Assume that $\dim \mathcal{V} = n$. Let $\{v_1, v_2, \ldots, v_k\}$ be a basis for $\ker(T)$, which can be completed to a basis

$$\{v_1, v_2, \ldots, v_k\} \cup \{u_{k+1}, u_{k+2}, \ldots, u_n\}$$

of $\mathcal{V}$. Let $\mathcal{S} = \operatorname{span}\{u_{k+1}, u_{k+2}, \ldots, u_n\}$. Then $\ker(T) \cap \mathcal{S} = \{0\}$ and so

$$\dim \mathcal{V} = \dim \mathcal{S} + \dim \ker(T).$$

Note that $\operatorname{range}(T) = T(\mathcal{S})$ and the restriction of T to $\mathcal{S}$ is injective. Thus $\dim \mathcal{S} = \dim T(\mathcal{S})$, which implies that

$$\dim \mathcal{S} = \dim \operatorname{range}(T) = \operatorname{rank}(T).$$

Therefore we have

$$\dim \mathcal{V} = \dim \ker(T) + \operatorname{rank}(T),$$

as claimed. □

Definition 1.50. Let A be an $m \times n$ matrix, and let $T_A : \mathbb{F}^n \to \mathbb{F}^m$ be the associated linear operator in the standard basis. That is, $T_A x = Ax$ for $x \in \mathcal{H} = \mathbb{F}^n$. The *rank* of A is defined to be the rank of T_A.

For an $m \times n$ matrix A, the *column space* is the linear span of the column vectors of A (which is a subspace of $\mathbb{F}^m$), and the *row space* is the linear span of the row vectors of A (which is a subspace of $\mathbb{F}^n$).

Proposition 1.51. *Let A be an $m \times n$ matrix.*

(i) *The rank of A is equal to the dimension of the column space of A, and also equal to the dimension of the row space of A.*

(ii) *If A is an $m \times m$ matrix, then A is invertible if and only if $\operatorname{rank}(A) = m$.*

Proof. (i) The range space of the operator T_A is exactly the linear span of the column vectors of A, so $\operatorname{rank}(A)$ is exactly the dimension of the column space of A. We must then show that the dimension of the row and column spaces are equal. Denote the columns of A by a_j for $j = 1, 2, \ldots, n$, and let R be the column space of A. Assume R has dimension k.

Let $\{b_i\}_{i=1}^k$ be a basis for R, so we can write each column of A as a linear combination of the basis elements:

$$a_j = c_{1j}b_1 + c_{2j}b_2 + \cdots + c_{kj}b_k \quad j = 1, 2, \ldots, n.$$

We can then write A in a matrix equation. If B is the $m \times k$ matrix with columns $\{b_i\}_{i=1}^k$ and C is the $k \times n$ matrix of scalars $C = [c_{ij}]$, then we have $A = BC$. Taking transposes gives the matrix equation $A^T = C^T B^T$. When we interpret this, we see that each column of A^T is now in the span of the k columns of C^T. Hence, the dimension of the column space of A^T, which is clearly also the dimension of the row space of A, can be at most k. In other words, $\text{rank}(A) \geq \dim \text{row} A$. To get the opposite inequality, substitute A^T into the above argument to obtain $\text{rank}(A^T) \geq \dim \text{row} A^T = \text{rank}(A)$, which completes the proof.

We leave part (ii) to Exercise 16. □

In the case where $\text{rank}(A) = \min\{m, n\}$, we say that A is a *full rank matrix*. In subsequent chapters we will see that full rank matrices are very important in finite frame theory.

From Proposition 1.51, we have the following useful fact:

Theorem 1.52. *Let $\{x_1, x_2, \ldots, x_m\}$ be the set of row vectors of an $m \times n$ matrix A, and suppose $n \leq m$. Then A is of full rank (i.e. $\text{rank}(A) = n$) if and only if $\text{span}\{x_1, x_2, \ldots, x_m\} = \mathbb{F}^n$.*

Proof. Exercise 17. □

1.5. Determinant and Trace

The determinant and trace are special scalar-valued functions defined on the set of square matrices. Although the definition of determinant can be given in a more abstract way, we use the following inductive definition:

Definition 1.53. The *determinant* of an $n \times n$ matrix, denoted by $\det(A)$, is defined as follows: If $A = [a]$ is 1×1 matrix, then $\det(A) = a$. If A is a 2×2 matrix, then $\det(A) = a_{11}a_{22} - a_{12}a_{21}$. Inductively, if we assume that the determinant of an arbitrary $(n-1) \times (n-1)$ matrix has been defined, then the determinant of an $n \times n$ matrix A is given by

$$\det(A) = \sum_{j=1}^{n} (-1)^{1+j} a_{1j} \det(M_{1j}),$$

where M_{ij} is the $(n-1) \times (n-1)$ matrix obtained from A by deleting the ith row and j^{th} column of A.

The following proposition summarizes some basic properties of the determinant.

Proposition 1.54. *Let A and B be $n \times n$ matrices.*

(i) $\det(A) = \sum_{j=1}^{n} (-1)^{i+j} a_{ij} \det(M_{ij})$.

(ii) $\det(AB) = \det(A)\det(B)$.

(iii) $\det(A^T) = \det(A)$.

(iv) *A is invertible if and only if* $\det(A) \neq 0$.

(v) *If A and B are similar matrices, then* $\det(A) = \det(B)$.

Proof. We refer the reader to an introductory linear algebra book such as [4] for the proofs of these properties. □

Definition 1.55. Let $A = [a_{ij}]$ be an $n \times n$ matrix. Then the *trace* of A is defined by

$$\operatorname{tr}(A) = \sum_{i=1}^{n} a_{ii}.$$

Proposition 1.56. *Let A, B be $n \times n$ matrices and $\alpha, \beta \in \mathbb{F}$.*

(i) $\operatorname{tr}(\alpha A + \beta B) = \alpha \operatorname{tr}(A) + \beta \operatorname{tr}(B)$.

(ii) $\operatorname{tr}(AB) = \operatorname{tr}(BA)$.

(iii) *If A and B are similar, then* $\operatorname{tr}(A) = \operatorname{tr}(B)$.

Proof. The proofs of parts (i) and (iii) are straightforward, so we will leave them as Exercise 18. For the proof of (ii), write $A = [a_{ij}]$

and $B = [b_{ij}]$. The diagonal elements of AB are given by $[AB]_{ii} = \sum_{k=1}^{n} a_{ik}b_{ki}$. Then we have:

$$\begin{aligned}
\operatorname{tr}(AB) &= \sum_{i=1}^{n} [AB]_{ii} \\
&= \sum_{i=1}^{n} \sum_{k=1}^{n} a_{ik}b_{ki} \\
&= \sum_{k=1}^{n} \sum_{i=1}^{n} b_{ki}a_{ik} \\
&= \sum_{k=1}^{n} [BA]_{kk} = \operatorname{tr}(BA).
\end{aligned}$$ □

1.6. Inner Products and Orthonormal Bases

Many applications involve the topological structure of the spaces. In this section we introduce the concept of inner product on a vector space , which will automatically infer the notion of distance between vectors, and so will lead to geometric and topological structures of the vector spaces.

Definition 1.57. Let $\mathcal{H}$ be a vector space over $\mathbb{F}$. An *inner product* is a map $\langle \cdot, \cdot \rangle : \mathcal{H} \times \mathcal{H} \to \mathbb{F}$ which satisfies the following properties for every $x, y, z \in \mathcal{H}$ and $\alpha \in \mathbb{F}$:

(i) $\langle x, x \rangle \geq 0$ for all $x \in \mathcal{H}$, with $\langle x, x \rangle = 0$ if and only if $x = 0$.

(ii) $\langle x + z, y \rangle = \langle x, y \rangle + \langle z, y \rangle$ and $\langle \alpha x, y \rangle = \alpha \langle x, y \rangle$.

(iii) $\overline{\langle x, y \rangle} = \langle y, x \rangle$, where $\overline{\langle x, y \rangle}$ denotes the complex conjugate of $\langle x, y \rangle$.

A vector space $\mathcal{H}$ equipped with an inner product is called an *inner product space*.

The third property in the definition of the inner product reduces to $\langle x, y \rangle = \langle y, x \rangle$ when the scalar field $\mathbb{F} = \mathbb{R}$. Notice that the three properties of inner products imply a fourth property: $\langle x, y + z \rangle =$

$\langle x, y \rangle + \langle x, z \rangle$ and $\langle x, \alpha y \rangle = \overline{\alpha} \langle x, y \rangle$ for every $x, y, z \in \mathcal{H}$ and $\alpha \in \mathbb{C}$.

Example 1.58. Let $\mathcal{H} = \mathbb{C}^n$ (or $\mathbb{R}^n$). For $x, y \in \mathcal{H}$ with components $\xi_1, \xi_2, \ldots, \xi_n$ and $\eta_1, \eta_2, \ldots, \eta_n$, respectively, the inner product of x and y is defined by

$$\langle x, y \rangle = \sum_{i=1}^{n} \xi_i \overline{\eta_i}.$$

This is referred as the standard inner product on $\mathbb{C}^n$.

Example 1.59. If $\langle x, y \rangle$ is any inner product on a vector space $\mathcal{H}$, then $\langle x, y \rangle' = r \langle x, y \rangle$ defines another inner product on $\mathcal{H}$ for any $r > 0$.

Example 1.60. Let $\mathcal{H}$ be the vector space $C[a, b]$ of all the continuous (real or complex-valued) functions on $[a, b]$. For $f, g \in \mathcal{H}$, define

$$\langle f, g \rangle = \int_a^b f(t)\overline{g(t)}dt.$$

Then $\langle f, g \rangle$ defines an inner product on $\mathcal{H}$.

Example 1.61. Let $\mathcal{H}$ be the vector space $\mathbb{P}_n$ of all the real polynomials of degree less than or equal to n, and let $\{a_1, a_2, \ldots, a_m\}$ be m different real numbers. Assume that $m \geq n$. For $f, g \in \mathcal{H}$, define

$$\langle f, g \rangle = \sum_{i=1}^{m} f(a_i) g(a_i).$$

Then $\langle f, g \rangle$ defines an inner product on $\mathcal{H}$.

Example 1.62. Let $\mathcal{I}$ be any finite or countably infinite index set. We define the vector space $\ell^2(\mathcal{I})$ to be the set of all finite or infinite sequences $a = (a_i)_{i \in \mathcal{I}}$ with entries in $\mathbb{F}$ such that

$$\sum_{i \in \mathcal{I}} |a_i|^2 < \infty,$$

with addition and scalar multiplication being defined as in Euclidean space $\mathbb{F}^n$. We can define the inner product of elements in $\ell^2(\mathcal{I})$ by:

$$\langle a, b \rangle = \sum_{i \in \mathcal{I}} a_i \overline{b_i}.$$

Note that the proof that this definition does indeed give an inner product will require a convergence argument if $\mathcal{I}$ is an infinite set.

Another notion we can define on a vector space is that of a norm. A norm yields a notion of "length" of vectors in the vector space. It is a special case of a metric, which can be defined on more general spaces. We will demonstrate here that every inner product space has a norm.

Definition 1.63. A *normed space* is a vector space $\mathcal{H}$ with a map $\| \cdot \| : \mathcal{H} \to [0, \infty)$ which satisfies the following properties for every $x, y \in \mathcal{H}$ and $\alpha \in \mathbb{F}$.

(i) $\|x\| = 0$ if and only if $x = 0$.

(ii) $\|\alpha x\| = |\alpha| \|x\|$.

(iii) $\|x + y\| \leq \|x\| + \|y\|$ (Triangle Inequality).

We call $\|x\|$ the *norm of* x.

Now let $\mathcal{H}$ be an inner product space and define $\|x\| = \langle x, x \rangle^{\frac{1}{2}}$ for each $x \in \mathcal{H}$. We see that $\|x\| \in [0, \infty)$, and we leave it as an exercise to show that this map is a norm on $\mathcal{H}$. This will require the following proposition. Notice that for the purposes of the proof of Proposition 1.64, we are taking $\| \cdot \|$ to be the above map from $\mathcal{H}$ to $\mathbb{R}$, but are not assuming it satisfies the norm properties from Definition 1.63.

Proposition 1.64. *Let $\mathcal{H}$ be an inner product space and let $x, y \in \mathcal{H}$. Let $\|x\| = \langle x, x \rangle^{\frac{1}{2}}$. Then the following properties hold:*

(i) (Cauchy-Schwarz Inequality) $|\langle x, y \rangle| \leq \|x\| \|y\|$, *with equality holding if and only if one is the scalar multiple of the other.*

(ii) (Triangle Inequality) $\|x + y\| \leq \|x\| + \|y\|$.

Proof. (i) Clearly we can assume that $x \neq 0$. Suppose that $\langle x, y \rangle$ is real. Then we have

$$\begin{aligned} 0 &\leq \|y - \frac{\langle x, y \rangle}{\langle x, x \rangle} x\|^2 \\ &= \langle y, y \rangle - 2\frac{\langle x, y \rangle^2}{\langle x, x \rangle} + \Big(\frac{\langle x, y \rangle}{\langle x, x \rangle}\Big)^2 \langle x, x \rangle \\ &= \frac{\langle y, y \rangle \langle x, x \rangle - \langle x, y \rangle^2}{\langle x, x \rangle}. \end{aligned}$$

Thus we have $|\langle x, y \rangle| \leq \|x\|\|y\|$, with equality if and only if y is a scalar multiple of x. In the case that $\langle x, y \rangle$ is complex, we can pick a scalar λ such that $|\lambda = 1|$ and $\lambda \langle x, y \rangle$ is real. So we get

$$|\langle x, y \rangle| = \langle \lambda x, y \rangle \leq \|\lambda x\|\|y\| = \|x\|\|y\|.$$

Hence we complete the proof of (i).

(ii) By using (i) we have

$$\begin{aligned} \|x + y\|^2 &= \|x\|^2 + 2\,\mathrm{Re}\,\langle x, y \rangle + \|y\|^2 \\ &\leq \|x\|^2 + 2|\langle x, y \rangle| + \|y\|^2 \\ &\leq \|x\|^2 + 2\|x\|\|y\| + \|y\|^2 \\ &= (\|x\| + \|y\|)^2. \end{aligned}$$

Thus $\|x + y\| \leq \|x\| + \|y\|$. □

Proposition 1.65. *Let $\mathcal{H}$ be an inner product space and $\|x\| = \langle x, x \rangle^{\frac{1}{2}}$. Then $\|\cdot\|$ defines a norm for $\mathcal{H}$.*

Proof. Exercise 19. □

Let $\mathcal{H}$ be an inner product space with norm given by the inner product: $\|x\| = |\langle x, x \rangle|^{\frac{1}{2}}$. Let $\{x_k\}_{k=1}^{\infty}$ be a sequence in $\mathcal{H}$. We say that $\{x_k\}$ is a Cauchy sequence if for every $\epsilon > 0$ there exists $N \in \mathbb{N}$ such that for all $k, \ell \geq N$, $\|x_k - x_\ell\| < \epsilon$. If $\|x_k - x\| \to 0$ as $k \to \infty$, then we say that $\{x_k\}$ is *convergent* to x, and x is called the *limit* of the sequence. Notice that the concept of a convergent sequence requires a vector space to have a norm, but not necessarily an inner product. A normed space $\mathcal{V}$ is called *complete* if every Cauchy sequence has a limit in $\mathcal{V}$. An inner product space which is complete in the norm arising from the inner product is called a *Hilbert space.*

Proposition 1.66. *Let $\mathcal{H}$ be an inner product space.*

(i) *The limit of a convergent sequence is unique.*

(ii) *If $\mathcal{H}$ is finite-dimensional, then every Cauchy sequence has a limit in $\mathcal{H}$; i.e. $\mathcal{H}$ is complete.*

Proof. Exercise 20. □

An immediate consequence of Proposition 1.66 is that the inner product spaces $\mathbb{F}^n$, $\mathbb{P}_n$, and $\ell^2(\mathcal{I})$ for $\mathcal{I}$ finite are all Hilbert spaces.

Definition 1.67. Two vectors x, y in an inner product space are called *orthogonal* if $\langle x, y \rangle = 0$. A subset $\mathcal{S}$ of $\mathcal{H}$ is called an *orthogonal set* if all the elements in $\mathcal{S}$ are mutually orthogonal.

Lemma 1.68. *If $S = \{x_1, x_2, \ldots, x_k\}$ is an orthogonal set of nonzero vectors, then S is linearly independent.*

Proof. Assume that $\sum_{i=1}^{k} \alpha_i x_i = 0$. Then for each j, by applying the inner product with x_j to both sides, we get $\alpha_j \langle x_j, x_j \rangle = 0$. Thus $\alpha_j = 0$ since $x_j \neq 0$. Therefore $S = \{x_1, x_2, \ldots, x_k\}$ is linearly independent. □

Definition 1.69. An *orthonormal basis* for a Hilbert space $\mathcal{H}$ is a basis whose elements are pairwise orthogonal unit vectors. A *scaled orthonormal basis* is a basis whose elements all have the same norm (perhaps not 1) and are pairwise orthogonal.

The significance of orthonormal bases lies in the following property.

Proposition 1.70. *Let $\{e_i\}_{i=1}^{n}$ be an orthonormal basis for a Hilbert space $\mathcal{H}$. Given $x \in \mathcal{H}$, the unique coefficients for the linear expansion of x in terms of $\{e_i\}_{i=1}^{n}$ are given by the inner products $\langle x, e_i \rangle$. In short,*

$$x = \sum \langle x, e_i \rangle e_i \qquad \forall x \in \mathcal{H}.$$

Proof. Since $x \in \mathcal{H}$ and $\{e_i\}_{i=1}^{n}$ is a basis, we have $x = c_1 e_1 + c_2 e_2 + \cdots + c_n e_n$, and the coefficients c_i are unique. Take the inner product with some e_k to get:

$$\begin{aligned}
\langle x, e_k \rangle &= \langle c_1 e_1 + c_2 e_2 + \cdots + c_n e_n, e_k \rangle \\
&= c_1 \langle e_1, e_k \rangle + c_2 \langle e_2, e_k \rangle + \cdots + c_n \langle e_n, e_k \rangle \\
&= c_k \langle e_k, e_k \rangle = c_k.
\end{aligned}$$

The final line above holds due to the orthonormality of $\{e_i\}_{i=1}^n$. □

This immediately yields another important formula:

Proposition 1.71 (Parseval's Identity). *Let $\{e_i\}_{i=1}^n$ be an orthonormal basis for a Hilbert space $\mathcal{H}$. Then, for every $x \in \mathcal{H}$,*

$$\|x\|^2 = \sum_{i=1}^{n} |\langle x, e_i \rangle|^2.$$

Proof.

$$\begin{aligned}
\langle x, x \rangle &= \left\langle \sum_{i=1}^{n} \langle x, e_i \rangle e_i, x \right\rangle \quad \text{by Proposition 1.70} \\
&= \sum_{i=1}^{n} \langle x, e_i \rangle \langle e_i, x \rangle \\
&= \sum_{i=1}^{n} |\langle x, e_i \rangle|^2.
\end{aligned}$$

□

A corollary to Parseval's Identity is the general version of the Pythagorean Theorem.

Corollary 1.72 (Pythagorean Theorem). *Given a Hilbert space $\mathcal{H}$ and vectors $\{x_1, x_1, \ldots, x_k\} \subset \mathcal{H}$ which are pairwise orthogonal, then we have*

$$\left\| \sum_{i=1}^{k} x_i \right\|^2 = \sum_{i=1}^{k} \|x_i\|^2.$$

Proof. Exercise 21. □

A natural question is whether there exists an orthonormal basis for every Hilbert space. This can be answered by the following well-known Gram-Schmidt orthogonalization procedure:

Theorem 1.73 (Gram-Schmidt). *Let $\mathcal{H}$ be a Hilbert space, and let $\{x_1, x_2, \ldots, x_k\}$ be a linearly independent set in $\mathcal{H}$. Then there exists an orthonormal set $\{u_1, u_2, \ldots, u_k\}$ with the same span.*

Proof. We define the set of vectors $\{v_1, v_2, \ldots, v_k\}$ recursively. For $j = 1, 2, \ldots, k$, let

$$v_j = x_j - \sum_{i=1}^{j-1} \frac{\langle x_j, v_i \rangle}{\|v_i\|^2} v_i.$$

Observe that this definition gives $v_1 = x_1$ and each vector v_j is in the span of $\{x_1, x_2, \ldots, x_j\}$. None of the vectors v_j can be the zero vector by linear independence of the original collection of vectors. It is straightforward to verify that $\langle v_i, v_j \rangle = 0$ for $i \neq j$. Therefore, $\{v_j\}_{j=1}^k$ is an orthogonal set. Define $u_i = \dfrac{v_i}{\|v_i\|}$. Then $\{u_1, u_2, \ldots, u_k\}$ is an orthonormal set having the same span as $\{x_i\}_{i=1}^k$. □

Corollary 1.74. *Every finite-dimensional Hilbert space has an orthonormal basis.*

The following lemma, the Polarization Lemma, will be used in the next chapter.

Lemma 1.75 (Polarization Lemma). *Let $\mathcal{H}$ be a Hilbert space over $\mathbb{R}$ or $\mathbb{C}$, and let x and y be arbitrary vectors in $\mathcal{H}$.*

(i) *If $\mathcal{H}$ is a vector space with scalar field $\mathbb{R}$, then*

$$\langle x, y \rangle = \frac{1}{4}[\|x+y\|^2 - \|x-y\|^2].$$

(ii) *If $\mathcal{H}$ is a vector space with scalar field $\mathbb{C}$, then*

$$\langle x, y \rangle = \frac{1}{4}[\|x+y\|^2 - \|x-y\|^2] + \frac{i}{4}[\|x+iy\|^2 - \|x-iy\|^2].$$

Proof. We have, whether $\mathbb{F}$ is real or complex,

$$\begin{aligned} \|x+y\|^2 - \|x-y\|^2 &= \langle x+y, x+y \rangle - \langle x-y, x-y \rangle \\ &= \langle x, x \rangle + \langle x, y \rangle + \langle y, x \rangle + \langle y, y \rangle \\ &\quad - \langle x, x \rangle + \langle x, y \rangle + \langle y, x \rangle - \langle y, y \rangle \\ &= 2\langle x, y \rangle + 2\langle y, x \rangle. \end{aligned}$$

(i) If $\mathcal{H}$ is real, then $\langle x, y \rangle = \langle y, x \rangle$, and it follows that

$$\langle x, y \rangle = \frac{1}{4}[\|x+y\|^2 - \|x-y\|^2].$$

(ii) If $\mathcal{H}$ is complex, then $\langle y, x \rangle = \overline{\langle x, y \rangle}$, so

$$\begin{aligned} 2\langle x, y \rangle + 2\langle y, x \rangle &= 2\langle x, y \rangle + 2\overline{\langle x, y \rangle} \\ &= 4\,\mathrm{Re}(\langle x, y \rangle), \end{aligned}$$

where we use $\mathrm{Re}(z)$ and $\mathrm{Im}(z)$ to denote the real part and imaginary part of a complex number z, respectively. Thus

$$\mathrm{Re}(\langle x, y \rangle) = \frac{1}{4}[\|x+y\|^2 - \|x-y\|^2]$$

for all vectors $x, y \in \mathcal{H}$. So for y replaced with the vector iy we have

$$\mathrm{Re}(\langle x, iy \rangle) = \frac{1}{4}[\|x+iy\|^2 - \|x-iy\|^2].$$

Next, by using the properties that $\langle x, iy \rangle = -i\langle x, y \rangle$ and $\mathrm{Re}(-i\langle x, y \rangle) = \mathrm{Im}(\langle x, y \rangle)$, we have that

$$\mathrm{Im}(\langle x, y \rangle) = \frac{1}{4}[\|x+iy\|^2 - \|x-iy\|^2].$$

Therefore

$$\begin{aligned} \langle x, y \rangle &= \mathrm{Re}(\langle x, y \rangle) + i\,\mathrm{Im}(\langle x, y \rangle) \\ &= \frac{1}{4}[\|x+y\|^2 - \|x-y\|^2] + \frac{i}{4}[\|x+iy\|^2 - \|x-iy\|^2]. \qquad \square \end{aligned}$$

1.7. Orthogonal Direct Sum

The notion of the direct sum of inner product spaces is slightly different than that of vector spaces. To differentiate the two, we use the symbol $\dot{+}$ to represent the algebraic direct sum of vector spaces, which we described in Section 1.2, and the symbol $\oplus$ for the orthogonal direct sum of Hilbert spaces.

Definition 1.76. If $\mathcal{K}_1$ and $\mathcal{K}_2$ are Hilbert spaces, we define the (orthogonal) *direct sum* of $\mathcal{K}_1$ and $\mathcal{K}_2$ to be

$$\mathcal{K}_1 \oplus \mathcal{K}_2 = \{(x_1, x_2) : x_1 \in \mathcal{K}_1, x_2 \in \mathcal{K}_2\}.$$

Proposition 1.77. *If $(\mathcal{K}_1, \langle\,\cdot,\cdot\,\rangle_{\mathcal{K}_1}), (\mathcal{K}_2, \langle\,\cdot,\cdot\,\rangle_{\mathcal{K}_2})$ are Hilbert spaces, the space $\mathcal{K}_1 \oplus \mathcal{K}_2$ is a vector space under the operations*

$$\alpha(x_1, x_2) = (\alpha x_1, \alpha x_2) \quad \textit{and} \quad (x_1, x_2) + (y_1, y_2) = (x_1 + y_1, x_2 + y_2).$$

Proof. Exercise 22. □

Proposition 1.78. *Given $\mathcal{K}_1 \oplus \mathcal{K}_2$ as defined above, let*

$$\langle\, (x_1, x_2), (y_1, y_2)\,\rangle = \langle\, x_1, y_1\,\rangle_{\mathcal{K}_1} + \langle\, x_2, y_2\,\rangle_{\mathcal{K}_2}.$$

Then this map is an inner product on $\mathcal{K}_1 \oplus \mathcal{K}_2$, and $\mathcal{K}_1 \oplus \mathcal{K}_2$ is a Hilbert space under this inner product.

Proof. Exercise 23. □

Given $\mathcal{H} = \mathcal{K}_1 \oplus \mathcal{K}_2$, let

$$\widetilde{\mathcal{K}}_1 = \{(x_1, 0) \,:\, x_1 \in \mathcal{K}_1\} \quad \text{and} \quad \widetilde{\mathcal{K}}_2 = \{(0, x_2) \,:\, x_2 \in \mathcal{K}_2\}.$$

It is clear that $\widetilde{\mathcal{K}}_1$ and $\widetilde{\mathcal{K}}_2$ are subspaces of $\mathcal{H}$. It is also easy to verify that $\widetilde{\mathcal{K}}_1 + \widetilde{\mathcal{K}}_2 = \mathcal{H}$ and that $\widetilde{\mathcal{K}}_1 \cap \widetilde{\mathcal{K}}_2 = \{(0,0)\}$, the zero vector in $\mathcal{H}$. We also see that the subspaces $\widetilde{\mathcal{K}}_1$ and $\widetilde{\mathcal{K}}_2$ are orthogonal; i.e. given $x \in \widetilde{\mathcal{K}}_1$ and $y \in \widetilde{\mathcal{K}}_2$, we have $\langle\, x, y\,\rangle = 0$. We denote the orthogonality of these subspaces by $\widetilde{\mathcal{K}}_1 \perp \widetilde{\mathcal{K}}_2$. This motivates the following subspace description of the direct sum.

Definition 1.79. Let $\mathcal{H}$ be a Hilbert space with subspaces $\mathcal{K}_1, \mathcal{K}_2$ which satisfy the following properties.

(i) $\mathcal{H} = \mathcal{K}_1 + \mathcal{K}_2$.

(ii) $\mathcal{K}_1 \cap \mathcal{K}_2 = \{0\}$.

(iii) $\mathcal{K}_1 \perp \mathcal{K}_2$.

Then we say $\mathcal{H}$ is the *direct sum* of $\mathcal{K}_1$ and $\mathcal{K}_2$, which we denote $\mathcal{H} = \mathcal{K}_1 \oplus \mathcal{K}_2$.

Remark 1.80. It requires some care to keep these two points of view straight. If we start with two Hilbert spaces $\mathcal{K}_1, \mathcal{K}_2$, then there is an isomorphic copy of each (the spaces $\widetilde{\mathcal{K}_1}$ and $\widetilde{\mathcal{K}_2}$ from Proposition 1.78) in $\mathcal{H} = \mathcal{K}_1 \oplus \mathcal{K}_2$. Both are subspaces of $\mathcal{H}$ satisfying the properties in Definition 1.79. Conversely, if $\mathcal{K}_1$ and $\mathcal{K}_2$ are subspaces of $\mathcal{H}$ that satisfy these three properties, then we can describe a Hilbert space $\widetilde{\mathcal{H}}$ isomorphic to $\mathcal{H}$ as follows:

$$\widetilde{\mathcal{H}} = \{(x_1, x_2) : x = x_1 + x_2 \in \mathcal{H}\}.$$

The map $x \mapsto (x_1, x_2)$ is well defined, since the expression $x = x_1 + x_2$ is unique. Under the given operations and inner product, we see that $\widetilde{\mathcal{H}}$ is a Hilbert space, and is isomorphic to $\mathcal{H}$. Using our first definition of direct sum, we have $\widetilde{\mathcal{H}} = \mathcal{K}_1 \oplus \mathcal{K}_2$.

In the obvious way, this notion can be extended to a direct sum of any finite number of Hilbert spaces.

Definition 1.81. If $\mathcal{K}_1, \mathcal{K}_2, \ldots, \mathcal{K}_n$ are Hilbert spaces, the *direct sum* of these spaces is the set

$$\mathcal{K}_1 \oplus \mathcal{K}_2 \oplus \cdots \oplus \mathcal{K}_n = \{(x_1, x_2, \ldots, x_n) : x_i \in \mathcal{K}_i, i = 1, 2, \ldots, n\}.$$

It is readily verified that $\mathcal{H} = \mathcal{K}_1 \oplus \mathcal{K}_2 \oplus \cdots \oplus \mathcal{K}_n$ is a Hilbert space with inner product $\langle x, y \rangle = \sum_{i=1}^{n} \langle x_1, y_i \rangle$.

1.8. Exercises from the Text

Exercise 1. Show that a nonempty set of at least two vectors is linearly dependent if and only if at least one of the vectors can be written as a linear combination of others in the set.

Exercise 2. Prove Lemma 1.12.

Exercise 3. Complete the proof of Proposition 1.16.

Exercise 4. Prove Lemma 1.24.

Exercise 5. If E, F are subspaces of a vector space $\mathcal{V}$, prove that $E + F = \operatorname{span}\{E, F\}$.

Exercise 6. Prove Lemma 1.29.

Exercise 7. Prove Proposition 1.31.

Exercise 8. Prove Proposition 1.32.

Exercise 9. Prove Theorem 1.33.

Exercise 10. Prove Proposition 1.37.

Exercise 11. Prove Lemma 1.39.

Exercise 12. Prove Lemma 1.41.

Exercise 13. Prove Proposition 1.43.

Exercise 14. Prove Proposition 1.44.

Exercise 15. Prove Proposition 1.47.

Exercise 16. Complete the proof of Proposition 1.51.

Exercise 17. Prove Theorem 1.52.

Exercise 18. Prove Proposition 1.56, parts (i) and (ii).

Exercise 19. Prove Proposition 1.65.

Exercise 20. Prove Proposition 1.66.

Exercise 21. Prove the Pythagorean Theorem, Corollary 1.72.

Exercise 22. Prove Proposition 1.77.

Exercise 23. Prove Proposition 1.78.

1.9. Additional Exercises

Some of the following exercises are intended to provide a reminder of the fundamental concepts from linear algebra. You may need to consult your favorite linear algebra textbook to refresh your memory.

Exercise 24. Define $\mathbb{M}_{m\times n}$ to be the set of all $m \times n$ matrices with entries in $\mathbb{F}$. Prove that $\mathbb{M}_{m\times n}$ is a vector space.

Exercise 25. Extend Lemma 1.13 to the case when $\mathcal{S}$ is an arbitrary subset of $\mathcal{V}$ (i.e., do not assume that $\mathcal{S}$ is finite).

Exercise 26. Let $T : \mathcal{V} \to \mathcal{V}$ be a linear operator.

(i) Prove that if T is injective and $\{x_i\}_{i=1}^n$ are linearly independent, then $\{Tx_i\}_{i=1}^n$ is also linearly independent.

(ii) Prove that if T is surjective and $\{x_i\}_{i=1}^n$ spans $\mathcal{V}$, then $\{Tx_i\}_{i=1}^n$ also spans $\mathcal{V}$.

(iii) Prove Theorem 1.33.

Exercise 27. Compute the rank and nullity (i.e. dimension of the null space) of the following matrix. Also, compute a basis for the null space of the following matrix.

$$\begin{bmatrix} 1 & 2 & 4 & 1 & 5 \\ 3 & 2 & 0 & 5 & 3 \\ 1 & 0 & 0 & 3 & 0 \\ 2 & 2 & 2 & 0 & 4 \end{bmatrix}$$

Exercise 28. Determine whether the set $\left\{ \begin{bmatrix} 1 \\ 3 \\ 1 \\ 3 \end{bmatrix}, \begin{bmatrix} 1 \\ 2 \\ 1 \\ 1 \end{bmatrix}, \begin{bmatrix} 1 \\ 5 \\ 4 \\ 2 \end{bmatrix} \right\}$ of vectors in $\mathbb{R}^4$ is linearly dependent or linearly independent. Prove your answer.

Exercise 29. Let $S = \operatorname{span} \left\{ \begin{bmatrix} 1 \\ 0 \\ 1 \\ 1 \end{bmatrix}, \begin{bmatrix} 1 \\ 2 \\ 0 \\ 0 \end{bmatrix} \right\}$. Compute a basis for the orthogonal complement of S in $\mathbb{R}^4$.

Exercise 30. Let $\mathbb{P}_2$ be the vector space of all polynomials of degree less than or equal to 2.

(i) Show that $\{x + 1, x^2 + x, x - 1\}$ is a basis for $\mathbb{P}_2$.

(ii) Define a transformation L from $\mathbb{P}_2$ into $\mathbb{P}_2$ by:

$$L(f) = (xf)'.$$

In other words, L acts on the polynomial $f(x)$ by first multiplying the function by x, then differentiating. The result is another polynomial in $\mathbb{P}_2$. Prove that L is a linear transformation.

(iii) Compute the matrix representation of the linear transformation L above with respect to the basis for $\mathbb{P}_2$ from the first part of this problem.

Exercise 31. Let A and B be $n \times n$ matrices. Prove that the rank of the product AB is no greater than the smaller of the ranks of A and B.

Exercise 32. Let V be the subspace of $\mathbb{R}^3$ spanned by the vectors $\left\{ \begin{bmatrix} 1 \\ 1 \\ 1 \end{bmatrix}, \begin{bmatrix} 3 \\ 1 \\ 3 \end{bmatrix} \right\} = \{\mathbf{u_1}, \mathbf{u_2}\}$. Let $\mathbf{w_1} = \begin{bmatrix} 2 \\ 1 \\ 2 \end{bmatrix}$ and $\mathbf{w_2} = \begin{bmatrix} 5 \\ 2 \\ 5 \end{bmatrix}$.

(i) Show that $\{\mathbf{u_1}, \mathbf{u_2}\}$ and $\{\mathbf{w_1}, \mathbf{w_2}\}$ are both bases for V.

(ii) Compute the coordinate vectors of $\mathbf{u_1}$ and $\mathbf{u_2}$ with respect to the basis $\{\mathbf{w_1}, \mathbf{w_2}\}$.

(iii) Find the transition matrix corresponding to the change of basis for V from $\{\mathbf{u_1}, \mathbf{u_2}\}$ to $\{\mathbf{w_1}, \mathbf{w_2}\}$.

Exercise 33. Given a vector space $\mathcal{V}$ and a subspace E of $\mathcal{V}$, prove that E has a nonzero subspace complement.

Exercise 34. Suppose $a_1, a_2, \ldots, a_n$ are real numbers. Use the Cauchy-Schwarz *equality* to find the minimum value of $a_1^2 + a_2^2 + \cdots + a_n^2$ over all possible values of $a_1, a_2, \ldots, a_n$ under the constraint that $a_1 + a_2 + \cdots + a_n = L$.

Exercise 35. Let $\mathcal{H}$ be a Hilbert space and $x, y \in \mathcal{H}$. Suppose that for all $z \in \mathcal{H}$, $|\langle z, x \rangle| = |\langle z, y \rangle|$. Prove that $x = \lambda y$, where $\lambda \in \mathbb{C}, |\lambda| = 1$. *Hint*: Use the Cauchy-Schwarz equality.

Exercise 36. Let $E_1, E_2, \ldots, E_n$ be subspaces of a vector space $\mathcal{V}$ with the property that every $v \in V$ can be written uniquely as $v = x_1 + x_2 + \cdots + x_n$ where $x_i \in E_i$ for $i = 1, 2, \ldots, n$. Then we say that $\mathcal{V}$ is a *direct sum* of $E_1, E_2, \ldots, E_n$, and we write

$$\mathcal{V} = E_1 \dot{+} E_2 \dot{+} \cdots \dot{+} E_n.$$

This generalizes Definition 1.27.

(i) Prove that if $\mathcal{V} = E_1 \dot{+} E_2 \dot{+} \cdots \dot{+} E_n$, and if for each $i = 1, 2, \ldots, n$, we have $\{b_{ij}\}_{j=1}^{k_i}$ is a basis for E_i, then

$$B = \{b_{1j}\}_{j=1}^{k_1} \cup \{b_{2j}\}_{j=1}^{k_2} \cup \cdots \cup \{b_{nj}\}_{j=1}^{k_n}$$

is a basis for $\mathcal{V}$. Consequently, $\dim \mathcal{V} = \dim E_1 + \dim E_2 + \cdots + \dim E_n$.

(ii) Prove that $\mathcal{V} = E_1 \dot{+} E_2 \dot{+} \cdots \dot{+} E_n$ if and only if $\mathcal{V} = \operatorname{span}(E_1, E_2, \ldots, E_n)$ and for each $i = 1, 2, \ldots, n$,

$$E_i \cap \operatorname{span}(E_1, \ldots, E_{i-1}, E_{i+1}, \ldots, E_n) = \{0\}.$$

Exercise 37. Let $\mathcal{V}$ and $\mathcal{W}$ be vector spaces. We define $\mathcal{L}(\mathcal{V}, \mathcal{W})$ to be the set of all linear operators from $\mathcal{V}$ to $\mathcal{W}$ and $\mathcal{L}(\mathcal{V})$ to be the set of linear operators from $\mathcal{V}$ to itself. Prove that under the definitions of addition and scalar multiplication on operators given in Definition 1.36 and Proposition 1.44, the set $\mathcal{L}(\mathcal{V}, \mathcal{W})$ is a vector space.

Chapter 2

Finite-Dimensional Operator Theory

Operator theory is the study of operators, or linear transformations. It involves an interesting combination of algebra and (functional) analysis. This chapter covers a few important topics from operator theory in finite dimensions. We have seen that all the linear operators between finite-dimensional vector spaces can be represented as matrices when bases have been prescribed in the underlying Hilbert spaces. When we investigate some important properties of operators, however, it is more common that the particular bases need not be involved. Therefore, most of the results in this chapter will be presented in a way that is independent of the choice of bases in the underlying Hilbert spaces. Many of the results presented in this chapter will be used in subsequent chapters.

2.1. Linear Functionals and the Dual Space

Linear functionals are the foundation of functional analysis, operator theory, as well as frame theory. Linear functionals give information about vectors in a vector space – enough information, we'll see, to uniquely determine any vector.

Definition 2.1. Let $\mathcal{V}$ be a finite-dimensional vector space. A *linear functional* is a linear transformation $\phi : \mathcal{V} \to \mathbb{F}$, i.e. a scalar-valued linear transformation. The collection of all linear functionals on $\mathcal{V}$ is called the *dual space*, and is denoted by $\mathcal{V}^*$.

The next theorem says that there are enough linear functionals on $\mathcal{V}$ to separate any two vectors in $\mathcal{V}$; i.e., for any two vectors $v_1, v_2 \in \mathcal{V}$, $v_1 \neq v_2$, there is a linear functional $\phi \in \mathcal{V}^*$ which distinguishes between v_1 and v_2.

Theorem 2.2. *Suppose $v_1, v_2 \in \mathcal{V}$ are distinct vectors. Then there is a $\phi \in \mathcal{V}^*$ such that $\phi(v_1) \neq \phi(v_2)$.*

Proof. Consider $e_1 = v_1 - v_2$, and let $\{e_2, \ldots, e_n\} \subset \mathcal{V}$ be such that $\{e_1, e_2, \ldots, e_n\}$ is a basis for $\mathcal{V}$. Define $\phi : \mathcal{V} \to \mathbb{F}$ by $\phi(e_1) = 1$; $\phi(e_k) = 0$ for $k = 2, \ldots, n$, and extend ϕ to all of $\mathcal{V}$ by linearity. Then $\phi \in \mathcal{V}^*$, and since $\phi(e_1) = \phi(v_1) - \phi(v_2) = 1$, we have that $\phi(v_1) \neq \phi(v_2)$ as required. □

The significance of this theorem is that if $\phi(v_1) = \phi(v_2)$ for all $\phi \in \mathcal{V}^*$, then in fact $v_1 = v_2$. Another way to think of this is if one knows the values $\phi(v)$ for all $\phi \in \mathcal{V}^*$, then one knows v.

It turns out that $\mathcal{V}^*$ is also a vector space by defining addition and scalar multiplication in the typical pointwise fashion:

$$[\phi_1 + \phi_2](v) = \phi_1(v) + \phi_2(v); \qquad [\lambda\phi](v) = \lambda\phi(v). \tag{2.1}$$

We leave it to Exercise 1 to show that these are well defined and that they turn $\mathcal{V}^*$ into a vector space.

Using the Riesz Representation Theorem in the next section, one can show that if $\mathcal{V}$ is finite-dimensional, with dimension n, then $\mathcal{V}^*$ is also finite-dimensional with dimension n.

Theorem 2.3. *Suppose $\mathcal{V}$ has dimension n and $\{\phi_1, \phi_2, \ldots, \phi_k\}$ is a subset of $\mathcal{V}^*$ which spans $\mathcal{V}^*$. If $v_1, v_2 \in \mathcal{V}$ and $\phi_j(v_1) = \phi_j(v_2)$ for $j = 1, 2, \ldots, k$, then $v_1 = v_2$.*

Proof. If we can show that $\phi(v_1) = \phi(v_2)$ for every $\phi \in \mathcal{V}^*$, then applying Theorem 2.2 will prove the statement. But we know this since there are scalars $a_1, a_2, \ldots, a_k \in \mathbb{F}$ such that $\phi = \sum_{j=1}^{k} a_j\phi_j$, whence

$$\phi(v_1) = \sum_{j=1}^{k} a_j \phi_j(v_1) = \sum_{j=1}^{k} a_j \phi_j(v_2) = \phi(v_2). \qquad \square$$

Therefore, if $\phi_1, \phi_2, \ldots, \phi_k$ span $\mathcal{V}^*$, then once the values $\phi_j(v)$ for each $j = 1, 2, \ldots, k$ are known, then v is known. The trick is to reconstruct v as a linear combination using the values $\phi_j(v)$ as coefficients.

2.2. Riesz Representation Theorem and Adjoint Operators

Let $A = [a_{ij}]$ be an $m \times n$ matrix. The *adjoint* matrix A^* of A is the $n \times m$ matrix $B = [b_{ij}]$ such that $b_{ij} = \overline{a_{ji}}$ for all i, j. Note that if A is a matrix of real numbers, then the adjoint is exactly the transpose of A. The following lemma consists of some easily verified properties for the adjoint matrices.

Proposition 2.4. *Let A and B be two matrices, and $\alpha, \beta \in \mathbb{F}$. Assume that they have the appropriate sizes that allow the following operations. Then the following properties hold:*

(i) $(\alpha A + \beta B)^* = \overline{\alpha} A^* + \overline{\beta} B^*$.

(ii) $(A^*)^* = A$.

(iii) $(AB)^* = B^* A^*$.

(iv) $(A^{-1})^* = (A^*)^{-1}$.

Proof. Exercise 2. $\square$

Suppose that $\{e_j\}_{j=1}^n$ and $\{f_i\}_{i=1}^n$ are the standard orthonormal bases for $\mathbb{F}^n$ and $\mathbb{F}^m$, respectively, and $A = [a_{ij}]$ is an $m \times n$ matrix. Then $a_{ij} = \langle Ae_j, f_i \rangle$. Therefore

$$\langle A^* f_j, e_i \rangle = \overline{a_{ji}} = \overline{\langle Ae_i, f_j \rangle} = \langle f_j, Ae_i \rangle .$$

This implies the following:

Lemma 2.5. *Let $A = [a_{ij}]$ be an $m \times n$ matrix with either real or complex entries. Then the adjoint matrix for A satisfies*

$$\langle Ax, y \rangle = \langle x, A^* y \rangle \quad \textit{for all } x \in \mathbb{F}^n, y \in \mathbb{F}^m.$$

We next describe the adjoint of an abstract linear operator, and identify this adjoint with the adjoint of the corresponding matrix. In order to prove that the adjoint of a linear operator is well defined and unique, we first will need to prove an important theorem by Riesz.

Theorem 2.6 (Riesz Representation Theorem). *Let Λ be a linear functional on a finite-dimensional Hilbert space $\mathcal{H}$. (In other words, Λ is a linear operator from $\mathcal{H}$ to $\mathbb{F}$.) Then there exists a unique vector $z \in \mathcal{H}$ such that $\Lambda x = \langle x, z \rangle$ $\forall x \in \mathcal{H}$.*

Proof. Let $\{e_1, e_2, \ldots, e_n\}$ be an orthonormal basis for $\mathcal{H}$. The matrix for $\Lambda : \mathcal{H} \to \mathbb{F}$ with respect to the basis $\{e_i\}_{i=1}^n$ is just the $1 \times n$ matrix $\begin{bmatrix} \Lambda e_1 & \Lambda e_2 & \cdots & \Lambda e_n \end{bmatrix}$. We define $z \in \mathcal{H}$ to be the vector

$$z = \sum_{i=1}^{n} (\overline{\Lambda e_n}) e_n.$$

For every $x \in \mathcal{H}$, x can be written uniquely in the form $x = \sum_{i=1}^n \alpha_i e_i$, where $\alpha_i = \langle x, e_i \rangle$. Taking the inner product of x and z gives:

$$\begin{aligned}
\langle x, z \rangle &= \left\langle \sum_{i=1}^{n} \alpha_i e_i, \sum_{j=1}^{n} \overline{\Lambda(e_j)} e_j \right\rangle \\
&= \sum_{i,j=1}^{n} \left\langle \alpha_i e_i, \overline{\Lambda(e_j)} e_j \right\rangle \\
&= \sum_{i=1}^{n} \alpha_i \Lambda(e_i) \qquad \text{(since } \{e_1\}_{i=1}^n \text{ is an o.n.b.)} \\
&= \Lambda\left(\sum_{i=1}^{n} \alpha_i e_i\right) \\
&= \Lambda(x).
\end{aligned}$$

□

Proposition 2.7. *For any linear operator T from a finite-dimensional inner product space $\mathcal{H}$ to $\mathcal{K}$, there exists a unique linear operator S from $\mathcal{K}$ to $\mathcal{H}$, such that for all $x \in \mathcal{H}, y \in \mathcal{K}$,*

$$\langle Tx, y \rangle = \langle x, Sy \rangle .$$

We call this operator the adjoint of T, and will denote it T^*.

Proof. Let $y \in \mathcal{K}$ be an arbitrary vector. It is readily verified that the map $\Lambda : \mathcal{H} \to \mathbb{F}$ defined by $\Lambda x = \langle Tx, y \rangle$ for $x \in \mathcal{H}$ is a linear map. By the Riesz Representation Theorem, there exists a unique vector $z_y \in \mathcal{H}$ such that $\langle Tx, y \rangle = \langle x, z_y \rangle$ $\forall x \in \mathcal{H}$.

By the uniqueness part of Riesz, the map from y to z_y is well defined from $\mathcal{K}$ to $\mathcal{H}$. We call this map S. It is straightforward to verify that S is linear and unique. Then for all x, y, we have the desired property

$$\langle Tx, y \rangle = \langle x, Sy \rangle . \qquad \square$$

Similar to the properties of adjoint matrices in Proposition 2.4, we also have

Proposition 2.8. *Let S, T be linear operators and $\alpha, \beta \in \mathbb{F}$. Then the following properties hold:*

(i) $(\alpha S + \beta T)^* = \overline{\alpha} S^* + \overline{\beta} T^*$.

(ii) $(T^*)^* = T$.

(iii) $(ST)^* = T^* S^*$.

(iv) *If T is invertible, then so is T^*, and $(T^{-1})^* = (T^*)^{-1}$.*

(v) $I^* = I$.

Proof. We will prove (i) and leave the other four parts to Exercise 3. Suppose $T, S : \mathcal{H} \to \mathcal{K}$ and $x \in \mathcal{H}, y \in \mathcal{K}$. Then we have

$$\begin{aligned}
\langle (\alpha S + \beta T)x, y \rangle &= \langle \alpha Sx, y \rangle + \langle \beta Tx, y \rangle \\
&= \alpha \langle Sx, y \rangle + \beta \langle Tx, y \rangle \\
&= \alpha \langle x, S^* y \rangle + \beta \langle x, T^* y \rangle \\
&= \langle x, \overline{\alpha} S^* y \rangle + \langle x, \overline{\beta} T^* y \rangle \\
&= \langle x, (\overline{\alpha} S^* + \overline{\beta} T^*) y \rangle .
\end{aligned}$$

Therefore, from the definition of adjoint operators, we have

$$(\alpha S + \beta T)^* = \overline{\alpha} S^* + \overline{\beta} T^* . \qquad \square$$

Let $\mathcal{H}$ and $\mathcal{K}$ be two Hilbert spaces with fixed orthonormal bases $\{v_1, v_2, \ldots, v_n\}$ and $\{w_1, w_2, \ldots, w_m\}$ respectively. Recall from Chapter 1 that there is a one-to-one correspondence between the linear operators from $\mathcal{H}$ to $\mathcal{K}$ and the $m \times n$ matrices. In the following proposition, we will denote by M_T the matrix associated to the operator T. These properties are related to those given in Proposition 1.44.

Proposition 2.9. *Let $T, S : \mathcal{H} \to \mathcal{K}$ be linear operators and let $\{v_1, v_2, \dots, v_n\}$ be a fixed orthonormal basis for $\mathcal{H}$ and $\{w_1, w_2, \dots, w_m\}$ a fixed orthonormal basis for $\mathcal{K}$. Let $\alpha, \beta \in \mathbb{F}$. Then the following properties hold:*

(i) $M_T = [m_{ij}]$, *where* $m_{ij} = \langle Tv_j, w_i \rangle$.

(ii) $M_{\alpha T + \beta S} = \alpha M_T + \beta M_S$.

(iii) $(M_T)^* = M_{T^*}$.

Proof. Exercise 4. □

2.3. Self-adjoint and Unitary Operators

In this section we introduce several classes of operators which are particularly useful in the study of operator theory. We start with the definition of self-adjoint operators.

Definition 2.10. Let $T : \mathcal{H} \to \mathcal{H}$ be a linear operator. If $T^* = T$, then we say that T is *self-adjoint*. In the case that $T^*T = TT^*$, we say that T is *normal*.

Clearly, if T is self-adjoint, then T is normal. However, normal operators are not necessarily self-adjoint. For example, let $T : \mathbb{C}^2 \to \mathbb{C}^2$ be defined by the matrix

$$\begin{bmatrix} 0 & 1 \\ -1 & 0 \end{bmatrix};$$

i.e., $T \begin{bmatrix} a \\ b \end{bmatrix} = \begin{bmatrix} b \\ -a \end{bmatrix}$ for $\begin{bmatrix} a \\ b \end{bmatrix} \in \mathbb{C}^2$. Then $T^*T = TT^* = I$. Hence, T is normal but it is clearly not self-adjoint.

Lemma 2.11. *If T is a normal operator on a Hilbert space $\mathcal{H}$, then for all $x \in \mathcal{H}$, $\|Tx\| = \|T^*x\|$.*

Proof. Using the definition of the adjoint operator, we have

$$\begin{aligned} \|Tx\|^2 &= \langle Tx, Tx \rangle \\ &= \langle T^*Tx, x \rangle \\ &= \langle TT^*x, x \rangle \\ &= \langle T^*x, T^*x \rangle \\ &= \|T^*x\|^2. \end{aligned}$$

Therefore, we have $\|Tx\| = \|T^*x\|$. □

Lemma 2.12. *Let $\mathcal{H}$ be a Hilbert space over $\mathbb{R}$ or $\mathbb{C}$ and let $T : \mathcal{H} \to \mathcal{H}$ be a self-adjoint linear operator. Then we have:*

(i) $\langle Tx, x \rangle$ *is real for all* $x \in \mathcal{H}$.

(ii) *If $\mathcal{H}$ is over $\mathbb{R}$, then for all $x, y \in \mathcal{H}$ we have*

$$\langle Tx, y \rangle = \frac{1}{4}[\langle T(x+y), x+y \rangle - \langle T(x-y), x-y \rangle].$$

(iii) *If $\mathcal{H}$ is over $\mathbb{C}$, then for all $x, y \in \mathcal{H}$ we have*

$$\begin{aligned} \langle Tx, y \rangle &= \frac{1}{4}[\langle T(x+y), x+y \rangle - \langle T(x-y), x-y \rangle] \\ &\quad + \frac{i}{4}[\langle T(x+iy), x+iy \rangle - \langle T(x-iy), x-iy \rangle]. \end{aligned}$$

Proof. Part (i) follows from

$$\langle Tx, x \rangle = \langle x, T^*x \rangle = \langle x, Tx \rangle = \overline{\langle Tx, x \rangle}$$

when $T^* = T$.

The proof of parts (ii) and (iii) are similar to the proof of Lemma 1.75 (Exercise 5). □

Proposition 2.13. *Let $T : \mathcal{H} \to \mathcal{H}$ be a linear operator on a complex inner-product space $\mathcal{H}$. Then there exist self-adjoint operators T_1 and T_2 on $\mathcal{H}$ such that*

$$T = T_1 + iT_2.$$

Moreover the above decomposition is unique.

Proof. Let $T_1 = \frac{1}{2}(T + T^*)$ and $T_2 = \frac{1}{2i}(T - T^*)$. Then T_1 and T_2 are self-adjoint and $T = T_1 + iT_2$.

In order to show the uniqueness, let $T = S_1 + iS_2$ with S_1, S_2 self-adjoint. Then we have

$$T_1 + iT_2 = S_1 + iS_2,$$

which implies that $(T_1 - S_1) + i(T_2 - S_2) = 0$.

Let $A = T_1 - S_1$ and $B = T_2 - S_2$. Then A and B are self-adjoint, and $A + iB = 0$. Thus

$$\langle Ax, x \rangle + i \langle Bx, x \rangle = 0$$

for all $x \in \mathcal{H}$. By Lemma 2.12, we have that $\langle Ax, x \rangle$ and $\langle Bx, x \rangle$ are real. Hence they both are zero, and so, again by Lemma 2.12, we have that

$$\langle Ax, y \rangle = \langle Bx, y \rangle = 0$$

for all $x, y \in \mathcal{H}$, which implies that $A = B = 0$. Hence $T_1 = S_1$ and $T_2 = S_2$. Therefore the decomposition is unique. $\square$

One interesting special type of self-adjoint operator occurs if all the inner products $\langle Tx, x \rangle$, $x \in \mathcal{H}$ are nonnegative. We introduce these operators, called positive operators, next.

Definition 2.14. Let $T : \mathcal{H} \to \mathcal{H}$ be a linear operator. Then T is called *positive* if T is self-adjoint and $\langle Tx, x \rangle \geq 0$ for all $x \in \mathcal{H}$. We write $T \geq 0$ for any positive operator.

We leave it as an exercise to prove that not every self-adjoint operator is positive (Exercise 6).

Definition 2.15. Let $T : \mathcal{H} \to \mathcal{K}$ be a linear operator.

(i) T is called an *isometry* if $||Tx|| = ||x||$ for every $x \in \mathcal{H}$.

(ii) T is called a *unitary* operator if it is an isometry and is also surjective.

Note that if T is a self-adjoint or positive operator with domain $\mathcal{H}$, then T necessarily maps $\mathcal{H}$ to itself. But if T is an isometry or a unitary operator T, then T may be a linear operator that maps $\mathcal{H}$ to a different inner product space $\mathcal{K}$. An operator T is called a *co-isometry* if T^* is an isometry.

Proposition 2.16. *Let $T : \mathcal{H} \to \mathcal{K}$ be a linear operator. Then the following are equivalent:*

(i) *T is an isometry.*

(ii) *T preserves the inner product, i.e., $\langle Tx, Ty \rangle = \langle x, y \rangle$ for $x, y \in \mathcal{H}$.*

(iii) *$T^*T = I_{\mathcal{H}}$, where $I_{\mathcal{H}}$ is the identity operator on $\mathcal{H}$.*

Proof. First, we will show the implication (i)$\to$(ii). Assume that T is an isometry. Then

$$\langle Tx, Tx \rangle = \langle x, x \rangle, \quad x \in \mathcal{H}.$$

By Lemma 2.12, we have that

$$\langle Tx, Ty \rangle = \langle x, y \rangle, \quad x, y \in \mathcal{H}.$$

Next, we address the implication (ii)$\to$(iii). Assume that

$$\langle Tx, Ty \rangle = \langle x, y \rangle, \quad x, y \in \mathcal{H}.$$

Then we have

$$\langle x, T^*Ty \rangle = \langle x, y \rangle, \quad x, y \in \mathcal{H},$$

which implies that $T^*Ty = y$ for all $y \in \mathcal{H}$. Hence $T^*T = I_{\mathcal{H}}$.

Finally, we show (iii)$\to$(i). Assume that $T^*T = I_{\mathcal{H}}$. Then for any $x \in \mathcal{H}$ we have

$$\|Tx\|^2 = \langle Tx, Tx \rangle = \langle x, T^*Tx \rangle = \langle x, x \rangle = \|x\|^2.$$

Therefore, T is an isometry. □

As a consequence of Proposition 2.16 we have the following characterization of unitary operators.

Theorem 2.17. *Let $T : \mathcal{H} \to \mathcal{K}$ be a linear operator. Then the following are equivalent:*

(i) *T is a unitary operator.*

(ii) *T preserves the inner product and is surjective.*

(iii) *T^* is a unitary operator.*

(iv) *$T^*T = I_{\mathcal{H}}$ and $TT^* = I_{\mathcal{K}}$.*

Proof. The equivalence of (i) and (ii) follows from the definition of unitary and Proposition 2.16. It also follows from Proposition 2.16 that T is unitary if and only if $T^* = T^{-1}$. This establishes (i)$\leftrightarrow$(iv), and since $(T^*)^* = T$, we also have (iii)$\leftrightarrow$(i). □

In the case that $\mathcal{H}$ and $\mathcal{K}$ have the same finite dimension, then isometries and unitary operators are the same.

Corollary 2.18. *Let $T : \mathcal{H} \to \mathcal{K}$ be a linear operator and suppose $\dim \mathcal{H} = \dim \mathcal{K} = n < \infty$. Then T is unitary if and only if it is an isometry.*

Proof. The forward direction holds by the definition of a unitary operator. For the reverse direction, assume that T is an isometry, which implies it is injective. Thus $n = \dim \mathcal{H} = \dim T\mathcal{H}$. Since $T\mathcal{H} \subseteq \mathcal{K}$ and $\mathcal{K}$ also has finite dimension n, we have $T\mathcal{H} = \mathcal{K}$. This proves that T is a surjective isometry, which implies that T is unitary by the definition. □

Isometries have the important property that they preserve orthonormal sets, and correspondingly, unitary operators preserve orthonormal bases.

Corollary 2.19. *Let $T : \mathcal{H} \to \mathcal{K}$ be a linear operator.*

(i) *If T is an isometry and $\{u_1, \dots, u_k\}$ is an orthonormal set of $\mathcal{H}$, then $\{Tu_1, \dots, Tu_k\}$ is an orthonormal set of $\mathcal{K}$.*

(ii) *If T is a unitary operator and $\{u_1, u_2, \dots, u_k\}$ is an orthonormal basis for $\mathcal{H}$, then $\{Tu_1, Tu_2, \dots, Tu_k\}$ is an orthonormal basis for $\mathcal{K}$.*

Proof. We prove (i) and leave (ii) for the reader to complete. Let $\{u_1, u_2, \dots, u_k\}$ be an orthonormal set of $\mathcal{H}$. Then, by Proposition 2.16, we have

$$\langle Tu_i, Tu_j \rangle = \langle u_i, u_j \rangle = \delta_{i,j},$$

where $\delta_{i,j} = 0$ if $i \neq j$ and $\delta_{i,i} = 1$. So $\{Tu_1, Tu_2, \dots, Tu_k\}$ is an orthonormal set of $\mathcal{K}$.

Part (ii) is the forward direction of the following proposition, whose proof is asked in Exercise 7. □

Proposition 2.20. *Let $T : \mathcal{H} \to \mathcal{K}$ be a linear operator and let $\{u_1, u_2, \ldots, u_k\}$ be an orthonormal basis for $\mathcal{H}$. Then the following are true:*

(i) *T is an isometry if and only if $\{Tu_1, Tu_2, \ldots, Tu_k\}$ is an orthonormal set in $\mathcal{K}$.*

(ii) *T is unitary if and only if $\{Tu_1, Tu_2, \ldots, Tu_k\}$ is an orthonormal basis for $\mathcal{K}$.*

Proof. Exercise 7. □

Remark 2.21. A matrix A is called *normal, self-adjoint, positive, isometry, or unitary* when the corresponding linear operator T_A has these properties. Therefore all the results given so far in this section apply to matrices as well as to their operators. We can, however, state some additional properties which apply to matrices.

Proposition 2.22. *Let A be an $m \times n$ matrix with entries in $\mathbb{F}$.*

(i) *A is an isometry if and only if the column vectors of A form an orthonormal set in $\mathbb{F}^m$.*

(ii) *A is a unitary matrix if and only if $m = n$ and the column vectors of A form an orthonormal basis in $\mathbb{F}^n$.*

(iii) *A is a unitary matrix if and only if $m = n$ and the row vectors of A form an orthonormal basis in $\mathbb{F}^m$.*

Proof. (i) Let $\{e_1, e_2, \ldots, e_n\}$ be the standard orthonormal basis of $\mathbb{F}^n$, and let C_j be the jth column vector of A. Then $C_j = Ae_j$. From Proposition 2.20(i), we have that A is an isometry if and only if $\{Ae_1, Ae_2, \ldots, Ae_n\}$ is an orthonormal set, which is the same as that $\{C_1, C_2, \ldots, C_n\}$ is an orthonormal set in $\mathbb{F}^m$.

(ii) By using Proposition 2.20(ii), the proof is similar to that of part (i).

(iii) This part follows from (ii) and Theorem 2.17. □

Let T be an isometry from a Hilbert space $\mathcal{H}$ to a Hilbert space $\mathcal{K}$. Then we can think of the subspace $\tilde{\mathcal{H}} = T\mathcal{H}$ as a copy of $\mathcal{H}$ inside of $\mathcal{K}$. In this case we say that $\mathcal{H}$ is *embedded* into $\mathcal{K}$, and we call T an *embedding*. Note that an isometry is always injective and so it preserves linearly independent sets. Therefore if $\mathcal{H}$ can be embedded into $\mathcal{K}$, then $\dim(\mathcal{H}) \leq \dim(\mathcal{K})$. (The converse is also true; see Proposition 2.24.) A typical example is to embed $\mathbb{F}^n$ into $\mathbb{F}^m$ when $m > n$.

Example 2.23. Let $m > n$. Define $T : \mathbb{F}^n \to \mathbb{F}^m$ by:

$$T \begin{bmatrix} x_1 \\ \vdots \\ x_n \end{bmatrix} = \begin{bmatrix} x_1 \\ \vdots \\ x_n \\ 0 \\ \vdots \\ 0 \end{bmatrix} \in \mathbb{F}^m$$

for all vectors $\begin{bmatrix} x_1 \\ \vdots \\ x_n \end{bmatrix} \in \mathbb{F}^n$. Then clearly T is an isometry. Therefore we can view $\mathbb{F}^n$ as a copy (subspace) inside of $\mathbb{F}^m$. Note that there are many different ways to embed one Hilbert space into another one.

Proposition 2.24. *Suppose $\mathcal{H}$ and $\mathcal{K}$ are Hilbert spaces. If $\dim(\mathcal{H}) \leq \dim(\mathcal{K})$, then $\mathcal{H}$ can be embedded into $\mathcal{K}$.*

Proof. Exercise 8. □

2.4. Orthogonal Complements and Projections

An inner product provides a quantity with which to study the geometric structure of a space. In particular, the inner product provides the notion of orthogonality of vectors. In this section we discuss two geometric concepts: the orthogonal complements of subspaces and orthogonal projection operators. We then state the important concept that given any subspace M of $\mathcal{H}$, we can think of $\mathcal{H}$ as a direct sum of M and the orthogonal complement of M.

Definition 2.25. Let M be a subspace of a Hilbert space $\mathcal{H}$. The *orthogonal complement of M* is defined to be the subset:

$$M^{\perp} = \{x \in \mathcal{H} : \langle x, y \rangle = 0 \text{ for all } y \in M\}.$$

It is straightforward to verify that $M^{\perp}$ is always a subspace of $\mathcal{H}$.

Definition 2.26. Given subspaces E and F of $\mathcal{H}$, we say the subspaces are *orthogonal subspaces* if for all $x \in E$ and $y \in F$, $\langle x, y \rangle = 0$. We denote this by $E \perp F$.

Notice that if $E \perp F$, we have $E \subseteq F^{\perp}$ and $F \subseteq E^{\perp}$.

Definition 2.27. A linear operator P from a Hilbert space $\mathcal{H}$ to $\mathcal{H}$ is called an *orthogonal projection* if P is self-adjoint and $P^2 = P$.

As is generally the assumption, we will use the term *projection* to mean an orthogonal projection unless stated otherwise. These are often also called *self-adjoint projections* to differentiate them from idempotent operators (satisfying $P^2 = P$) which are not self-adjoint.

The following result tells us that for any given subspace of a Hilbert space, there exists an orthogonal projection with that subspace as its range. This is an explicit correspondence between subspaces and projections.

Lemma 2.28. *Let M be a subspace of a Hilbert space $\mathcal{H}$. Then there exists an orthogonal projection P on $\mathcal{H}$ such that $P\mathcal{H} = M$.*

Proof. Pick an orthonormal basis $\{u_1, u_2, \ldots, u_k\}$ for M. Define P by

$$Px = \sum_{j=1}^{k} \langle x, u_j \rangle u_j, \quad x \in \mathcal{H}.$$

One can verify that P is a linear operator. Moreover, it is clear from the definition that for all $x \in \mathcal{H}$, Px is in the span of the basis for M, so we have $P\mathcal{H} \subseteq M$. Let $x \in \mathcal{H}$ and compute P^2x:

$$\begin{aligned}
P^2x &= \sum_{j=1}^{k} \langle Px, u_j \rangle u_j \\
&= \sum_{j=1}^{k} \left\langle \sum_{i=1}^{k} \langle x, u_i \rangle u_i, u_j \right\rangle u_j \\
&= \sum_{j=1}^{k} \sum_{i=1}^{k} \langle x, u_i \rangle \langle u_i, u_j \rangle u_j \\
&= \sum_{j=1}^{k} \langle x, u_j \rangle u_j \\
&= Px.
\end{aligned}$$

This verifies that $P^2 = P$. In the case that $x \in M$, we have $x = \sum_{j=1}^{k} \langle x, u_j \rangle u_j$. So the above calculation also shows that $Px = x$ for all $x \in M$. This implies that $P\mathcal{H} = M$.

Finally we verify that P is self-adjoint by showing that $\langle Px, y \rangle = \langle x, Py \rangle$ for all $x, y \in \mathcal{H}$.

$$\begin{aligned}
\langle Px, y \rangle &= \left\langle \sum_{j=1}^{k} \langle x, u_j \rangle u_j, y \right\rangle \\
&= \sum_{j=1}^{k} \langle x, u_j \rangle \langle u_j, y \rangle \\
&= \left\langle x, \sum_{j=1}^{k} \overline{\langle u_j, y \rangle} u_j \right\rangle \\
&= \left\langle x, \sum_{j=1}^{k} \langle y, u_j \rangle u_j \right\rangle \\
&= \langle x, Py \rangle .
\end{aligned}$$

□

Next, we prove the orthogonal decomposition result we described at the start of this section.

Proposition 2.29. *Let M be a subspace of a Hilbert space $\mathcal{H}$.*

(i) *For each* $x \in \mathcal{H}$*, there exists a unique decomposition of* x*:*

$$x = x_1 + x_2$$

with $x_1 \in M$ *and* $x_2 \in M^\perp$.

(ii) *The projection* P *defined in Lemma 2.28 is the unique orthogonal projection on* $\mathcal{H}$ *such that* $P\mathcal{H} = M$.

Proof. Let $x \in \mathcal{H}$ and P be the projection defined in Lemma 2.28. Then let $x_1 = Px \in M$ and $x_2 = (I - P)x$. We see that $x_2 \in M^\perp$, since given any $y \in M$, we have

$$\langle x_2, y \rangle = \langle x - Px, y \rangle = \langle x, y \rangle - \langle Px, y \rangle = \langle x, y \rangle - \langle x, Py \rangle .$$

The right-hand quantity is equal to zero, since $Py = y$ when $y \in M$. We also see that $x = x_1 + x_2$, so we have verified that this is an orthogonal decomposition of x.

To prove the uniqueness, let $x = y_1 + y_2$ be another orthogonal decomposition, which gives $0 = x - x = (x_1 - y_1) + (x_2 - y_2)$. This means that $x_1 - y_1$ and $x_2 - y_2$ are linearly dependent, but we also have $x_1 - y_1 \in M$, and $x_2 - y_2 \in M^\perp$. The only possibility is that both $x_1 - y_1$ and $x_2 - y_2$ are zero. Thus $x_1 = y_1$ and $x_2 = y_2$, which completes the proof of part (i).

For part (ii), let Q be another orthogonal projection on $\mathcal{H}$ such that $Q\mathcal{H} = M$. Then, clearly $Px = Qx = x$ when $x \in M$. If $x \in M^\perp$, then $\langle Px, y \rangle = \langle x, Py \rangle = 0$ for any $y \in \mathcal{H}$ since $Py \in M$. Thus $Px = 0$. Similarly, $Qx = 0$. Now let $x = x_1 + x_2$ with $x_1 \in M$ and $x_2 \in M^\perp$. Then we have

$$Px = Px_1 + Px_2 = x_1 = Qx_1 + Qx_2 = Qx.$$

Thus $P = Q$. □

The two parts of this proposition imply that $\mathcal{H}$ has an orthogonal decomposition $\mathcal{H} = M \oplus M^\perp$, where $\oplus$ denotes the orthogonal direct sum defined in Section 1.7; i.e., $\mathcal{H} = M + M^\perp$ and $M \perp M^\perp$.

Lemma 2.30. *Let* M *be a subspace of* $\mathcal{H}$*. Then the following statements hold:*

(i) $(M^\perp)^\perp = M$.

(ii) *If P is the (unique) orthogonal projection from $\mathcal{H}$ onto M, then $(I - P)$ is the orthogonal projection from $\mathcal{H}$ onto $M^{\perp}$.*

Proof. Exercise 10. □

We will use the common notation P_M to denote the unique orthogonal projection of a Hilbert space $\mathcal{H}$ to the subspace M.

Corollary 2.31. *Let $\mathcal{H}$ be an n-dimensional Hilbert space, and let $\{u_1, u_2, \ldots, u_k\}$ be an orthonormal set of vectors from $\mathcal{H}$. Then we can extend it to an orthonormal basis $\{u_1, u_2, \ldots, u_k, u_{k+1}, \ldots, u_n\}$ for $\mathcal{H}$.*

Proof. Let $M = \text{span}\{u_1, u_2, \ldots, u_k\}$. Since $M^{\perp}$ is also a Hilbert space, it has an orthonormal basis. If $M^{\perp} = \{0\}$, then we have $\mathcal{H} = M$ and hence $\{u_1, u_2, \ldots, u_k\}$ is already an orthonormal basis for $\mathcal{H}$. Otherwise, let $\{v_1, v_2, \ldots, v_m\}$ be an orthonormal basis for $M^{\perp}$.

We can now conclude that $\mathcal{B} = \{u_1, u_2, \ldots, u_k\} \cup \{v_1, v_2, \ldots, v_m\}$ forms an orthonormal basis for $\mathcal{H}$ since $\mathcal{H}$ is the orthogonal direct sum of M and $M^{\perp}$. By the orthogonality of all elements from M with the elements of $M^{\perp}$, it is clear that the vectors in $\mathcal{B}$ are pairwise orthogonal. The vectors of $\mathcal{B}$ span $\mathcal{H}$ since any $x \in \mathcal{H}$ can be written as $x = x_1 + x_2$ with $x_1 \in M$ and $x_2 \in M^{\perp}$. □

The following lemma verifies that a well-understood fact about projections on Euclidean space $\mathbb{F}^n$ also holds on an arbitrary Hilbert space. Using the norm on $\mathcal{H}$, the lemma demonstrates that the element in a subspace M closest in norm to a given vector $v \in \mathcal{H}$ is exactly the orthogonal projection of v onto M.

Lemma 2.32. *Let M be a subspace of $\mathcal{H}$ and $v \in \mathcal{H}$. Then*

$$\|v - P_M v\| \leq \|v - u\|$$

for every $u \in M$. Moreover if $\|v - P_M v\| = \|v - u\|$ for some $u \in M$, then $u = P_M v$.

Proof. Note that $v - P_M v \in M^\perp$ and $P_M v - u \in M$, and hence they are orthogonal. Therefore we have

$$\begin{aligned} \|v - P_M v\|^2 &\leq \|v - P_M v\|^2 + \|P_M v - u\|^2 \\ &= \|v - P_M v + P_M v - u\|^2 \\ &= \|v - u\|^2. \end{aligned}$$

From the above argument we have that $\|v - P_M v\| = \|v - u\|$ if and only if $\|P_M v - u\|^2 = 0$, which happens if and only if $u = P_M v$. □

Definition 2.33. Let T be a linear operator on $\mathcal{H}$. Recall from Section 1.3 that the *kernel* of T is the set:

$$\ker(T) = \{x \in \mathcal{H} : Tx = 0\}.$$

It is easy to verify that $\ker(T)$ is a linear subspace of $\mathcal{H}$. We also denote by $\operatorname{range}(T)$ the range space of T.

Proposition 2.34. *Assume that* $T : \mathcal{H} \to \mathcal{K}$ *is a linear operator. Then* $\ker(T) = [\operatorname{range}(T^*)]^\perp$, *and so*

$$\mathcal{H} = \ker(T) \oplus \operatorname{range}(T^*).$$

In particular we have $\dim \mathcal{H} = \dim \ker(T) + \dim \operatorname{range}(T^*)$.

Proof. The orthogonality of the spaces $\ker(T)$ and $\operatorname{range}(T^*)$ follows from $\langle x, T^* y \rangle = \langle Tx, y \rangle = 0$ for $x \in \ker(T)$ and any $y \in \mathcal{K}$. Therefore, $\ker(T) \subseteq [\operatorname{range}(T^*)]^\perp$. Next, let $x \in \mathcal{H}$ and let $x = x_1 + x_2$ with $x_2 \in M = \operatorname{range}(T^*)$ and $x_1 \in M^\perp$. Then for every $y \in \mathcal{K}$ we have

$$\langle Tx_1, y \rangle = \langle x_1, T^* y \rangle = 0.$$

Hence $Tx_1 = 0$ which means $x_1 \in \ker(T)$. Therefore $\ker(T) = [\operatorname{range}(T^*)]^\perp$ and so

$$\mathcal{H} = \ker(T) \oplus \operatorname{range}(T^*).$$ □

We will call the orthogonal projection onto $\operatorname{range}(T)$ the *range projection* of T.

Definition 2.35. The *support* of an operator $T : \mathcal{H} \to \mathcal{K}$ is the orthogonal complement $[\ker(T)]^\perp$ of its kernel. We write this $\operatorname{supp}(T)$. We call the orthogonal projection onto $\operatorname{supp}(T)$ the *support projection* of T.

Remark 2.36. If T is a nonzero operator, then the restriction operator $T|_{\text{supp}(T)}$ of T to its support is injective. (Try to verify this.) Moreover, when considered as a linear operator from supp(T) to range(T), T is both injective and surjective, hence invertible. This rather geometric viewpoint is useful.

Finally we present a result that will be used in the frame theory we will present in the main portion of this book.

Proposition 2.37. *If E and F are subspaces of a finite-dimensional Hilbert space $\mathcal{H}$ with $E \cap F = \{0\}$, then the following properties hold:*

(i) $\dim(F) \leq \dim(E^{\perp})$.

(ii) *There exists an invertible operator $A : \mathcal{H} \to \mathcal{H}$ such that AE is orthogonal to AF.*

Proof. Let $n = \dim(\mathcal{H})$. Choose an orthonormal basis $\{e_1, e_2, \ldots, e_k\}$ for E and an orthonormal basis $\{f_1, f_2, \ldots, f_\ell\}$ for F. Since $E \cap F = \{0\}$, we have that

$$\{e_1, e_2, \ldots, e_k\} \cup \{f_1, f_2, \ldots, f_\ell\}$$

is a linearly independent set. Thus $k+\ell \leq n$. Also let $\{g_1, g_2, \ldots, g_m\}$ be an orthonormal basis for $E^{\perp}$, where we note that $m = n-k$. Then

$$\{e_1, e_2, \ldots, e_k\} \cup \{g_1, g_2, \ldots, g_m\}$$

is an orthonormal basis for $\mathcal{H}$. So $k + \ell \leq k + m$ which implies that $\ell \leq m$. Hence $\dim(F) \leq \dim(E^{\perp})$, establishing (i).

Now we prove (ii). First, using Proposition 1.18, we can extend the linearly independent set $\{e_1, e_2, \ldots, e_k, f_1, f_2, \ldots, f_\ell\}$ to a basis (not necessarily orthonormal) for $\mathcal{H}$. Since $\dim(\mathcal{H}) = n$, this basis has cardinality n. So there are nonzero vectors $\{h_1, h_2, \ldots, h_{n-k-\ell}\}$ so that the set

$$\{e_1, e_2, \ldots, e_k, f_1, f_2, \ldots, f_\ell, h_1, h_2, \ldots, h_{n-k-\ell}\}$$

is a basis for $\mathcal{H}$. Let $\mathcal{K} = \text{span}\{f_1, f_2, \ldots, f_\ell, h_1, h_2, \ldots, h_{n-k-\ell}\}$. Then $\mathcal{K}$ has dimension $n-k$. By Corollary 2.31, the orthonormal set $\{f_1, f_2, \ldots, f_\ell\}$ can be extended to an orthonormal basis

$$\{f_1, f_2, \ldots, f_\ell, f_{\ell+1}, \ldots, f_{n-k}\}$$

for $\mathcal{K}$.

Since $\mathcal{K} \cap E = \{0\}$ and $\mathcal{K} + E = \mathcal{H}$, the combined set

$$\{e_1, e_2, \ldots, e_k, f_1, f_2, \ldots, f_{n-k}\}$$

is also a basis for $\mathcal{H}$. Define A by $Ae_i = e_i$ for $1 \leq i \leq k$, and $Af_i = g_i$ for $1 \leq i \leq n-k$ and then extend it by linearity to $\mathcal{H}$. Then A is an invertible operator from $\mathcal{H}$ to $\mathcal{H}$ since it has trivial kernel by the way it has been defined and is also surjective since the range contains n linearly independent vectors. Therefore, we have

$$AE = \operatorname{span}\{Ae_1, Ae_2, \ldots, Ae_k\} = \operatorname{span}\{e_1, e_2, \ldots, e_k\} = E$$

and

$$AF = \operatorname{span}\{Af_1, Af_2, \ldots, Af_\ell\} = \operatorname{span}\{g_1, g_2, \ldots, g_\ell\}.$$

Since $g_i \in E^\perp$, this shows that $AF \subset E^\perp$ and so $AF \perp AE$, as required. $\square$

2.5. The Moore-Penrose Inverse

The Moore-Penrose inverse is a generalized inverse of linear transformations. Not every linear transformation is invertible, but the Moore-Penrose inverse allows certain linear transformations to be "inverted as much as possible".

Suppose $T : \mathcal{H} \to \mathcal{K}$ is linear and is also one-to-one. If we consider the range of T, call it M, as a subspace of $\mathcal{K}$, then T is invertible as a linear transformation from $\mathcal{H}$ to M. The Moore-Penrose inverse is a linear transformation $T^\dagger : \mathcal{K} \to \mathcal{H}$ such that for every $v \in \mathcal{H}$, $T^\dagger T(v) = v$, so it is a one-sided inverse. This operator has additional properties, which we will describe shortly.

Definition 2.38. Suppose $T : \mathcal{H} \to \mathcal{K}$ is a linear transformation which is one-to-one. Define the Moore-Penrose inverse of T, which we will denote $T^\dagger$, by:

$$T^\dagger = (T^*T)^{-1}T^*.$$

Let us first show that $T^\dagger$ is a well-defined operator. We will leave it as an exercise to prove that it is a one-sided inverse of T.

Lemma 2.39. *If $T : \mathcal{H} \to \mathcal{K}$ is a linear transformation which is one-to-one, then $T^*T : \mathcal{H} \to \mathcal{H}$ is invertible.*

Proof. This follows almost immediately from Proposition 2.34: applying Proposition 2.34 to T^*, we see that $\mathcal{K} = \ker(T^*) \oplus \text{range}(T)$. This implies that if we restrict $T^* : \mathcal{K} \to \mathcal{H}$ to the subspace range(T), that $T^*|_{\text{range}(T)}$ is one-to-one, since the only vector in range(T) which T^* maps to 0 is the zero vector in $\mathcal{K}$. Therefore, we have that $T : \mathcal{H} \to \mathcal{K}$ is one-to-one, and $T^*|_{\text{range}(T)}$ is also one-to-one, whence $T^*T : \mathcal{H} \to \mathcal{H}$ is one-to-one and thus is invertible. □

Theorem 2.40. *If $T : \mathcal{H} \to \mathcal{K}$ is a linear transformation which is one-to-one, then $T^\dagger T : \mathcal{H} \to \mathcal{H}$ is the identity; i.e. $T^\dagger T(v) = v$ for all $v \in \mathcal{H}$.*

Proof. Exercise 11. □

We see that $T^\dagger$ performs the role of the inverse of T on range$(T) \subset \mathcal{K}$; it is important to know what $T^\dagger$ does on all of $\mathcal{K}$. If $w \in \mathcal{K}$, since $\mathcal{K} = \ker(T^*) \oplus \text{range}(T)$, we know that $T^\dagger$ first projects w onto range(T), and then maps that projected vector to $\mathcal{H}$. Thinking of this in the opposite direction, if $w \in \mathcal{K}$, $T^\dagger w$ is as we just described, so $T(T^\dagger w)$ ends up in range(T); in fact $TT^\dagger w$ is exactly the projection of w onto range(T). Therefore, $T^\dagger w$ is as close to the vector $T^{-1}w$ as possible, since the operator T^{-1} may not actually exist.

2.6. Eigenvalues for Operators

Since eigenvalues and eigenspaces for matrices can be viewed as special cases of these concepts for general linear operators, we start by reviewing the definitions of eigenvalues, eigenvectors, and eigenspaces of a matrix.

Definition 2.41. Let A be an $n \times n$ matrix with entries in Euclidean space $\mathbb{F}$. A scalar $\lambda \in \mathbb{F}$ is called an *eigenvalue* of A if there exists a nonzero vector $v \in \mathbb{F}^n$ such that

$$Av = \lambda v.$$

Any nonzero vector v satisfying the above equation is called an *eigenvector* of A corresponding to λ. The *eigenspace* of A corresponding to λ is defined to be:

$$E_\lambda = \{v \in \mathbb{F}^n : Av = \lambda v\}.$$

We leave it to the reader to verify that E_λ is a subspace of $\mathbb{F}^n$. We will define the *geometric multiplicity* of λ to be the dimension of E_λ. The set of all the eigenvalues of A is called the *spectrum* of A, which we denote by $\sigma(A)$.

As an example, if $D = \operatorname{diag}(\lambda_1, \lambda_2, \ldots, \lambda_n)$ is a diagonal $n \times n$ matrix, then the spectrum $\sigma(D)$ is the set of distinct diagonal elements of D. We leave the proof of this claim to the first part of Exercise 33.

Eigenvalues and geometric multiplicities are invariant under similarity of matrices. Recall that two $n \times n$ matrices A and B are said to be *similar* if there exists an invertible matrix S such that $A = S^{-1}BS$.

Proposition 2.42. *Let A and B be similar matrices. Then the following properties are true:*

(i) $\sigma(A) = \sigma(B)$.

(ii) $\dim E_\lambda(A) = \dim E_\lambda(B)$.

Proof. (i) Assume that $A = S^{-1}BS$. Let $\lambda \in \sigma(A)$. Then there exits $v \neq 0$ such that $Av = \lambda v$. This implies that $S^{-1}BSv = \lambda v$, and hence $BSv = \lambda Sv$. Note that $Sv \neq 0$ since S is invertible. Therefore $\lambda \in \sigma(B)$ which implies that $\sigma(A) \subseteq \sigma(B)$. Because of the symmetric property for the similarity, we also have $\sigma(B) \subseteq \sigma(A)$, and hence (i) follows.

(ii) By the proof of (i), we have $SE_\lambda(A) = E_\lambda(B)$. Therefore $\dim E_\lambda(A) = \dim E_\lambda(B)$. □

The matrix determinant is useful in computing the eigenvalues of a matrix, as demonstrated by the following result.

Proposition 2.43. *Let A be an $n \times n$ matrix with entries in $\mathbb{F}$. Then the eigenvalues of A are the roots in $\mathbb{F}$ of the polynomial* $\det(\lambda I - A)$.

The polynomial $\det(\lambda I - A)$ is called the *characteristic polynomial* of A.

Proof. Recall that a square matrix M is invertible if and only if $\det(M) \neq 0$.

If $\det(\lambda I - A) = 0$ for some $\lambda \in \mathbb{F}$, then $\lambda I - A$ is not invertible. Thus, there exists a nonzero vector v in $\mathbb{F}^n$ such that $(\lambda I - A)v = 0$ and so $Av = \lambda v$. This implies that λ is an eigenvalue of A.

Clearly we can reverse the above argument. Hence if λ is an eigenvalue of A, it is a root of the polynomial $\det(\lambda I - A)$. □

Lemma 2.44. *Let μ and λ be two distinct eigenvalues for an $n \times n$ matrix. Then for any two eigenvectors $x \in E_\mu$ and $y \in E_\lambda$, the pair $\{x, y\}$ is linearly independent.*

Proof. For purposes of contradiction, assume that x and y are linearly dependent. This is equivalent to the assumption that $x = cy$ for some scalar c. Then

$$Ax = A(cy) = cAy = c\lambda y = \lambda(cy) = \lambda x,$$

and so $\mu x = Ax = \lambda x$, which implies that $(\mu - \lambda)x = 0$. Since $x \neq 0$, we have $\mu - \lambda = 0$ which contradicts the assumption that μ and λ are distinct. □

This result extends to the more general fact that if $\{x_1, x_2, \ldots, x_k\}$ are eigenvectors of a matrix corresponding to distinct eigenvalues, then the set $\{x_1, x_2, \ldots, x_k\}$ is linearly independent (see Exercise 12).

An *invariant subspace* of an $n \times n$ matrix is a subspace E of $\mathbb{F}^n$ such that $AE \subset E$. From the definition, it is clear that all the eigenspaces $E_\lambda(A)$ are invariant under A. We have the following:

Proposition 2.45. *Suppose that $\{\lambda_1, \lambda_2, \ldots, \lambda_k\}$ are all the distinct eigenvalues of an $n \times n$ matrix A. Then the following are equivalent:*

(i) *A is similar to a diagonal matrix; i.e., A is diagonalizable.*

(ii) *$\mathbb{F}^n$ has a basis consisting of eigenvectors of A.*

(iii) $\dim \mathbb{F}^n = \dim E_{\lambda_1} + \dim E_{\lambda_2} + \cdots + \dim E_{\lambda_k}$.

(iv) $\mathbb{F}^n = E_{\lambda_1} \dotplus E_{\lambda_2} \dotplus \cdots \dotplus E_{\lambda_k}$, *where $\dotplus$ denotes the (not necessarily orthogonal) direct sum from Definition* 1.27.

(v) *There exist one-dimensional A-invariant subspaces V_1, $V_2, \ldots, V_n$ such that $\mathbb{F}^n = V_1 \dot{+} V_2 \dot{+} \cdots \dot{+} V_n$.*

Moreover, if $A = A^*$, then A is always similar to a diagonal matrix.

Proof. See the Student Presentation in Section 10.1. □

Next, we define the eigenvalues and eigenvectors of general linear operators. These definitions are similar to those for matrices.

Definition 2.46. Let T be a linear operator from a Hilbert space $\mathcal{H}$ to itself. A scalar $\lambda \in \mathbb{F}$ is called an *eigenvalue* of T if there exists a nonzero vector $v \in \mathcal{H}$ such that

$$Tv = \lambda v.$$

The nonzero vector v is called an *eigenvector* of T corresponding to λ. The *eigenspace* of T corresponding to λ is defined to be

$$E_\lambda(T) = \{v \in \mathcal{H} : Tv = \lambda v\}.$$

Moreover, the set of all eigenvalues of T is called the *spectrum* of T. We denote the spectrum as we did for matrices by $\sigma(T)$.

Lemma 2.47. *If T is a linear operator on an n-dimensional Hilbert space, then T has at most n distinct eigenvalues.*

Proof. Exercise 13. □

In addition to the properties listed in the previous sections, we also discuss some important properties related to special classes of operators.

Proposition 2.48. *Let T be an operator on a Hilbert space $\mathcal{H}$.*

(i) *If T is unitary, then every eigenvalue λ has modulus one; i.e., $|\lambda| = 1$.*

(ii) *If T is self-adjoint, then $\sigma(T) \subset \mathbb{R}$.*

(iii) *If T is positive, then $\sigma(T) \subset \mathbb{R}^+$, the set of nonnegative real numbers.*

Proof. (i) Let v be an eigenvector in E_λ. Then $Tv = \lambda v$. So

$$\langle Tv, Tv \rangle = \langle \lambda v, \lambda v \rangle = |\lambda|^2 \|v\|^2.$$

Since T is unitary, we have that $T^*T = I$. Thus

$$\langle Tv, Tv \rangle = \langle T^*Tv, v \rangle = \langle v, v \rangle = \|v\|^2.$$

Therefore $\|v\|^2 = |\lambda|^2\|v\|^2$ which implies that $|\lambda| = 1$ since $\|v\| \neq 0$.

(ii) Let $\lambda \in \sigma(T)$ and v be an eigenvector corresponding to λ. Then we have

$$\langle Tv, v \rangle = \langle \lambda v, v \rangle = \lambda \|v\|^2.$$

Since T is self-adjoint, we have that $\langle Tv, v \rangle$ is real, and therefore λ is real since $\|v\|^2 \neq 0$. So (ii) is proved. In the case that T is positive, we have $\langle Tv, v \rangle \geq 0$ and hence $\lambda \geq 0$. This proves (iii). □

Proposition 2.49. *Let T be an operator on a finite-dimensional Hilbert space $\mathcal{H}$. Then λ is an eigenvalue of T if and only if its complex conjugate $\overline{\lambda}$ is an eigenvalue of T^*. In other words, $\sigma(T^*) = \overline{\sigma(T)}$. If T is a normal operator, then x is an eigenvector for T with eigenvalue λ if and only if x is an eigenvector for T^* with eigenvalue $\overline{\lambda}$.*

Proof. Suppose that v is an eigenvector of T corresponding to the eigenvalue λ. Then for any $x \in \mathcal{H}$ we have

$$\begin{aligned} 0 &= \langle 0, x \rangle = \langle (T - \lambda I)v, x \rangle \\ &= \langle v, (T - \lambda I)^* x \rangle = \left\langle v, (T^* - \overline{\lambda} I)x \right\rangle. \end{aligned}$$

Hence v is orthogonal to range$(T^* - \overline{\lambda}I)$ and therefore $T^* - \overline{\lambda}I$ is not surjective and therefore not injective. This implies that there exists a nonzero vector, say $u \in \mathcal{H}$, such that $(T^* - \overline{\lambda}I)u = 0$. Therefore, $\overline{\lambda}$ is an eigenvalue of T^*. The other direction follows from the same computation and the fact that $(T^*)^* = T$.

Let T be normal, so $T^*T = TT^*$. We know from the properties of the adjoint that for any constant λ, we have $(T - \lambda I)^* = T^* - \overline{\lambda}I$. Then we can demonstrate that $T - \lambda I$ is also a normal operator.

$$\begin{aligned} (T - \lambda I)(T^* - \overline{\lambda} I) &= TT^* - (\overline{\lambda} T) - \lambda T^* + |\lambda^2| I \\ &= T^*T - \overline{\lambda} T - \lambda T^* + |\lambda^2| I \\ &= (T^* - \overline{\lambda} I)(T - \lambda I). \end{aligned}$$

Using Lemma 2.11, we can conclude that for any $x \in \mathcal{H}$, we have $\|(T - \lambda I)x\| = \|(T^* - \overline{\lambda})x\|$. Now, we see that x is an eigenvector for T with eigenvalue λ if and only if $\|Tx - \lambda x\| = 0$, which is true exactly when $\|T^*x - \overline{\lambda}x\| = 0$, which means x is an eigenvector for T^* with eigenvalue $\overline{\lambda}$. □

Proposition 2.49 shows that if T is normal, it has the same eigenspaces as T^*. We can further say that these eigenspaces are orthogonal subspaces of $\mathcal{H}$.

Proposition 2.50. *Let T be a normal operator on a Hilbert space $\mathcal{H}$. If x and y are eigenvectors of T for distinct eigenvalues λ and μ respectively, then x and y are orthogonal.*

Proof. By definition of eigenvalues and eigenvectors, we know $Tx = \lambda x$ and $Ty = \mu y$. We can then compute

$$\begin{aligned} \langle Tx, y \rangle &= \langle \lambda x, y \rangle \\ &= \lambda \langle x, y \rangle . \end{aligned}$$

But we also have from Proposition 2.49, that

$$\begin{aligned} \langle Tx, y \rangle &= \langle x, T^* y \rangle \\ &= \langle x, \overline{\mu} y \rangle \\ &= \mu \langle x, y \rangle , \end{aligned}$$

where we use Proposition 2.49 and the hypothesis that T is normal to replace T^*y with $\overline{\mu}y$. Therefore $\lambda \langle x, y \rangle = \mu \langle x, y \rangle$ and since $\lambda \neq \mu$, we must have $\langle x, y \rangle = 0$. □

Let $p(t) = a_0 + a_1 t + \cdots + a_k t^k$ be a polynomial and let T be a linear operator on a Hilbert space $\mathcal{H}$. We can now define the operator $p(T) = a_0 I + a_1 T + \cdots + a_k T^k$, where the powers of T indicate compositions of T with itself. $p(T)$ is again a linear operator on $\mathcal{H}$.

Theorem 2.51. *Let T be an operator on a Hilbert space $\mathcal{H}$.*

(i) *If T is invertible, then $\sigma(T^{-1}) = \{\lambda^{-1} : \lambda \in \sigma(T)\}$.*

(ii) *We have $\sigma(T^k) = \{\lambda^k : \lambda \in \sigma(T)\}$ for any positive integer k.*

(iii) (Spectral Mapping Theorem) *Given the operator $p(T)$ defined as above, $\sigma(p(T)) = \{p(\lambda) : \lambda \in \sigma(T)\}$ for any polynomial $p(t)$.*

Proof. (i) For any $\lambda \neq 0$, we have

$$T^{-1} - \lambda^{-1}I = \lambda^{-1}T^{-1}(\lambda I - T).$$

If $\lambda \in \sigma(T)$, then $\lambda \neq 0$ since T^{-1} exists. Let $v \in \mathcal{H}$ be such that $Tv = \lambda v$ and $v \neq 0$. Then we get $(T^{-1} - \lambda^{-1}I)v = \lambda^{-1}T^{-1}(\lambda I - T)v = 0$ and hence $\lambda^{-1} \in \sigma(T^{-1})$. On the other side, assume that $T^{-1}u = \alpha u$ for some $0 \neq u \in \mathcal{H}$ and some scalar α. Then $\alpha \neq 0$ since T^{-1} is invertible. We need to show that $\alpha^{-1} \in \sigma(T)$. This follows from

$$(T - \alpha^{-1}I)u = \alpha^{-1}T(\alpha I - T^{-1})u = 0.$$

Clearly (ii) is a special case of (iii), so once we have proven (iii), we will also have proven (ii).

(iii) Let $p(t)$ be a polynomial of degree k. First assume that $\lambda \in \sigma(T)$. Then there exists $0 \neq v \in \mathcal{H}$ such that $(T - \lambda I)v = 0$. Since λ is a root of the polynomial $p(t) - p(\lambda)$, we can write $p(t) - p(\lambda) = q(t)(t - \lambda)$ with q being a polynomial of degree $k - 1$. This yields the operator equation

$$(p(T) - p(\lambda)I)v = q(T)(T - \lambda I)v = 0,$$

which implies that $p(\lambda) \in \sigma(p(T))$.

Secondly, let $\alpha \in \sigma(p(T))$. Then there exists a nonzero $v \in \mathcal{H}$ such that $(p(T) - \alpha I)v = 0$. We need to show that $\alpha \in \{p(\lambda) : \lambda \in \sigma(T)\}$.

Write the polynomial $p(t) - \alpha$ in its factored form,

$$p(t) - \alpha = \prod_{i=1}^{k}(t - \lambda_i),$$

where we assume that $p(t)$ has leading coefficient 1. Therefore, $p(\lambda_i) - \alpha = 0$ for all $i = 1, 2, \ldots, k$. Given the eigenvector v of $p(T)$ corresponding to α, let j be the smallest integer such that

$\prod_{i=1}^{j-1}(T-\lambda_i I)v \neq 0$, but

$$(T-\lambda_j I)\prod_{i=1}^{j-1}(T-\lambda_i I)v = \prod_{i=1}^{j}(T-\lambda_i I)v = 0.$$

Note that such a j exists because $v \neq 0$ and $\prod_{i=1}^{k}(T-\lambda_i I)v = 0$. Then we have $\lambda_j \in \sigma(T)$ and hence $\alpha = p(\lambda_j) \in \{p(\lambda) : \lambda \in \sigma(T)\}$. $\square$

2.7. Square Roots of Positive Operators

Recall that a positive operator on a Hilbert space $\mathcal{H}$ is a self-adjoint operator such that $\langle Tx, x \rangle \geq 0$ for all $x \in \mathcal{H}$, and we denote this as $T \geq 0$. More generally, we will use the notation $S \geq T$ when both S and T are self-adjoint and $(S-T) \geq 0$.

Let us first look at the special case of positive matrices, and then extend to operators on a general finite-dimensional Hilbert space. An $n \times n$ matrix A is positive if $A^* = A$ and $\langle Ax, x \rangle \geq 0$ for all $x \in \mathbb{F}^n$. Now suppose that A is a positive matrix. Then, from Proposition 2.45, A is similar to a diagonal matrix D; i.e., $A = P^{-1}DP$ for some invertible matrix P. Let $D = \operatorname{diag}(\lambda_1, \lambda_2, \ldots, \lambda_n)$. Then $\sigma(D) = \{\lambda_1, \lambda_2, \ldots, \lambda_n\}$ (allowing repetition). Note that the positivity of A and Proposition 2.48 imply that $\lambda_j \geq 0$ for all $j = 1, 2, \ldots, n$.

For each real number $\alpha > 0$, we define $A^\alpha = P^{-1}D_\alpha P$, where

$$D_\alpha = \operatorname{diag}(\lambda_1^\alpha, \lambda_2^\alpha, \ldots, \lambda_n^\alpha).$$

In particular, we call $A^{\frac{1}{2}}$ the *square root* of the matrix A. It can be shown that $A^{\frac{1}{2}}$ is the unique positive operator B satisfying $B^2 = A$.

Now let us generalize the concept of square roots of positive matrices to general positive operators.

Let T be a positive operator on a Hilbert space $\mathcal{H}$. Pick an orthonormal basis $\{e_1, e_2, \ldots, e_n\}$ for $\mathcal{H}$. Let $A = [a_{ij}]$ be the $n \times n$ matrix representation of T with respect to the basis $\{e_1, e_2, \ldots, e_n\}$, so that

$$Te_j = \sum_{i=1}^{n} a_{ij}e_i, \quad j = 1, 2, \ldots, n.$$

Then A is a positive matrix (Exercise 14). Let $[b_{ij}] = A^{\frac{1}{2}}$ be the square root of A. Define a linear operator S on $\mathcal{H}$ by

$$Se_j = \sum_{i=1}^{n} b_{ij} e_i, \quad j = 1, 2, \ldots, n.$$

Proposition 2.52. *Let S be defined as above.*

(i) *S is a positive operator and $S^2 = T$.*

(ii) *The operator S is independent of the choice of orthonormal basis $\{e_1, e_2, \ldots, e_n\}$ for $\mathcal{H}$.*

(iii) *If there exists another positive operator S_1 such that $S_1^2 = T$, then $S = S_1$.*

Proof. See Student Presentations, Section 10.2. □

Definition 2.53. The unique positive operator S defined in Proposition 2.52 is called the *square root* of T, and will be denoted by $T^{\frac{1}{2}}$.

Proposition 2.54. *Let T be an operator on a Hilbert space $\mathcal{H}$. Then the following are equivalent:*

(i) *T is positive.*

(ii) *$T = S^2$ for some positive operator S.*

(iii) *$T = V^*V$ for some linear operator V.*

Proof. In order to show (i)→(ii), assume that T is positive. Let $S = T^{\frac{1}{2}}$. Then S is positive and $S = T^2$.

We obviously have (ii)→(iii) since $S^* = S$ when S is a positive operator. For (iii)→ (i), let $T = V^*V$ for some linear operator V on $\mathcal{H}$. Then for any $x \in \mathcal{H}$, we have

$$\langle V^*Vx, x \rangle = \langle Vx, Vx \rangle = \|Vx\|^2 \geq 0$$

and

$$T^* = (V^*V)^* = V^*(V^*)^* = V^*V = T.$$

This shows that $T = V^*V$ satisfies the properties of a positive operator. □

Remark 2.55. In the above proposition we have that $T = V^*V \geq 0$ for any linear operator on a Hilbert space $\mathcal{H}$. It is clear from the proof that $T = V^*V$ is also positive for any linear operator V from $\mathcal{H}$ to a different Hilbert space $\mathcal{K}$.

Corollary 2.56. *Let T be a positive invertible operator on a Hilbert space $\mathcal{H}$. Then T^{-1} is also positive.*

Proof. By Proposition 2.54, $T = S^2$ for some positive operator S on $\mathcal{H}$. Since T is invertible, we know that $T\mathcal{H} = \mathcal{H}$ and $\ker(T) = \{0\}$. Thus $\mathcal{H} = T\mathcal{H} = S^2\mathcal{H} = S(S\mathcal{H}) \subset S\mathcal{H}$. If $Sx = 0$, then $Tx = S(Sx) = 0$ and hence $x = 0$. Therefore S is also invertible. Hence

$$T^{-1} = S^{-1}S^{-1}$$

with $(S^{-1})^* = (S^*)^{-1} = S^{-1}$. Therefore, T^{-1} is positive by Proposition 2.54. □

2.8. The Polar Decomposition

Let T be a linear operator from a Hilbert space $\mathcal{H}$ to a Hilbert space $\mathcal{K}$. Since T^*T is a positive operator, we know T^*T has a unique square root which is also positive. We denote this operator by the absolute value symbol. That is, $|T|$ is used to denote the unique square root of T^*T. The following lemma is useful:

Lemma 2.57. *If T is an operator acting on a Hilbert space $\mathcal{H}$, and if x is any vector in $\mathcal{H}$, then*

$$\|Tx\| = \||T|x\|.$$

Proof. We have

$$\||T|x\|^2 = \langle\, |T|x, |T|x \,\rangle = \langle\, |T| \cdot |T|x, x \,\rangle.$$

Since $|T| \cdot |T| = T^*T$, we have that

$$\langle\, |T| \cdot |T|x, x \,\rangle = \langle\, T^*Tx, x \,\rangle = \langle\, Tx, Tx \,\rangle = \|Tx\|^2.$$

Therefore $\||T|x\| = \|Tx\|$. □

Lemma 2.57 results in the following two immediate corollaries.

Corollary 2.58. *The operators T and $|T|$ have the same kernels.*

Corollary 2.59. *If T is invertible, then so is $|T|$.*

Definition 2.60. A *partial isometry* is a linear operator $U : \mathcal{H} \to \mathcal{K}$ such that the restriction of U to its support is an isometry.

Clearly isometries, co-isometries and unitary operators are all special cases of partial isometries. There are several ways of using and understanding partial isometries.

Proposition 2.61. *An operator U is a partial isometry if and only if U^*U is a projection. This is true if and only if UU^* is a projection. In this case U^*U is the support projection of U and UU^* is the range projection of U.*

Proof. Assume that U is a partial isometry. Let P denote the support projection of U, and let $x, y \in \operatorname{supp}(U)$. Then

$$\langle Px, y \rangle = \langle x, y \rangle = \langle Ux, Uy \rangle = \langle U^*Ux, y \rangle .$$

Since y is an arbitrary vector in $\operatorname{supp}(U)$, this implies that $Px = U^*Ux$ for all $x \in \operatorname{supp}(U)$. If $v \in \mathcal{H}$, then $v = x + z$ with $x \in \operatorname{supp}(U)$ and $z \in \ker(U)$. Thus $Pz = 0 = Uz$, and so

$$Pv = Px = x = U^*Ux = U^*Uv.$$

Since v is arbitrary in $\mathcal{H}$, this implies that $P = U^*U$. We have proven that if U is an isometry, then U^*U is the support projection of U.

Conversely, suppose that $U : \mathcal{H} \to \mathcal{K}$ is a linear operator with the property that U^*U is a projection. Let $P = U^*U$, and $E = P\mathcal{H}$. Then for any $x \in E$ we have $Px = x$ and so

$$\|x\|^2 = \langle x, x \rangle = \langle Px, x \rangle = \langle U^*Ux, x \rangle = \|Ux\|^2.$$

Thus $U|_E$ is an isometry. Moreover, for $y \in E^\perp$, we have

$$\|Uy\|^2 = \langle U^*Uy, y \rangle = \langle Py, y \rangle = 0.$$

This, together with $U|_E$ being an isometry, implies that $\operatorname{supp}(U) = E$. Hence U is a partial isometry.

For the second statement, it suffices to show that if an operator U is a partial isometry, then so is U^*. In fact, assume that U is a partial isometry. Then by what we have just proved, U^*U is a projection onto $\operatorname{supp}(U)$. Note that $\operatorname{supp}(U^*) = (\ker U^*)^\perp = \operatorname{range}(U)$. So if $z \in \operatorname{supp}(U^*)$, then $z = Ux$ for some $x \in \operatorname{supp}(U)$, and thus $\|z\| = \|x\|$ since U is isometric on $\operatorname{supp}(U)$. This implies that

$$\|U^*z\| = \|U^*Ux\| = \|x\| = \|z\|.$$

Hence U^* is a partial isometry, as claimed. □

Similarly, an $m \times n$ matrix A is called a *partial isometry matrix* if A^*A is a projection matrix, and this is equivalent to AA^* being a projection. If $P = AA^*$ and $Q = A^*A$, then P is called the range projection of A, and Q is called the support projection of A.

If $U : \mathcal{H} \to \mathcal{K}$ is a linear transformation, and if A is the matrix representation of U with respect to some choices of orthonormal basis for $\mathcal{H}$ and orthonormal basis for $\mathcal{K}$, then U is a partial isometry if and only if A is a partial isometry matrix. Moreover, $P = AA^*$ and $Q = A^*A$ are the matrix representations of the range space of U and, respectively, the support projection of U.

Example 2.62. (i) An elementary matrix is a matrix such that exactly one entry is 1 and the rest are 0. Every elementary matrix is a partial isometry matrix. We denote the elementary matrix with $a_{ij} = 1$ as E_{ij}. Some examples are the 2×2 matrix

$$E_{12} = \begin{bmatrix} 0 & 1 \\ 0 & 0 \end{bmatrix}$$

and the 3×2 matrix

$$E_{31} = \begin{bmatrix} 0 & 0 \\ 0 & 0 \\ 1 & 0 \end{bmatrix}.$$

The range projection of E_{12} is $E_{12}E_{12}^* = E_{12}E_{21} = E_{11}$, and the support projection of E_{12} is $E_{12}^*E_{12} = E_{21}E_{12} = E_{22}$. More generally, the matrix unit E_{ij} is a partial isometry with range projection E_{ii} and support projection E_{jj}.

(ii) Every orthogonal projection P is a partial isometry with both the support and range projections being P itself.

(iii) If u and v are unit vectors in a Hilbert space $\mathcal{H}$, then the *rank-one* operator on $\mathcal{H}$ denoted by $u \otimes v$ and defined by

$$(u \otimes v)(x) = \langle\, x, v \,\rangle\, u, \quad \forall x \in \mathcal{H},$$

is a partial isometry. (The reader should verify this.) Its range and support projections are, respectively, $u \otimes u$ and $v \otimes v$. We will be using these rank-one operators to learn about frames in Chapter 7.

Remark 2.63. In Theorem 2.64 which follows, the Hilbert spaces are assumed to be finite-dimensional. However, this result is also valid for infinite-dimensional Hilbert spaces if the operator is also assumed to be bounded.

Theorem 2.64 (The Polar Decomposition). *Let T be an operator from a Hilbert space $\mathcal{H}$ to a Hilbert space $\mathcal{K}$. Then there is a partial isometry U from $\mathcal{H}$ to $\mathcal{K}$ such that*

$$T = U|T|.$$

Moreover, if T is invertible, then U is unitary and is also unique.

Proof. The proof of this proposition is interesting and illustrates a variety of common techniques from operator theory. A detailed tutorial-style proof is given in the Student Presentations in Section 10.3. ☐

2.9. Traces of Operators

In Chapter 1 we introduced the trace of square matrices. This concept can be generalized to linear operators on both finite- and infinite-dimensional Hilbert spaces. For simplicity we assume that $\mathcal{H}$ is finite-dimensional.

Lemma 2.65. *Let T be a linear operator on $\mathcal{H}$ having dimension n. If $\{e_i\}_{i=1}^n$ and $\{f_i\}_{i=1}^n$ are any two orthonormal bases for $\mathcal{H}$, then*

$$\sum_{i=1}^{n} \langle Te_i, e_i \rangle = \sum_{i=1}^{n} \langle Tf_i, f_i \rangle .$$

Proof. By the properties of an orthonormal basis, we have

$$\begin{aligned}
\sum_{i=1}^{n} \langle Te_i, e_i \rangle &= \sum_{i=1}^{n} \left\langle \sum_{j=1}^{n} \langle Te_i, f_j \rangle f_j, \sum_{k=1}^{n} \langle e_i, f_k \rangle f_k \right\rangle \\
&= \sum_{i=1}^{n} \sum_{j=1}^{n} \langle Te_i, f_j \rangle \langle f_j, e_i \rangle \\
&= \sum_{i=1}^{n} \sum_{j=1}^{n} \langle e_i, T^* f_j \rangle \langle f_j, e_i \rangle \\
&= \sum_{j=1}^{n} \sum_{i=1}^{n} \langle f_j, e_i \rangle \langle e_i, T^* f_j \rangle \\
&= \sum_{j=1}^{n} \left\langle \sum_{i=1}^{n} \langle f_j, e_i \rangle e_i, T^* f_j \right\rangle \\
&= \sum_{j=1}^{n} \langle f_j, T^* f_j \rangle \\
&= \sum_{j=1}^{n} \langle Tf_j, f_j \rangle .
\end{aligned}$$

□

The quantity $\sum_{i=1}^{n} \langle Te_i, e_i \rangle$ is therefore independent of the choice of orthonormal basis for $\mathcal{H}$.

Definition 2.66. Let T be a linear operator on a Hilbert space $\mathcal{H}$ which has dimension n. Then the *trace* of T is the sum $\sum_{i=1}^{n} \langle Te_i, e_i \rangle$, where $\{e_i\}_{i=1}^{n}$ is any orthonormal basis for $\mathcal{H}$. We denote it by $\operatorname{tr}(T)$.

We have the following properties, which have already been shown in the matrix case.

Proposition 2.67. *Let S, T be linear operators on a Hilbert space $\mathcal{H}$ and $\alpha, \beta \in \mathbb{F}$.*

(i) $\operatorname{tr}(\alpha S + \beta T) = \alpha \operatorname{tr}(S) + \beta \operatorname{tr}(T)$.

(ii) $\operatorname{tr}(ST) = \operatorname{tr}(TS)$.

(iii) *If S and T are similar, then* $\operatorname{tr}(S) = \operatorname{tr}(T)$.

Proof. Exercise 15. □

Finally we give the following dimension formula:

Proposition 2.68. *Let M be a subspace of $\mathcal{H}$ and P be the orthogonal projection from $\mathcal{H}$ onto M. Then* $\text{tr}(P) = \dim(M)$.

Proof. Let $\{u_1, u_2, \ldots, u_k\}$ be an orthonormal basis for M and extend it to an orthonormal basis $\{u_1, u_2, \ldots, u_k, \ldots, u_n\}$ of $\mathcal{H}$. Then $Pe_j = e_j$ if $j \le k$ and $Pe_j = 0$ if $j > k$. Thus,

$$\text{tr}(P) = \sum_{j=1}^{n} \langle Pu_j, u_j \rangle = \sum_{j=1}^{k} \langle u_j, u_j \rangle = k = \dim(M). \qquad \square$$

2.10. The Operator Norm

Recall from Exercise 37 that $\mathcal{L}(\mathcal{V}, \mathcal{W})$ is the set of linear operators from vector space $\mathcal{V}$ to $\mathcal{W}$, which we showed is a vector space under the operator addition and scalar multiplication operations. Let $\mathcal{H}$ and $\mathcal{K}$ be Hilbert spaces. We will give a natural definition of a norm on the operators in $\mathcal{L}(\mathcal{H}, \mathcal{K})$.

Definition 2.69. Let $T : \mathcal{H} \to \mathcal{K}$ be a linear operator. The *operator norm* of T is defined by:

$$\|T\| = \sup\{\|Tx\| : x \in \mathcal{H}, \|x\| = 1\},$$

if this supremum exists. If the supremum exists, we call T a *bounded operator*.

Lemma 2.70. *Let $\mathcal{H}$ and $\mathcal{K}$ be two Hilbert spaces.*

(i) *The operator norm is a norm on the vector space $L(\mathcal{H}, \mathcal{K})$.*

(ii) *There are two equivalent definitions of $\|T\|$:*

$$\begin{aligned} \|T\| &= \sup\{\|Tx\| : x \in \mathcal{H}, \|x\| \le 1\} \\ &= \inf\{C : \|Tx\| \le C\|x\|, \forall x \in \mathcal{H}\}. \end{aligned}$$

Proof. See Exercise 16. $\square$

Let $\mathcal{B}(\mathcal{H}, \mathcal{K})$ denote the set of all bounded linear operators from a Hilbert space $\mathcal{H}$ to a Hilbert space $\mathcal{K}$. As a special case, we denote the bounded operators mapping $\mathcal{H}$ to itself by $\mathcal{B}(\mathcal{H})$. In finite-dimensional

Hilbert spaces, every linear operator is bounded, but there exist unbounded operators on infinite-dimensional spaces. Despite this, the notations $\mathcal{B}(\mathcal{H},\mathcal{K})$ and $\mathcal{L}(\mathcal{H},\mathcal{K})$ are often used interchangeably in the literature. In most of this book we are restricting to finite dimensions, so we will primarily use the notation $\mathcal{B}(\mathcal{H},\mathcal{K})$ to denote the operators from $\mathcal{H}$ to $\mathcal{K}$.

Proposition 2.71. *Let $T:\mathcal{H}\to\mathcal{K}$ and $S:\mathcal{K}\to\mathcal{V}$ be bounded linear operators. Then the following properties hold, where each operator norm given below is on the appropriate vector space of linear operators.*

(i) $\|Tx\|\le\|T\|\cdot\|x\|$ *for every* $x\in\mathcal{H}$.

(ii) $\|ST\|\le\|S\|\cdot\|T\|$.

(iii) $\|T\|=\|T^*\|$.

(iv) $\|T^*T\|=\|T\|^2$.

Proof. Part (i) follows from part (ii) of Lemma 2.70.

Part (ii): Let $x\in\mathcal{H}$ with $\|x\|=1$. By (i) we have:

$$\begin{aligned}\|STx\|=\|S(Tx)\| &\le \|S\|\cdot\|Tx\|\\ &\le \|S\|\cdot\|T\|\cdot\|x\|\\ &= \|S\|\cdot\|T\|.\end{aligned}$$

Taking the supremum over all unit vectors x yields:

$$\|ST\|\le\|S\|\cdot\|T\|.$$

Part (iii): For $x\in\mathcal{H}$, we have:

$$\begin{aligned}\|Tx\|^2 &= \langle Tx,Tx\rangle\\ &= \langle T^*Tx,x\rangle\\ &\le \|T^*Tx\|\cdot\|x\|\\ &\le \|T^*T\|\cdot\|x\|^2.\end{aligned}$$

The first inequality uses the Cauchy-Schwarz inequality. For $\|x\|=1$, this yields $\|Tx\|^2\le\|T^*T\|$, and taking the supremum over all unit vectors x yields:

$$\|T\|^2\le\|T^*T\|.$$

Hence $\|T\|^2 \leq \|T^*\| \cdot \|T\|$. If $T = 0$, then naturally $\|T\| = \|T^*\| = 0$. If $T \neq 0$, then $\|T\| > 0$, so dividing this last inequality by $\|T\|$ yields $\|T\| \leq \|T^*\|$. Now replace T with T^* and use the fact that $(T^*)^* = T$, obtaining $\|T^*\| \leq \|T\|$. Hence $\|T\| = \|T^*\|$.

Part (iv): From the proof of (iii) we have obtained that $\|T\|^2 \leq \|T^*T\|$, and from part (iii) we also have $\|T\| = \|T^*\|$. Thus

$$\|T\|^2 \leq \|T^*T\| \leq \|T\| \cdot \|T^*\| = \|T\|^2.$$

Hence $\|T\|^2 = \|T^*T\|$. □

Proposition 2.72. *If $U \in \mathcal{B}(\mathcal{H}, \mathcal{K})$ is a nonzero partial isometry, then $\|U\| = 1$. In particular, the norm of a unitary operator, an isometry, or an orthogonal projection is 1.*

Proof. Let $M = \ker(U)$, and let x be any unit vector in $\mathcal{H}$. Then $x = y + z$, where $y \in M$ and $z \in M^\perp$, and $\|y\|^2 + \|z\|^2 = 1$ by the Pythagorean Theorem, Corollary 1.72. Since U is an isometry on $M^\perp$, we have $\|Uz\| = \|z\| \leq 1$. So $\|Ux\| = \|Uy + Uz\| = \|Uz\| \leq 1$ for any unit vector $x \in \mathcal{H}$. Hence $\|U\| \leq 1$. To show we have equality, since U is not the zero operator, we have $M \neq \mathcal{H}$. Thus $M^\perp \neq \{0\}$. Choose $x \in M^\perp$ such that $\|x\| = 1$. Then $\|Ux\| = \|x\| = 1$, which implies that $\|U\| \geq 1$. Hence $\|U\| = 1$, as claimed. □

Proposition 2.73. *If $T : \mathcal{H} \to \mathcal{K}$ is any linear operator, and if $U_1 : \mathcal{K} \to \mathcal{N}$ and $U_2 : \mathcal{M} \to \mathcal{H}$ are unitary operators, then*

$$\|U_1 T U_2\| = \|T\|.$$

Proof. For any unit vector $x \in \mathcal{H}$ we have $\|U_1 T x\| = \|Tx\|$ because U_1 is unitary. Thus $\|U_1 T\| = \|T\|$. Replacing T by TU_2 in this argument yields $\|U_1 T U_2\| = \|TU_2\|$.

Since U_2 is unitary, it maps the unit sphere of M onto the unit sphere of $\mathcal{H}$. That is:

$$\{U_2 y : y \in M, \|y\| = 1\} = \{x : x \in \mathcal{H}, \|x\| = 1\}.$$

Thus

$$\begin{aligned} \|TU_2\| &= \sup\{\|TU_2 y\| : y \in M, \|y\| = 1\} \\ &= \{\|Tx\| : x \in \mathcal{H}, \|x\| = 1\} \\ &= \|T\|. \end{aligned}$$

Therefore, we have our result that $\|U_1TU_2\| = \|T\|$. □

2.11. The Spectral Theorem

The Spectral Theorem is a powerful theorem which states that if T is a normal operator on a finite-dimensional Hilbert space $\mathcal{H}$, the eigenspaces of T form an orthogonal direct sum decomposition of $\mathcal{H}$. This is an extension of the results given in Proposition 2.45. We should first note that while Proposition 2.45 is stated for $n \times n$ matrices on Euclidean space $\mathbb{F}^n$, there are exact analogs of these equivalent properties for linear operators on finite-dimensional Hilbert spaces.

Theorem 2.74 (The Spectral Theorem). *Let T be a normal linear operator on a finite-dimensional Hilbert space $\mathcal{H}$ with distinct eigenvalues $\lambda_1, \lambda_2, \ldots, \lambda_k$, and let P_j be the orthogonal projection of $\mathcal{H}$ onto the eigenspace E_{λ_j} for $1 \leq j \leq k$. Then the following are true:*

(i) $\mathcal{H} = E_{\lambda_1} \oplus \lambda_2 \oplus \cdots \oplus E_{\lambda_k}$.

(ii) $P_iP_j = 0$ *for* $i \neq j$.

(iii) $P_1 + P_2 + \cdots + P_k = I$.

(iv) $T = \lambda_1 P_1 + \lambda_2 P_2 + \cdots + \lambda_k P_k$.

Proof. We will prove part (i) using Definition 1.79 of the orthogonal direct sum. By Proposition 2.50, we know that the eigenspaces of a normal operator are pairwise orthogonal; i.e., if $x_i \in E_{\lambda_i}$ and $x_j \in E_{\lambda_j}$ for $i \neq j$, we have $\langle x_i, x_j \rangle = 0$. By the definition of the eigenspaces, we also have $E_{\lambda_i} \cap E_{\lambda_j} = \{0\}$ when $i \neq j$.

Define $K^\perp$ to be the orthogonal complement of $K = E_{\lambda_1} \oplus \cdots \oplus E_{\lambda_k}$. It remains to be proved that $K^\perp = \{0\}$. We first claim that the subspace $K^\perp$ is invariant under T and T^*. To see this, let $x \in \mathcal{H}$ with $x = x_1 + x_2$ where $x_1 \in K$ and $x_2 \in K^\perp$. Then by Proposition 2.50 we have $\langle x_1, x_2 \rangle = 0$. Therefore, $Tx = T(x_1 + x_2) = Tx_1 + Tx_2$. Since x_1 is a linear combination of eigenvectors for T, we have $Tx_1 \in K$, which means $\langle Tx_1, x_2 \rangle = 0$ since they are in orthogonal subspaces. But K is invariant under T^* as well, by Proposition 2.49, which means $T^*Tx_1 \in K$ and hence $\langle T^*Tx_1, x_2 \rangle = 0$. Therefore, $\langle Tx_1, Tx_2 \rangle = 0$, and also $\langle TT^*x_1, x_2 \rangle = \langle T^*x_1, T^*x_2 \rangle = 0$, which shows $Tx_2 \in K^\perp$ and $T^*x_2 \in K^\perp$. This proves $K^\perp$ is invariant under both T and T^*.

Using this invariance, we can define $T_{K^\perp}$ and $T^*_{K^\perp}$ to be the linear operators which are the restrictions of T and T^* respectively to the subspace $K^\perp$. If $K^\perp$ is a nontrivial subspace, there exists by Schur's result, Proposition 10.1, a matrix representation for $T_{K^\perp}$ which is upper triangular. There exists then at least one eigenvector for $T_{K^\perp}$ since the vector $\begin{bmatrix} 1 & 0 & 0 & \cdots & 0 \end{bmatrix}^T$ is always an eigenvector for an upper triangular matrix. Let $T_{K^\perp}x = \mu x$. We find, though, that x is an eigenvector not only for $T_{K^\perp}$, but also for T, since by invariance we have $Tx = T_{K^\perp}x = \mu x$. This contradicts the definition of the subspace K as containing all the eigenspaces of T. We therefore find that $\mathcal{H} = E_{\lambda_1} \oplus E_{\lambda_2} \oplus \cdots \oplus E_{\lambda_k}$.

Property (ii) follows readily because the eigenspaces are orthogonal. Property (iii) follows from (i) since given $x \in \mathcal{H}$ we can write $x = x_1 + x_2 + \cdots + x_k$ with $x_i \in E_{\lambda_i}$ for each $i = 1, 2, \ldots, k$. Then $(P_1 + P_2 + \cdots + P_k)x = \sum_{j=1}^k \sum_{i=1}^k P_j x_i$. Since the terms when $i \neq j$ are zero, this sum becomes $\sum_{i=1}^k P_i x_i$. Then, by definition of a projection, $P_i x_i = x_i$ and therefore $(P_1 + P_2 + \cdots + P_k)x = \sum_{i=1}^k x_i = x$ which proves $P_1 + P_2 + \cdots + P_k = I$. Similarly we can write

$$\begin{aligned} Tx &= T(x_1 + x_2 + \cdots + x_k) \\ &= Tx_1 + Tx_2 + \cdots + Tx_k \\ &= \lambda_1 x_1 + \lambda_2 x_2 + \cdots + \lambda_k x_k \\ &= \lambda_1 P_1 x + \lambda_2 P_2 x + \cdots + \lambda_k P_k x. \end{aligned}$$

This proves property (iv). □

An immediate consequence of part (i) of the Spectral Theorem is that the matrix representation of a normal operator is diagonalizable. This is true because part (i) implies part (iv) of Proposition 2.45.

The Spectral Theorem shows that if T is a normal operator on $\mathcal{H}$, then $\mathcal{H}$ has an orthonormal basis of eigenvectors which can be constructed by combining orthonormal bases from each eigenspace. This leads to the following result about the operator norm of a normal operator.

Proposition 2.75. *Let T be a linear operator on a Hilbert space $\mathcal{H}$.*

(i) $|\lambda| \leq \|T\|$ *for any* $\lambda \in \sigma(T)$.

(ii) *If T is a normal operator, then*

$$\|T\| = \max\{|\lambda| : \lambda \in \sigma(T)\}.$$

Proof. (i) Let $\lambda \in \sigma(T)$ and let x be a unit eigenvector for λ. Then $Tx = \lambda x$, so $\|Tx\| = \|\lambda x\| = |\lambda| \cdot \|x\| = |\lambda|$. We assumed that x is a unit vector, so $\|Tx\| \leq \|T\|$ by definition of the operator norm. Therefore $|\lambda| \leq \|T\|$ for all $\lambda \in \sigma(T)$.

(ii) Let $\{E_{\lambda_i}\}_{i=1}^k$ be the eigenspaces for T and let $|\lambda|_{\max} = \max\{|\lambda| : \lambda \in \sigma(T)\}$. Using the Spectral Theorem for normal operators and the definition of the orthogonal direct sum, we can write $x \in \mathcal{H}$ as a sum of pairwise orthogonal vectors $x = \sum_{i=1}^k x_i$, where $x_i \in E_{\lambda_i}$. Then $Tx = \sum_{i=1}^k Tx_i = \sum_{i=1}^k \lambda_i x_i$. If we take x to be a unit vector, we find

$$\begin{aligned}
\|Tx\|^2 &= \|\sum_{i=1}^k \lambda_i x_i\|^2 \\
&= \sum_{i=1}^k |\lambda_i| \|x_i\|^2 \quad \text{by the Pythagorean Theorem} \\
&\leq |\lambda|_{\max} \sum_{i=1}^k \|x_i\|^2 \\
&= |\lambda|_{\max} \|x\|^2 = |\lambda|_{\max}.
\end{aligned}$$

Therefore, we have $|\lambda|_{\max} \geq \|T\|$ and together with (i), we have $\|T\| = |\lambda|_{\max}$. □

The following is an immediate corollary of Proposition 2.75(i).

Corollary 2.76. *Let T be a linear operator on a Hilbert space $\mathcal{H}$. Then $\lambda I + T$ is invertible for any scalar λ such that $|\lambda| > \|T\|$.*

Recall from Section 2.7 that, given operators S, T on a Hilbert space $\mathcal{H}$, we will write $S \geq T$ to denote that the operator $S - T$ is a positive operator.

Proposition 2.77. *Let T be a self-adjoint operator on a Hilbert space $\mathcal{H}$. Then*

$$-\|T\| \cdot I \leq T \leq \|T\| \cdot I.$$

In particular, $0 \leq T \leq \|T\| \cdot I = \lambda_{\max} I$ *when T is positive and where* $\lambda_{\max} = \max\{\lambda : \lambda \in \sigma(T)\}$.

Proof. Recall from Lemma 2.12 that when T is self-adjoint, $\langle Tx, x \rangle$ is a real number for all $x \in \mathcal{H}$. We then have by the Cauchy-Schwarz Inequality,

$$|\langle Tx, x \rangle| \leq \|Tx\| \cdot \|x\| \leq \|T\| \cdot \|x\|^2.$$

Thus

$$-\|T\| \cdot \|x\|^2 \leq \langle Tx, x \rangle \leq \|T\| \cdot \|x\|^2,$$

which implies that

$$\langle (\|T\| \cdot I - T)x, x \rangle \geq 0$$

and

$$\langle (T + \|T\| \cdot I)x, x \rangle \geq 0.$$

Therefore

$$-\|T\| \cdot I \leq T \leq \|T\| \cdot I.$$

Since every positive operator is self-adjoint, and also therefore normal, by Proposition 2.75 we have $\|T\| = \lambda_{\max}$. □

The Spectral Theorem leads to the result that if S and T commute, then the eigenspaces of S are invariant under T. As a particular example, we show that if a positive operator S commutes with T, then the operator S^α as defined in Section 2.7 also commutes with T.

Corollary 2.78. *Let S be a positive operator on a Hilbert space $\mathcal{H}$ and let T be an operator on $\mathcal{H}$ such that $TS = ST$.*

(i) *If E_λ is an eigenspace of S, then $TE_\lambda \subset E_\lambda$.*

(ii) *If $S = PDP^{-1}$, we define $S^\alpha = PD^\alpha P^{-1}$, for $\alpha > 0$. Then S and S^α have the same eigenspaces, and $TS^\alpha = S^\alpha T$.*

Proof. (i) Suppose $ST = TS$. Since S is self-adjoint, there exists an orthonormal basis $\{u_i\}_{i=1}^n$ for $\mathcal{H}$ consisting of eigenvectors of S. Let $Su_i = \lambda_i u_i$. We see that for each i, $S(Tu_i) = TSu_i = T(\lambda_i u_i) =$

$\lambda_i(Tu_i)$, which proves that $Tu_i \in E_{\lambda_i}$. In other words, each E_{λ_i} is invariant under T.

(ii) It is clear from the definition of S^α that the spectrum of S^α is $\sigma(S^\alpha) = \{\lambda^\alpha : \lambda \in \sigma(S)\}$. Suppose $Sx = \lambda x$. Then $PDP^{-1}x = \lambda x$, and hence $D(P^{-1}x) = P^{-1}\lambda x = \lambda(P^{-1}x)$. Since D is a diagonal operator, we have $D^\alpha(P^{-1}x) = \lambda^\alpha(P^{-1}x)$, which then gives $PD^\alpha P^{-1}x = \lambda^\alpha x$. Therefore, we have $E_\lambda(S) = E_{\lambda^\alpha}(S^\alpha)$.

Given $x \in \mathcal{H}$, we can write $x = \sum_{i=1}^n a_i u_i$, where we have $S^\alpha u_i = \lambda_i^\alpha u_i$ for $i = 1, 2, \ldots, n$. We then find

$$\begin{aligned} S^\alpha Tx &= \sum_{i=1}^n a_i S^\alpha(Tu_i) \\ &= \sum_{i=1}^n a_i \lambda_i^\alpha (Tu_i) \\ &= T\sum_{i=1}^n a_i \lambda_i^\alpha u_i \\ &= TS^\alpha x, \end{aligned}$$

which proves $S^\alpha T = TS^\alpha$. □

2.12. Exercises from the Text

Exercise 1. If $\mathcal{V}$ is a vector space, show that the dual space $\mathcal{V}^*$ is a vector space under the operations defined in Equation (2.1).

Exercise 2. Prove Proposition 2.4.

Exercise 3. Prove parts (ii), (iii), (iv), and (v) of Proposition 2.8.

Exercise 4. Prove Proposition 2.9

Exercise 5. Complete the proof of Lemma 2.12(ii) and (iii).

Exercise 6. Let $T : \mathbb{C}^2 \to \mathbb{C}^2$ be defined by $T\begin{bmatrix} a \\ b \end{bmatrix} = \begin{bmatrix} -a \\ b \end{bmatrix}$ for $\begin{bmatrix} a \\ b \end{bmatrix} \in \mathbb{C}^2$. Show that T is self-adjoint but not positive.

Exercise 7. Prove Proposition 2.20.

Exercise 8. Prove Proposition 2.24.

Exercise 9. Let A be an $m \times n$ matrix. Prove that A is unitary if and only if both of the following conditions are satisfied.

(i) The column vectors of A form an orthonormal set in $\mathbb{F}^m$.

(ii) The row vectors of A form an orthonormal set in $\mathbb{F}^n$.

Hint: First show that $m = n$, then use Proposition 2.22 and consider A^*.

Exercise 10. Prove Lemma 2.30.

Exercise 11. Prove Theorem 2.40.

Exercise 12. Show that if $\{x_1, x_2, \ldots, x_k\}$ are eigenvectors of a matrix corresponding to distinct eigenvalues, then the set $\{x_1, x_2, \ldots, x_k\}$ is linearly independent.

Exercise 13. Prove Lemma 2.47.

Exercise 14. Let T be a positive operator on a Hilbert space $\mathcal{H}$. Pick an orthonormal basis $\{e_1, e_2, \ldots, e_n\}$ for $\mathcal{H}$. Let $A = [a_{ij}]$ be the $n \times n$ matrix representation of T with respect to the basis $\{e_1, e_2, \ldots, e_n\}$, so that

$$Te_j = \sum_{i=1}^{n} a_{ij} e_i, \quad j = 1, 2, \ldots, n.$$

Show that A is a positive matrix,; i.e., for all $x \in \mathbb{C}^n$, $x^* A x \geq 0$.

Exercise 15. Prove Proposition 2.67. Also, show that Part (ii) remains valid for linear operators between two different Hilbert spaces. That is, prove that if $T : \mathcal{H} \to \mathcal{K}$ and $S : \mathcal{K} \to \mathcal{H}$ are linear operators, so that $ST \in \mathcal{B}(\mathcal{H})$ and $TS \in \mathcal{B}(\mathcal{K})$, then $\operatorname{tr}(ST) = \operatorname{tr}(TS)$.

Exercise 16. Prove Lemma 2.70.

2.13. Additional Exercises

Exercise 17. Let S be the subspace of $\mathbb{R}^4$ that is spanned by the three vectors

$$\left\{ \begin{bmatrix} 1 \\ 2 \\ 0 \\ 1 \end{bmatrix}, \begin{bmatrix} 0 \\ 1 \\ 1 \\ 0 \end{bmatrix}, \begin{bmatrix} 1 \\ 0 \\ 1 \\ 1 \end{bmatrix} \right\}.$$

Show that S has dimension three. Use the Gram-Schmidt process on these vectors to compute an orthonormal basis for S.

Exercise 18. Let $\mathcal{H} = \mathbb{P}_2([-1,1])$ be the vector space of polynomials of degree less than or equal to 2 restricted to the domain $[-1,1]$. Give $\mathcal{H}$ the inner product

$$\langle\, p(t), q(t)\,\rangle = \int_{-1}^{1} p(t)q(t)dt.$$

(i) Use the Gram-Schmidt orthonormalization process on the set $\{1, t, t^2\}$ to get an orthonormal basis for $\mathcal{H}$.

(ii) Fix $\alpha \in \mathbb{R}$, and then $F_\alpha(p) = p(\alpha)$ for every $p \in \mathcal{H}$. Prove that F_α is a linear functional on $\mathcal{H}$. By the Riesz representation theorem, there exist $q_\alpha \in \mathcal{H}$ such that

$$F_\alpha(p) = \langle\, p, q_\alpha\,\rangle\,, \quad p \in \mathcal{H}.$$

Find $q_0, q_{1/2}$, and q_1.

Exercise 19. Let $W = \text{span}\{(i, 0, 1)\}$ in $\mathbb{C}^3$. Find $W^\perp$ and an orthonormal basis for $W^\perp$.

Exercise 20. Prove that if M is a subspace of a Hilbert space $\mathcal{H}$ and $M \neq \mathcal{H}$, then $M^\perp \neq \{0\}$.

Exercise 21. Compute all the eigenvalues for the following matrix, and for each eigenvalue, find all corresponding eigenvectors.

$$\begin{bmatrix} 3 & 2 & 1 \\ 4 & 1 & 0 \\ 0 & 0 & 5 \end{bmatrix}$$

Exercise 22. Show that the matrix A given below is diagonalizable (i.e., it is similar to a diagonal matrix) and compute an invertible matrix X and a diagonal matrix D such that $X^{-1}AX = D$.

$$A = \begin{bmatrix} 2 & 2 & 1 \\ 0 & 1 & 2 \\ 0 & 0 & -1 \end{bmatrix}$$

Exercise 23. For $z \in \mathbb{C}$, define $T_z : \mathbb{C} \to \mathbb{C}$ by $T_z(u) = zu$ for every $u \in \mathbb{C}$. Characterize those z for which T_z is normal, self-adjoint, positive, or unitary.

Exercise 24. Let $T : \mathbb{R}^2 \to \mathbb{R}^2$ be rotation by an angle θ. Show that T is a unitary operator and the matrix representation in the standard basis of $\mathbb{R}^2$ is given by

$$\begin{bmatrix} \cos\theta & -\sin\theta \\ \sin\theta & \cos\theta \end{bmatrix}.$$

Exercise 25. Show directly, by using a matrix and vector equation, that the row space of an $m \times n$ matrix A can be identified with the orthogonal complement of the kernel (or null space) of the matrix. Then use this to prove the theorem that states $\ker(A) = \text{range}(A^T)^\perp$, where $\ker(A)$ is the kernel and $\text{range}(A)$ is the range or column space.

Exercise 26. Let $\mathbb{P}_2$ be the set of polynomials of degree less than or equal to 2. In a previous exercise, we showed that $\{x+1, x^2+x, x-1\}$ is a basis for $\mathbb{P}_2$. Suppose L is a linear transformation from $\mathbb{P}_2$ to $\mathbb{P}_2$, and suppose the matrix representation for L with respect to the basis $\{x+1, x^2+x, x-1\}$ is given by the matrix:

$$A = \begin{bmatrix} 1 & 3 & 1 \\ 2 & 1 & 0 \\ 1 & 0 & 1 \end{bmatrix}.$$

Compute $L(x^2)$.

Exercise 27. Let T be a normal operator on a finite-dimensional Hilbert space $\mathcal{H}$. Prove the following results.

(i) $\|Tx\| = \|T^*x\|$ for all $x \in \mathcal{H}$.

(ii) $\ker(T) = \ker(T^*)$ and $\text{range}(T) = \text{range}(T^*)$.

(iii) If x is an eigenvector of T, then x is also an eigenvector of T^*.

(iv) If μ and λ are two distinct eigenvalues of T with corresponding eigenvectors x and y, prove that x and y are orthogonal.

Exercise 28. Prove that the rank of an orthogonal projection is equal to its trace.

Exercise 29. Let T and S be two positive operators on a Hilbert space $\mathcal{H}$.

(i) Show that $T + S$ and cT $(c > 0)$ are also positive.

(ii) Prove that if $ST = TS$, then ST is positive. Give an example showing that ST may not be positive in general. *Hint*: This requires use of the Spectral Theorem, part (i) of Theorem 2.74.

Exercise 30. Let $\mathcal{H}$ be a finite-dimensional Hilbert space, and let T be a positive invertible operator on $\mathcal{H}$. Prove that $\langle x, y \rangle_T := \langle Tx, y \rangle$ $(x, y \in \mathcal{H})$ defines another inner product on $\mathcal{H}$.

Exercise 31. Let P be an orthogonal projection from a Hilbert space $\mathcal{H}$ onto a proper subspace M of $\mathcal{H}$ (i.e. $M \neq \{0\}, \mathcal{H}$). Prove that $\sigma(P) = \{0, 1\}$.

Exercise 32. Let $T : \mathbb{C}^3 \to \mathbb{C}^3$ be the linear operator defined by the matrix:

$$\begin{bmatrix} 4 & 2 & 2 \\ 2 & 4 & 2 \\ 2 & 2 & 4 \end{bmatrix}.$$

Find the square root of T. *Hint*: Diagonalize the matrix first.

Exercise 33. Let $T : \mathbb{C}^n \to \mathbb{C}^n$ be the linear operator defined by a diagonal matrix $D = \operatorname{diag}(a_1, a_2, \dots, a_n)$.

(i) Show that $\sigma(T)$ is exactly the set of distinct diagonal elements of D.

(ii) Find the operator norm of T.

Exercise 34. Let T be a linear operator on a Hilbert space $\mathcal{H}$. Is it true that $\|T\| \neq 0$ implies T is invertible? Explain why.

Exercise 35. Let T be a linear operator on a Hilbert space $\mathcal{H}$. Prove the following statements.

(i) For every $x \in \mathcal{H}$,

$$\|x\| = \sup\{|\langle x, y \rangle| : y \in \mathcal{H}, \|y\| = 1\}.$$

(ii) $\|T\| = \sup\{|\langle Tx, y \rangle| \ : \ x, y \in \mathcal{H}, \|x\| = \|y\| = 1\}$.

Exercise 36. Let T be a positive invertible operator on a finite-dimensional Hilbert space $\mathcal{H}$, and let $\lambda_{\min} = \min\{\lambda : \lambda \in \sigma(T)\}$, $\lambda_{\max} = \max\{\lambda : \lambda \in \sigma(T)\}$. Prove the following statements.

(i) $T \geq \lambda_{\min} I$.

(ii) $\|T\| = \lambda_{\max}$.

(iii) $\|T^{-1}\| = \dfrac{1}{\lambda_{\min}}$.

Exercise 37. Define two operators A and B on a Hilbert space $\mathcal{H}$ to be *unitarily equivalent* if there is a unitary operator U on $\mathcal{H}$ such that $B = U^*AU$. We call matrices A and B *unitarily equivalent* if there is a unitary matrix U such that $B = U^*AU$. In other words, matrices A and B are unitarily equivalent if they are similar (see Definition 1.46) and the invertible operator S in that definition can be taken to be unitary.

(i) Prove that operators A and B on $\mathcal{H}$ are unitarily equivalent if and only if there are two orthonormal bases $\{e_i\}_{i=1}^n$ and $\{f_i\}_{i=1}^n$ for $\mathcal{H}$ such that the matrix of A with respect to $\{e_i\}_{i=1}^n$ coincides with the matrix of B with respect to $\{f_i\}_{i=1}^n$.

(ii) Prove that two orthogonal projections P and Q on $\mathcal{H}$ (where $\mathcal{H}$ is finite-dimensional) are unitarily equivalent if and only if they have the same rank.

(iii) Prove that two rank-one operators $x \otimes y$ and $z \otimes w$ are unitarily equivalent if and only if they have the same norms and $\langle x, y \rangle = \langle z, w \rangle$.

(iv) Use the Spectral Theorem to prove that two normal operators A and B on $\mathcal{H}$ are unitarily equivalent if and only if they have the same sets of eigenvalues, counting multiplicities. That is, if and only if they have the same eigenvalues and for each eigenvalue the dimensions of their corresponding eigenspaces are equal. (This is, in fact, an abstract form of the Spectral Theorem.)

Chapter 3

Introduction to Finite Frames

One of the important concepts in the study of vector spaces is the concept of a basis for the vector space, which allows every vector to be uniquely represented as a linear combination of the basis elements. However, the linear independence property for a basis is restrictive; sometimes it is impossible to find vectors which both fulfill the basis requirements and also satisfy external conditions demanded by applied problems. For such purposes, we need to look for more flexible types of spanning sets. Frames provide these alternatives. They not only have great variety for use in applications, but also have a rich theory from a pure analysis point of view.

This chapter will introduce the concept of a frame for a finite-dimensional Hilbert space. We begin with the basic characteristics of frames, then proceed in later chapters to more advanced topics. The reader who already has adequate linear algebra background and is using this book to learn about frames can begin with this chapter and refer to the background linear algebra materials in the previous two chapters as needed. The first section of this chapter discusses frames in $\mathbb{R}^n$, giving a nonstandard but equivalent definition of a frame. We use this as a first definition in hopes that it lends some intuition about frames that carry over into the more general setting.

We then proceed to give the standard definition of a frame in a finite-dimensional Hilbert space.

Many of the topics in this chapter have an analog or a generalization in infinite-dimensional spaces. We will point these out as they come up, and will refer the interested reader to further readings on the subjects.

3.1. $\mathbb{R}^n$-Frames

We begin our discussion of frames by restricting ourselves to real Euclidean space $\mathbb{R}^n$. The definition we give for a frame in this setting differs from, but is equivalent to, the definition of a more general frame (Definition 3.17). We are choosing this definition first because it is more intuitive for a first exposure to frames. The equivalence between the definitions is not obvious, and is discussed in Section 5.2.

The results in this section are equally valid in the complex spaces $\mathbb{C}^n$, and in fact, we use the complex version of the inner product to emphasize this fact.

Definition 3.1. Let $k \geq n$ and let $\{v_1, v_2, \ldots, v_k\}$ be a finite sequence of vectors in $\mathbb{R}^n$. We say that the sequence $\{v_1, v_2, \ldots, v_k\}$ has an *extension to a basis for* $\mathbb{R}^k$ if there exist vectors $\{w_1, w_2, \ldots, w_k\}$ in $\mathbb{R}^{k-n}$ such that

$$\left\{ \begin{bmatrix} v_1 \\ w_1 \end{bmatrix}, \begin{bmatrix} v_2 \\ w_2 \end{bmatrix}, \ldots, \begin{bmatrix} v_k \\ w_k \end{bmatrix} \right\}$$

is a basis for $\mathbb{R}^k$.

Definition 3.2. An $\mathbb{R}^n$*-frame* is a finite sequence of vectors $F = \{v_1, v_2, \ldots, v_k\}$ in $\mathbb{R}^n$, with $k \geq n$, such that there exists an extension of F to a basis for $\mathbb{R}^k$.

Example 3.3. Consider the collection of vectors

$$\{v_1, v_2, v_3\} = \left\{ \begin{bmatrix} 1 \\ 0 \end{bmatrix}, \begin{bmatrix} 0 \\ 2 \end{bmatrix}, \begin{bmatrix} 0 \\ 0 \end{bmatrix} \right\} \subset \mathbb{R}^2.$$

If the vectors $\{w_1, w_2, w_3\} = \{[0], [0], [3]\} \subset \mathbb{R}$ are appended to these, we have a basis for $\mathbb{R}^3$:

$$\left\{ \begin{bmatrix} v_1 \\ w_1 \end{bmatrix}, \begin{bmatrix} v_2 \\ w_2 \end{bmatrix}, \begin{bmatrix} v_3 \\ w_3 \end{bmatrix} \right\} = \left\{ \begin{bmatrix} 1 \\ 0 \\ 0 \end{bmatrix}, \begin{bmatrix} 0 \\ 2 \\ 0 \end{bmatrix}, \begin{bmatrix} 0 \\ 0 \\ 3 \end{bmatrix} \right\}.$$

Therefore, $\{v_1, v_2, v_3\}$ is an $\mathbb{R}^2$ frame.

It is clear from the definition that the $\mathbb{R}^n$-frames having exactly n elements (so $k = n$) are precisely the bases for $\mathbb{R}^n$.

Lemma 3.4. *A collection of vectors in $\mathbb{R}^n$ is an $\mathbb{R}^n$-frame if and only if it is a spanning set for $\mathbb{R}^n$.*

Proof. If the set $\{v_1, v_2, \ldots, v_k\}$ spans $\mathbb{R}^n$, then the matrix $V = \begin{bmatrix} v_1 & v_2 & \cdots & v_k \end{bmatrix}$ with the vectors v_i as its columns, has rank n. Since the column space, and therefore the row space, has dimension n, the n rows of this matrix must be linearly independent vectors in $\mathbb{R}^k$. There exists a basis for the orthogonal complement to the span of these n vectors. This basis will have $n - k$ vectors from $\mathbb{R}^k$, and these can be filled in as row vectors to extend the row vectors from the matrix V to a basis for $\mathbb{R}^k$.

If, on the other hand, the vectors do not span $\mathbb{R}^n$, the dimension of the span of the rows of the matrix is less than n, so we cannot extend to a basis for $\mathbb{R}^k$ with only $n - k$ row vectors from $\mathbb{R}^k$. □

Definition 3.5. A finite sequence of vectors $\{v_1, v_2, \ldots, v_k\}$ in $\mathbb{R}^n$ is called a *Parseval sequence* if it satisfies an identity like Parseval's identity. Specifically, for every $x \in \mathbb{R}^n$,

$$\|x\|^2 = \sum_{i=1}^{k} |\langle x, v_i \rangle|^2. \tag{3.1}$$

Orthonormal bases for $\mathbb{R}^n$ are naturally examples of Parseval sequences, since they satisfy Parseval's identity, but there are other examples as well. Notice that for a sequence to be a Parseval sequence for $\mathbb{R}^n$, it must have at least n elements.

Proposition 3.6. *Every Parseval sequence for $\mathbb{R}^n$ is necessarily an $\mathbb{R}^n$-frame.*

Proof. Exercise 6. □

We will henceforth call such sequences Parseval frames rather than Parseval sequences. The term Parseval frame will be given a more general definition in Section 3.3.

Lemma 3.7. *A Parseval frame* $\{v_1, v_2, \ldots, v_k\}$ *for* $\mathbb{R}^n$ *has an extension to an orthonormal basis of* $\mathbb{R}^k$.

Proof. The $n \times k$ matrix $\Theta^* = \begin{bmatrix} v_1 & v_2 & \cdots & v_k \end{bmatrix}$ has linearly independent rows. We will show that these rows are also orthonormal. The Gram-Schmidt algorithm (see Theorem 1.73) then gives a way to construct vectors in $\mathbb{R}^k$ which combine with the rows of Θ^* to form an orthonormal basis for $\mathbb{R}^k$. Appending these $k - n$ vectors as the final rows in our matrix gives a $k \times k$ matrix with orthonormal rows, and thus orthonormal columns as well.

Using the notation x^* for the conjugate-transpose $\overline{x}^T$ of the vector x, notice that $x^*y = \langle y, x \rangle$, where we are using the complex inner product. We can write Equation (3.1) as follows:

$$\begin{aligned} \langle x, x \rangle &= \sum_{i=1}^{k} \langle x, v_i \rangle \langle v_i, x \rangle, \\ x^*x &= \sum_{i=1}^{k} x^* v_i v_i^* x \\ &= x^* \left(\sum_{i=1}^{k} v_i v_i^* \right) x. \end{aligned}$$

From the last line above, it must follow that $\sum_{i=1}^{k} v_i v_i^* = I_n$, the $n \times n$ identity matrix. (Use Exercise 7 to verify this.) If we use the notation $\langle v_i, e_j \rangle = v_i(j)$ to give the components of each vector v_i, it follows that $\sum_{i=1}^{k} v_i(j)\overline{v_i(l)}$ equal to 1 if $j = l$ and 0 otherwise. It is also true, however, that $\sum_{i=1}^{k} v_i(j)\overline{v_i(l)}$ is exactly the inner product of the jth and l^{th} rows of the matrix Θ^*. This leads to the conclusion that the rows of the matrix Θ^* are orthonormal. □

The following is an immediate consequence of Lemma 3.7.

Lemma 3.8. *A finite sequence of vectors $\{v_1, v_2, \ldots, v_k\}$ in $\mathbb{R}^n$ is a Parseval sequence if and only if the rows of the matrix*

$$V = \begin{bmatrix} v_1 & v_2 & \cdots & v_k \end{bmatrix}$$

are orthonormal vectors in $\mathbb{R}^k$.

Consider the following example in $\mathbb{R}^2$. This collection of vectors is neither linearly independent nor an orthonormal set, but it shares some properties, including Parseval's identity, with an orthonormal basis.

Example 3.9. Let $\mathcal{H} = \mathbb{R}^2$, and let $\{x_1, x_2, x_3\}$ be the vectors

$$\left\{ \sqrt{\frac{2}{3}} \begin{bmatrix} 1 \\ 0 \end{bmatrix}, \sqrt{\frac{2}{3}} \begin{bmatrix} -\frac{1}{2} \\ \frac{\sqrt{3}}{2} \end{bmatrix}, \sqrt{\frac{2}{3}} \begin{bmatrix} -\frac{1}{2} \\ -\frac{\sqrt{3}}{2} \end{bmatrix} \right\}.$$

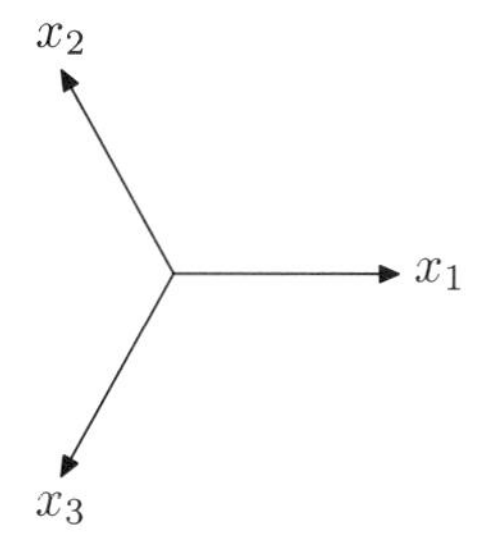

Figure 3.1. Vectors in Example 3.9. (This frame is often called the Mercedes-Benz frame. The likeness is apparent if you rotate the frame vectors by 90 degrees and also draw in the circle of radius $\sqrt{\frac{2}{3}}$.)

By showing that the 2 rows of the matrix $\begin{bmatrix} v_1 & v_2 & v_3 \end{bmatrix}$ are orthonormal (Exercise 8), we obtain that this is an example of a Parseval sequence for $\mathbb{R}^2$. This can also be verified by demonstrating that Equation (3.1) holds for every $x = \begin{bmatrix} a \\ b \end{bmatrix}$ in $\mathbb{R}^2$.

Notice that for every vector $x = \begin{bmatrix} a \\ b \end{bmatrix} \in \mathbb{R}^2$, we have the following equation:

$$x = \langle x, x_1 \rangle x_1 + \langle x, x_2 \rangle x_2 + \langle x, x_3 \rangle x_3. \tag{3.2}$$

This can be easily verified by direct computation. We have $\langle x, x_1 \rangle = \sqrt{\frac{2}{3}}(a)$, $\langle x, x_2 \rangle = \sqrt{\frac{2}{3}}(-\frac{1}{2}a + \frac{\sqrt{3}}{2}b)$, and $\langle x, x_3 \rangle = \sqrt{\frac{2}{3}}(-\frac{1}{2}a - \frac{\sqrt{3}}{2}b)$. When we substitute these into the right-hand side of the above formula, we find:

$$\begin{aligned}
&\langle x, x_1 \rangle x_1 + \langle x, x_2 \rangle x_2 + \langle x, x_3 \rangle x_3 \\
&= \frac{2}{3}(a)\begin{bmatrix}1\\0\end{bmatrix} + \frac{2}{3}(-\frac{1}{2}a + \frac{\sqrt{3}}{2}b)\begin{bmatrix}-\frac{1}{2}\\ \frac{\sqrt{3}}{2}\end{bmatrix} + \frac{2}{3}(-\frac{1}{2}a - \frac{\sqrt{3}}{2}b)\begin{bmatrix}-\frac{1}{2}\\ -\frac{\sqrt{3}}{2}\end{bmatrix} \\
&= a\begin{bmatrix}\frac{2}{3}+\frac{1}{6}+\frac{1}{6}\\ \frac{\sqrt{3}}{6}-\frac{\sqrt{3}}{6}\end{bmatrix} + b\begin{bmatrix}-\frac{\sqrt{3}}{6}+\frac{\sqrt{3}}{6}\\ \frac{1}{2}+\frac{1}{2}\end{bmatrix} \\
&= \begin{bmatrix}a\\b\end{bmatrix} = x.
\end{aligned}$$

Let's take a minute and think about this example. The vectors form a spanning set, so we know that we can always write x as a linear combination of these three vectors. The extraordinary feature, however, is that the coefficients in the expansion of x are calculated exactly as they are for an orthonormal basis. That is, the coefficient for the vector x is given by $\{\langle x, x_i \rangle\}$. Note however that since there are three vectors in a two-dimensional space, this set of vectors is linearly dependent. Therefore, this set of vectors does not form a basis, so these coefficients $\langle x, x_i \rangle$ are not unique.

3.2. Parseval Frames

Let $\mathcal{H}$ be a Hilbert space with finite dimension n. Our primary examples of such spaces will be the Euclidian spaces $\mathbb{R}^n$ and $\mathbb{C}^n$.

The set of vectors in Example 3.9 form a special type of frame called a Parseval frame. A formula such as Equation (3.2) which gives an algorithm for computing a vector from the frame elements is called a reconstruction formula for the frame.

Definition 3.10. A sequence of vectors $\{x_i\}_{i=1}^k \subset \mathcal{H}$ is called a *Parseval frame* for $\mathcal{H}$ if for every $x \in \mathcal{H}$:

$$\|x\|^2 = \sum_{i=1}^{k} |\langle x, x_i \rangle|^2. \tag{3.3}$$

Parseval frames are so named because Equation (3.3) looks like Parseval's identity for orthonormal bases. As we observed in the previous section, every orthonormal basis is a Parseval frame but there do exist Parseval frames which are not orthonormal bases.

Equation (3.3) gives the definition of a Parseval frame, but it turns out we could also have used, as the defining property, the fact that every vector x can be reconstructed using the inner products $\langle x, x_i \rangle$ for coefficients. We now prove that the two notions are equivalent.

Proposition 3.11. *A collection of vectors* $\{x_i\}_{i=1}^k$ *is a Parseval frame for a Hilbert space* $\mathcal{H}$ *if and only if the following formula holds for every* x *in* $\mathcal{H}$*:*

$$x = \sum_{i=1}^{k} \langle x, x_i \rangle x_i. \tag{3.4}$$

Equation (3.4) is called the *reconstruction formula* for a Parseval frame.

Proof. Let $\{x_i\}_{i=1}^k$ satisfy Equation (3.4). Then, for every $x \in \mathcal{H}$, we show that Equation (3.3) holds. In fact,

$$\begin{aligned} \|x\|^2 = \langle x, x \rangle &= \left\langle \sum_{i=1}^{k} \langle x, x_i \rangle x_i, x \right\rangle \\ &= \sum_{i=1}^{k} \langle \langle x, x_i \rangle x_i, x \rangle \\ &= \sum_{i=1}^{k} \langle x, x_i \rangle \langle x_i, x \rangle \\ &= \sum_{i=1}^{k} | \langle x, x_i \rangle |^2. \end{aligned}$$

Conversely, assume that $\{x_i\}_{i=1}^k$ satisfies Equation (3.3), so that $\|x\|^2 = \sum_{i=1}^k | \langle x, x_i \rangle |^2$ for every $x \in \mathcal{H}$. Let Θ be the linear operator from $\mathcal{H}$ to $\mathbb{C}^k$ given by

$$\Theta x = \begin{bmatrix} \langle x, x_1 \rangle \\ \langle x, x_2 \rangle \\ \vdots \\ \langle x, x_k \rangle \end{bmatrix} = \sum_{i=1}^{k} \langle x, x_i \rangle e_i,$$

where $\{e_i\}_{i=1}^k$ is the standard orthonormal basis for $\mathbb{C}^k$. (This operator, called the analysis operator, will be prominent in later sections.)

Then, using the vector norm on $\mathbb{C}^k$, we find that

$$\|\Theta x\|^2 = \sum_{i=1}^{k} |\langle x, x_i \rangle|^2 = \|x\|^2$$

for all $x \in \mathcal{H}$. Recall from Proposition 2.16 that such a norm-preserving operator is an isometry, and that Θ will also preserve inner products. In other words, for $x, y \in \mathcal{H}$, $\langle \Theta x, \Theta y \rangle = \langle x, y \rangle$. We can now verify that Equation (3.4) holds for every $x \in \mathcal{H}$. In the computation below, let $\{u_j\}_{j=1}^n$ be an orthonormal basis for $\mathcal{H}$.

$$\begin{aligned} x &= \sum_{j=1}^{n} \langle x, u_j \rangle u_j \\ &= \sum_{j=1}^{n} \langle \Theta x, \Theta u_j \rangle u_j \\ &= \sum_{j=1}^{n} \sum_{i=1}^{k} \langle x, x_i \rangle \overline{\langle u_j, x_i \rangle} u_j \\ &= \sum_{i=1}^{k} \langle x, x_i \rangle \sum_{j=1}^{n} \langle x_i, u_j \rangle u_j \\ &= \sum_{i=1}^{k} \langle x, x_i \rangle x_i. \end{aligned}$$

□

Remark 3.12. If $\{x_i\}_{i=1}^k$ is a Parseval frame, we can deduce that $\|x_i\| \leq 1$ for each i. To see this, compute for any i in $\{1, 2, \ldots, k\}$:

$$\|x_i\|^2 = \sum_{j=1}^{k} |\langle x_i, x_j \rangle|^2 \geq |\langle x_i, x_i \rangle|^2 = \|x_i\|^4.$$

Since $\|x_i\|^2 \geq \|x_i\|^4$, we know $\|x_i\| \leq 1$.

Remark 3.13. Following on the previous remark, we also find that if $x_i \neq 0$, then $\|x_i\| = 1$ if and only if x_i is orthogonal to each x_j when $j \neq i$. To verify this, assume $\|x_i\| = 1$. Then we see that:

$$1 = \|x_i\|^2 = \sum_{j=1}^{k} |\langle x_i, x_j \rangle|^2 = |\langle x_i, x_i \rangle|^2 + \sum_{j \neq i} |\langle x_i, x_j \rangle|^2,$$

which implies that $\langle x_i, x_j \rangle = 0$ for all $j \neq i$. To prove the converse, if x_i is orthogonal to each x_j, for $j \neq i$, then

$$\|x_i\|^2 = \sum |\langle x_i, x_j \rangle|^2 = |\langle x_i, x_i \rangle|^2 = \|x_i\|^4.$$

This gives $\|x_i\|^2 = \|x_i\|^4$, so $\|x_i\|$ is either equal to zero or 1.

These two remarks yield the following observation, which illustrates an important difference between an orthonormal basis and a general Parseval frame.

Proposition 3.14. *Let $\{x_i\}_{i=1}^k$ be a Parseval frame for a Hilbert space $\mathcal{H}$. Then it is an orthonormal basis if and only if each x_i is a unit vector.*

Proof. The forward direction is obvious by the definition of orthonormal basis, so we need to show that $\{x_i\}_{i=1}^k$ is an orthonormal basis when $\|x_i\| = 1$ for all $i = 1, 2, \ldots, k$. By Remark 3.13 above, we know that it is an orthonormal set. Since we assumed $\{x_i\}_{i=1}^k$ is a Parseval frame for $\mathcal{H}$, the set must span $\mathcal{H}$, and therefore must be an orthonormal basis for $\mathcal{H}$. □

We also have the following formula on the dimension of the Hilbert space $\mathcal{H}$.

Proposition 3.15. *Let $\mathcal{H}$ be a finite-dimensional Hilbert space. If $\{x_i\}_{i=1}^k$ is a Parseval frame for $\mathcal{H}$, then*

$$\dim \mathcal{H} = \sum_{i=1}^{k} \|x_i\|^2.$$

Proof. Let $n = \dim \mathcal{H}$ and $\{e_1, e_2, \ldots, e_n\}$ be an orthonormal basis for $\mathcal{H}$. Then we have

$$\begin{aligned} n &= \sum_{j=1}^{n} \|e_j\|^2 \\ &= \sum_{j=1}^{n} \sum_{i=1}^{k} |\langle e_j, x_i \rangle|^2 \\ &= \sum_{i=1}^{k} \sum_{j=1}^{n} |\langle x_i, e_j \rangle|^2 \\ &= \sum_{i=1}^{k} \|x_i\|^2. \end{aligned}$$

□

From the above result, we also have a new formula for the trace of a linear operator (recall Definition 2.66) using a Parseval frame.

Corollary 3.16 (Trace Formula). *Let $\{x_i\}_{i=1}^k$ be a Parseval frame for $\mathcal{H}$, and let A be a linear operator on $\mathcal{H}$. Then*

$$\operatorname{tr}(A) = \sum_{i=1}^{k} \langle Ax_i, x_i \rangle .$$

Proof. Let $\{e_j\}_{j=1}^n$ be an orthonormal basis for $\mathcal{H}$. Then by Definition 2.66, we have:

$$\operatorname{tr}(A) = \sum_{j=1}^{n} \langle Ae_j, e_j \rangle .$$

We then use the reconstruction formula $Ae_j = \sum_{i=1}^{k} \langle Ae_j, x_i \rangle x_i$ from Proposition 3.11, together with the linearity properties of the inner product and the adjoint of A to compute the following:

$$\begin{aligned}
\operatorname{tr}(A) &= \sum_{j=1}^{n} \left\langle \sum_{i=1}^{k} \langle Ae_j, x_i \rangle x_i, e_j \right\rangle \\
&= \sum_{j=1}^{n} \sum_{i=1}^{k} \langle Ae_j, x_i \rangle \langle x_i, e_j \rangle \\
&= \sum_{j=1}^{n} \sum_{i=1}^{k} \langle e_j, A^* x_i \rangle \langle x_i, e_j \rangle .
\end{aligned}$$

In the next calculation, we switch the order of the sums. We can then use the linearity properties of the inner product again, which will prove the trace formula.

$$\begin{aligned}
\operatorname{tr}(A) &= \sum_{i=1}^{k} \sum_{j=1}^{n} \langle x_i, e_j \rangle \langle e_j, A^* x_i \rangle \\
&= \sum_{i=1}^{k} \left\langle \sum_{j=1}^{n} \langle x_i, e_j \rangle e_j \, , \, A^* x_i \right\rangle \\
&= \sum_{i=1}^{k} \langle x_i, A^* x_i \rangle \\
&= \sum_{i=1}^{k} \langle Ax_i, x_i \rangle .
\end{aligned}$$

□

The reconstruction formula in Equation (3.4) and the Parseval-like identity from Equation (3.3) are two important properties shared by Parseval frames and orthonormal bases. There certainly are differences between them, too. Notice that the Parseval frame in Example 3.9 consists of three vectors, while any orthonormal basis for $\mathbb{R}^2$ must have exactly two vectors. We also readily see that the vectors in Example 3.9 are not orthogonal. They do all have the same norm, however, just like the vectors in an orthonormal basis.

Remark 3.12 points out that the vectors can have at most norm 1 if they belong to a Parseval frame, but does not address any further restrictions on the norms. Are equal norms required for the reconstruction formula to hold? Try to come up with a Parseval frame in which the norms of the vectors are not equal. (The paragraph following the proof of Proposition 3.19 may give you an idea about how to do this.) Nonuniform frames will be discussed often in the following sections.

3.3. General Frames and the Canonical Reconstruction Formula

Parseval frames are a special example of sets of vectors called frames. We introduced them first to emphasize the similarity with orthonormal bases. Frames, too, are related to bases, but they are more general than the Parseval frames. The following definition is the general frame analog of Definition 3.10.

Definition 3.17. A *frame* for a Hilbert space $\mathcal{H}$ is a sequence of vectors $\{x_i\} \subset \mathcal{H}$ for which there exist constants $0 < A \leq B < \infty$ such that, for every $x \in \mathcal{H}$,

$$A\|x\|^2 \leq \sum_i |\langle x, x_i \rangle|^2 \leq B\|x\|^2. \tag{3.5}$$

The constants A and B are known respectively as lower and upper *frame bounds.* Notice that any $A' < A$ is also a lower frame bound and any $B' > B$ is also an upper frame bound. We will often presume without stating it that A and B are the optimal frame bounds for a frame; i.e., A is the greatest lower frame bound and B is the least upper frame bound. A frame is called a *tight frame* if the optimal upper and lower frame bounds are equal; $A = B$. A frame is a *Parseval frame* if $A = B = 1$. A *uniform frame* is a frame in which all the vectors have equal norm.

The sum in Equation (3.5) will be considered throughout most of this book to be a finite sum, since we are considering primarily finite frames for finite-dimensional Hilbert spaces. As we have previously mentioned, though, this definition carries over into the infinite-dimensional setting.

We introduced frames for $\mathbb{R}^n$ in Section 3.1 and discovered that they are exactly the spanning sets of $\mathbb{R}^n$. The same result holds for general finite-dimensional Hilbert spaces.

Proposition 3.18. *Suppose that $\mathcal{H}$ is a finite-dimensional Hilbert space and $\{x_i\}_{i=1}^k$ is a finite collection of vectors from $\mathcal{H}$. Then the following are equivalent:*

(i) $\{x_i\}_{i=1}^k$ *is a frame for* $\mathcal{H}$.

(ii) $\operatorname{span}\{x_i\}_{i=1}^k = \mathcal{H}$.

The hypothesis here that the Hilbert space is finite-dimensional cannot be dropped. The statement is not valid in infinite dimensions.

Proof. (i)→(ii): Using the contrapositive, suppose $\{x_i\}_{i=1}^k$ does not span $\mathcal{H}$. Then there exists a nonzero vector x in the orthogonal complement $M^\perp$ of the subspace $M = \operatorname{span}\{x_i\}_{i=1}^k$. Since x is orthogonal to each x_i, the sum $\sum_{i=1}^k |\langle x, x_i \rangle|^2 = 0$, so the collection would not have a positive lower frame bound and thus would not be a frame.

(ii)→(i): Again use the contrapositive and assume that $\{x_i\}_{i=1}^k$ is not a frame for $\mathcal{H}$. Then the lower frame bound condition must be violated. (The upper frame bound condition always holds for finite sequences; see Exercise 9.) So for each positive integer m, there exists an element $y_m \in \mathcal{H}$ such that $\|y_m\| = 1$ and

$$\sum_{i=1}^k |\langle y_m, x_i \rangle|^2 < \frac{1}{m}.$$

Since $\{y_m\}_{m=1}^\infty$ is a bounded sequence, we recall from the Bolzano-Weierstrass Theorem in analysis that $\{y_m\}_{m=1}^\infty$ must have a convergent subsequence, say $\{y_{m_j}\}$. Let y be the limit vector, so $\|y_{m_j} - y\| \to 0$ as $j \to \infty$. Then we have

$$0 = \lim_{j\to\infty} \sum_{i=1}^k \left|\left\langle y_{m_j}, x_i \right\rangle\right|^2 = \sum_{i=1}^k |\langle y, x_i \rangle|^2.$$

This shows that y is orthogonal to every x_i for $i = 1, 2, \dots, k$, which implies that either $y = 0$ or $\operatorname{span}\{x_i\}_{i=1}^k \neq \mathcal{H}$. But we know that $\|y\| = 1$ because each $\|y_{m_j}\| = 1$ and we have shown that $\|y_{m_j} - y\| \to 0$. This proves $\{x_i\}_{i=1}^k$ does not span $\mathcal{H}$. □

For general frames, we can also work out a reconstruction formula which resembles the reconstruction formula (3.4) for Parseval frames.

Proposition 3.19. *Let* $\{x_i\}_{i=1}^k$ *be a frame for* $\mathcal{H}$. *Then there exists a frame* $\{y_i\}_{i=1}^k$ *such that every* $x \in \mathcal{H}$ *can be reconstructed with the formula:*

$$x = \sum_{i=1}^{k} \langle x, y_i \rangle x_i = \sum_{i=1}^{k} \langle x, x_i \rangle y_i. \tag{3.6}$$

Such a frame $\{y_i\}_{i=1}^k$ is called a *dual frame* to $\{x_i\}_{i=1}^k$. These are discussed in more detail in Chapter 6.

Proof. In this proof we will use the analysis operator, which we defined in the proof of Proposition 3.11. Let Θ be the linear map from $\mathcal{H}$ to $\mathbb{C}^k$ defined by:

$$\Theta x = \begin{bmatrix} \langle x, x_1 \rangle \\ \langle x, x_2 \rangle \\ \vdots \\ \langle x, x_k \rangle \end{bmatrix}.$$

We show that Θ is injective (one-to-one) by showing that the kernel is $\{0\}$. Let $\Theta x = 0$, which gives $\langle x, x_i \rangle = 0$ for $i = 1, 2, \ldots, k$. Since $\{x_i\}_{i=1}^k$ is a spanning set for $\mathcal{H}$, we can conclude that $x = 0$. Hence Θ is a bijection onto its range. If we let Θ^* be the adjoint matrix of Θ, we may also conclude that the operator $S = \Theta^*\Theta : \mathcal{H} \to \mathcal{H}$ is invertible. (We call S the *frame operator* for the collection $\{x_i\}_{i=1}^k$.)

Let $\{e_i\}_{i=1}^k$ be the standard orthonormal basis for $\mathbb{C}^k$. Then we see that

$$\Theta x = \sum_{i=1}^{k} \langle x, x_i \rangle e_i.$$

For each $x \in \mathcal{H}$ and each j, we have by the definition of adjoint,

$$\begin{aligned} \langle x, \Theta^* e_j \rangle &= \langle \Theta x, e_j \rangle \\ &= \left\langle \sum_{i=1}^{k} \langle x, x_i \rangle e_i, e_j \right\rangle \\ &= \langle x, x_j \rangle. \end{aligned}$$

Thus $\Theta^* e_j = x_j$. This implies that for each $x \in \mathcal{H}$ we have

$$\begin{aligned} Sx &= \Theta^*\Theta x \\ &= \Theta^*\left(\sum_{i=1}^{k} \langle x, x_i \rangle e_i\right) \\ &= \sum_{i=1}^{k} \langle x, x_i \rangle \Theta^* e_i ; \end{aligned}$$

$$Sx = \sum_{i=1}^{k} \langle x, x_i \rangle x_i. \tag{3.7}$$

We now define $y_i = S^{-1}x_i$ for $i = 1, 2, \ldots, k$. Then we have for each $x \in \mathcal{H}$ that

$$\begin{aligned} x = S^{-1}Sx &= S^{-1}\sum_{i=1}^{k} \langle x, x_i \rangle x_i \\ &= \sum_{i=1}^{k} \langle x, x_i \rangle S^{-1}x_i \\ &= \sum_{i=1}^{k} \langle x, x_i \rangle y_i. \end{aligned}$$

This gives one of the equalities in Equation (3.6). To see the other, we note that S, and therefore also S^{-1}, are self-adjoint:

$$\begin{aligned} x = SS^{-1}x &= \sum_{i=1}^{k} \left\langle S^{-1}x, x_i \right\rangle x_i \\ &= \sum_{i=1}^{k} \left\langle x, S^{-1}x_i \right\rangle x_i \\ &= \sum_{i=1}^{k} \langle x, y_i \rangle x_i. \end{aligned}$$

To prove that $\{y_i\}_{i=1}^k$ is a frame, we can demonstrate the existence of appropriate frame bounds. These bounds will make use of the operator norms of S and S^{-1}. (See Section 2.10.) Let A and B be lower and upper frame bounds (respectively) for the frame $\{x_i\}_{i=1}^k$.

We use the frame inequality and fact that S^{-1} is self-adjoint to find frame bounds on $\{S^{-1}x_1\}_{i=1}^k$:

$$\begin{aligned}
\frac{A}{\|S\|^2}\|x\|^2 &\leq A\|S^{-1}x\|^2 \\
&\leq \sum_{i=1}^{k} |\langle x, S^{-1}x_i \rangle|^2 \\
&= \sum_{i=1}^{k} |\langle S^{-1}x, x_i \rangle|^2 \\
&\leq B\|S^{-1}x\|^2 \\
&\leq B\|S^{-1}\|^2\|x\|^2.
\end{aligned}$$

The first inequality above follows from the properties of the operator norm, $\|x\|^2 = \|SS^{-1}x\|^2 \leq \|S\|^2\|S^{-1}x\|^2$. □

We have already noted that an orthonormal basis is always a Parseval frame. It is also easy to verify that the union of Parseval or tight frames will form another tight frame, so long as we clarify that the union must allow repeated vectors. For example, if $\{e_1, e_2\}$ is the standard orthonormal basis for $\mathbb{R}^2$, then $\{e_1, -e_2\}$ is also an orthonormal basis, and the collection $\{e_1, e_2, e_1, -e_2\}$ therefore forms a tight frame.

As a remark on the notation here, notice that although we are using set or sequence notation for frames, neither is exactly the right notion. For example, in the previous paragraph, we need the vector e_1 to be in the collection twice in order for $\{e_1, e_2, e_1, -e_2\}$ to be a tight frame. To allow for repeated vectors, frames are often regarded as finite sequences rather than sets. But the sequence notation is also an imperfect model, since the ordering it imposes would require us to regard a rearrangement of the same set of vectors as a different frame. We will generally use the word *collection* of vectors, by which we mean to consider rearrangements to be equivalent but to allow elements to appear more than once.

In a finite dimensional Hilbert space, a sequence of vectors is a spanning set if and only if it is a frame. Therefore, it is clear that if $\mathcal{H}$ has dimension n, any frame for $\mathcal{H}$ must have at least n vectors.

When a frame has more vectors than the dimension of the Hilbert space, we say it has an increased redundancy.

Definition 3.20. Let $\mathcal{H}$ have dimension n and let $\{x_i\}_{i=1}^k$ be a frame for $\mathcal{H}$ having k elements. The *redundancy* of the frame is the quantity $\frac{k}{n}$, which must be greater than or equal to 1.

The frame in Example 3.9, then, must have redundancy $\frac{3}{2}$. The redundancy of a frame gives a way to describe the size of the frame in comparison to the vector space it spans. In an application where the representation of a signal or image might be subjected to noise or erasures, redundancy helps to reduce the losses and errors that can occur. Think of a vector x in $\mathcal{H}$ as a sentence spoken into a cell phone. The voice message is broken down into a series of coefficients which are digitized, transmitted, and read by a receiver which knows how to transform the coefficients back into an audible sentence. During the transmission, however, some of those coefficients may be scrambled up or erased. If there were some extra coefficients used, we have a better chance of understanding the message on the other end, even if it isn't perfectly identical to the message that was sent.

Another advantage to redundancy is the variety of frames that exist. Frames are used in a wide variety of applications, each having unique constraints. Orthonormal bases are very restrictive. The elements in an orthonormal basis must all be orthogonal, there can only be exactly as many elements as the dimension of the space, and they must all have unit norm. Frames can be structured to adjust the weight on each component by having vectors with varying norms. Frames exist which pay special attention to some parts of a signal by grouping more vectors in these areas. This is accomplished by constructing a frame with varied spacing (measured by the inner products) between vectors.

The property that is present in orthonormal bases and lost for frames with redundancy greater than 1 is the uniqueness of the coefficients. In certain applications, however, uniqueness may be less important than the benefits from redundancy and variety of structures.

In an infinite-dimensional space, the analog of a spanning set is a complete sequence, and it turns out to be untrue that every complete sequence is a frame. There is a rich theory of frames in infinite dimensions, which we hope the reader will be motivated to explore after reading this book.

3.4. Frames and Matrices

In the previous section, we introduced the map Θ which led to the reconstruction formula in Equation (3.6). In this section we give a more detailed investigation of this operator. For convenience we always assume that every vector $x \in \mathcal{H}$ has a vector form with respect to a fixed basis $\{u_1, u_2, \ldots, u_n\}$ of $\mathcal{H}$.

Definition 3.21. Let $\{x_i\}_{i=1}^k \subset \mathcal{H}$. The matrix (operator) $\Theta : \mathcal{H} \to \mathbb{C}^k$ defined by

$$\Theta x = \begin{bmatrix} \langle x, x_1 \rangle \\ \vdots \\ \langle x, x_k \rangle \end{bmatrix} = \sum_{i=1}^{k} \langle x, x_i \rangle e_i$$

is called the analysis matrix (or operator) of $\{x_i\}_{i=1}^k$, where $\{e_i\}_{i=1}^k$ is the standard orthonormal basis for $\mathbb{C}^k$.

As we have seen in the proof of Proposition 3.19, if Θ^* is the adjoint operator of Θ, then $\Theta^* e_i = x_i$, which gives $\Theta^*(\sum_{i=1}^k c_i e_i) = \sum_{i=1}^k c_i x_i$. The composition $\Theta^*\Theta$ is therefore given by the following formula:

$$\Theta^*\Theta x = \sum_{i=1}^{n} \langle x, x_i \rangle x_i, \quad x \in \mathcal{H}. \tag{3.8}$$

Definition 3.22. The adjoint Θ^* of the analysis operator, which will map $\mathbb{C}^k$ to $\mathcal{H}$, is called the *synthesis operator*. The operator $S = \Theta^*\Theta : \mathcal{H} \to \mathcal{H}$ is called the *frame operator*. We will leave it to the exercises to prove that S is a positive self-adjoint operator. Note that we can define these operators for any sequence of vectors $\{x_i\}_{i=1}^k$ from $\mathcal{H}$, although $\{x_i\}_{i=1}^k$ may not be a frame.

Remark 3.23. The definition of a Parseval frame and Proposition 3.11 combine to prove that the frame operator is exactly the identity operator for $\mathcal{H}$; i.e., $Sx = x \ \forall x \in \mathcal{H}$, if and only if $\{x_i\}_{i=1}^k$ is a Parseval frame for $\mathcal{H}$. It is an immediate corollary that $\{x_i\}_{i=1}^k$ is a tight frame if and only if the frame operator for $\{x_i\}_{i=1}^k$ is a scalar multiple of the identity operator.

Recall the handy equation from Proposition 3.19, using the norm in $\mathbb{C}^k$:

$$\|\Theta x\|^2 = \sum_{i=1}^{k} |\langle x, x_i \rangle|^2. \tag{3.9}$$

This will lead us to the following equivalent ways to describe a frame for a finite-dimensional Hilbert space.

Lemma 3.24. *Let $\mathcal{H}$ be a Hilbert space and let $\{x_i\}_{i=1}^k \subset \mathcal{H}$. Let Θ be the analysis operator for $\{x_i\}_{i=1}^k$. Then the following are equivalent:*

(i) *$\{x_i\}_{i=1}^k$ is a frame for $\mathcal{H}$.*

(ii) *Θ is a one-to-one operator from $\mathcal{H}$ to $\mathbb{C}^k$.*

(iii) *The frame operator $S = \Theta^*\Theta$ is an invertible operator on $\mathcal{H}$.*

Moreover, if $\{x_i\}_{i=1}^k$ is a frame for $\mathcal{H}$, then $A = \frac{1}{\|\Theta^{-1}\|^2}$ and $B = \|\Theta\|^2$ are frame bounds, where $\Theta^{-1} : \Theta(\mathcal{H}) \to \mathcal{H}$ is the inverse of Θ.

Proof. (i)$\rightarrow$(ii): We will prove the contrapositive. Suppose $\Theta x = 0$ for some $x \neq 0$ in $\mathcal{H}$. This means that $\langle x, x_i \rangle = 0$ for each $i = 1, 2, \dots, k$, so x is orthogonal to each x_i. Therefore, x is not in the span of $\{x_i\}_{i=1}^k$. In the comments following Proposition 3.19, we noted that a frame must be a spanning set, so this shows that $\{x_i\}_{i=1}^k$ is not a frame for $\mathcal{H}$.

(ii)$\rightarrow$(iii): This is a result of Proposition 2.34. Since $\mathbb{C}^k = \ker(\Theta^*) \oplus \operatorname{range}(\Theta)$, if $y \neq 0$ is in $\Theta(\mathcal{H})$, then $\Theta^* y \neq 0$. If we assume that Θ is one-to-one, we know for any $x \neq 0$ in $\mathcal{H}$, that $\Theta x \neq 0$; hence $\Theta^*\Theta x \neq 0$. Therefore, since $\Theta^*\Theta$ is a linear operator on $\mathcal{H}$, it must be invertible.

(iii)$\rightarrow$(i): If $S = \Theta^*\Theta$ is an invertible operator on $\mathcal{H}$, we let $y_i = S^{-1}x_i$ for $i = 1, 2, \dots, k$. Then $x = \sum_{i=1}^k \langle x, y_i \rangle x_i$, using the computation shown in Proposition 3.19. (Note that the computation did not rely on $\{x_i\}_{i=1}^k$ being a frame.) Therefore, $\{x_i\}_{i=1}^k$ spans $\mathcal{H}$, and is hence a frame for $\mathcal{H}$.

The frame bounds follow from Equation (3.9). Supposing that $\{x_i\}_{i=1}^k$ is a frame, $\sum_{i=1}^k |\langle x, x_i \rangle|^2 = \|\Theta x\|^2 \leq \|\Theta\|^2\|x\|^2$ for all $x \in \mathcal{H}$, which proves $\|\Theta\|^2$ is an upper frame bound. Since Θ is a bijection onto its range $\Theta(\mathcal{H})$, we have $\|x\|^2 = \|\Theta^{-1}\Theta x\|^2 \leq \|\Theta^{-1}\|^2\|\Theta x\|^2$ for all $x \in \mathcal{H}$, which gives $\frac{\|x\|^2}{\|\Theta^{-1}\|^2} \leq \|\Theta x\|^2$. Therefore, as required, $\frac{1}{\|\Theta^{-1}\|^2}$ is a lower frame bound for $\{x_i\}_{i=1}^k$. □

Now we view Θ as a $k \times n$ matrix with respect to the standard orthonormal basis $\{e_i\}_{i=1}^k$ for $\mathbb{C}^k$ and a fixed orthonormal basis $\{u_1, u_2, \ldots, u_n\}$ for $\mathcal{H}$. Write $\Theta = [\Theta_{ij}]_{k\times n}$. Then we have

$$\Theta_{ij} = \langle \Theta u_j, e_i \rangle = \langle u_j, \Theta^* e_i \rangle = \langle u_j, x_i \rangle = \overline{\langle x_i, u_j \rangle}.$$

The rows of the matrix Θ are $x_i^* = \overline{x_i}^T$ if we view each vector x_i as a column vector in $\mathcal{H}$:

$$\Theta = \begin{bmatrix} \leftarrow x_1^* \rightarrow \\ \leftarrow x_2^* \rightarrow \\ \vdots \\ \leftarrow x_k^* \rightarrow \end{bmatrix}.$$

Similarly, the synthesis operator Θ^* is an $n \times k$ matrix with the vectors x_i as its columns:

$$\Theta^* = \begin{bmatrix} \uparrow & \uparrow & & \uparrow \\ x_1 & x_2 & \cdots & x_k \\ \downarrow & \downarrow & & \downarrow \end{bmatrix}.$$

Using the matrix representations of the analysis and synthesis operator, we find the following properties:

Proposition 3.25. *Let $T = \begin{bmatrix} x_1 & x_2 & \cdots & x_k \end{bmatrix}$ be an $n \times k$ matrix with x_i being the column vectors of T.*

(i) *$\{x_1, x_2, \ldots, x_k\}$ is a frame for $\mathbb{C}^n$ if and only if T has rank n.*

(ii) *$\{x_1, x_2, \ldots, x_k\}$ is a tight frame for $\mathbb{C}^n$ if and only if the set of row vectors of T is a pairwise orthogonal collection of vectors all having the same norm. In particular, $\{x_i\}_{i=1}^k$ is a Parseval frame for $\mathbb{C}^n$ if and only if the set of row vectors of T is an orthonormal set.*

Proof. Note that $T = \Theta^*$, where Θ is the analysis operator of $\{x_1, x_2, \ldots, x_k\}$. Thus from Proposition 1.51, we have $\{x_1, x_2, \ldots, x_k\}$ is a frame if and only if T^* has rank n if and only if T has rank n, which proves (i).

For (ii), the columns of T form a tight frame with frame bound A if and only if the analysis operator $\Theta = T^*$ is a scalar multiple of an isometry. In particular, using Equation (3.9) and the definition of a tight frame, we see that $\{x_i\}_{i=1}^k$ is an A-tight frame for $\mathbb{C}^n$ if and only if

$$\|\Theta x\| = \sqrt{A}\|x\| \qquad \text{for all } x \in \mathbb{C}^n.$$

By Proposition 2.22, this is equivalent to the matrix $\frac{1}{\sqrt{A}}T$ having orthonormal rows; hence the rows of T are orthogonal and all have norm $\sqrt{A}$ if and only if $\{x_i\}_{i=1}^k$ is an A-tight frame. The Parseval frame case occurs when $A = 1$. □

Motivated by the above result, we give the following definitions:

Definition 3.26. A matrix T of size $n \times k$ is called a *frame matrix* if it has rank n. T is called a *Parseval frame matrix* if $TT^* = I_{n\times n}$. It is called a *tight frame matrix* if $TT^* = \lambda I_{n\times n}$ for some $\lambda > 0$. If T is a tight frame matrix and, in addition, all of the columns of T have the same norm, then T is called an *equi-norm tight frame matrix.*

Proposition 3.27. *Let $T = \begin{bmatrix} x_1 & x_2 & \cdots & x_k \end{bmatrix}$ be an $n \times k$ matrix and let $\lambda_{\min}$ and $\lambda_{\max}$ respectively be the minimal and maximal eigenvalues of TT^*. Then following are equivalent:*

(i) $\lambda_{\min} > 0$.

(ii) *$\{x_i\}_{i=1}^k$ is a frame for $\mathbb{C}^n$.*

Moreover, when the above statements hold, the optimal lower and upper frame bounds for $\{x_i\}_{i=1}^k$ are $\lambda_{\min}$ and $\lambda_{\max}$, respectively.

Proof. Since $TT^* = S$ – the frame operator for $\{x_i\}_{i=1}^k$ – is shown in Exercise 2 to be a positive operator, its eigenvalues are all real and nonnegative by Proposition 2.48. Then $\lambda_{\min} > 0$ if and only if S is invertible, so by Lemma 3.24, $\{x_i\}_{i=1}^k$ is a frame if and only if $\lambda_{\min} > 0$.

We leave the proof of the optimal frame bounds for the reader to show in Exercise 13. □

If $\{x_i\}_{i=1}^k$ is a frame with optimal frame bounds A and B, then $\frac{B}{A} = \frac{\lambda_{\max}}{\lambda_{\min}} = c(S)$ is the *condition number* of the frame operator S, which is an important quantity in the numerical computation of S^{-1}, and will be discussed later in more detail.

Given the analysis operator Θ for a sequence $\{x_i\}_{i=1}^k$, we have been describing the importance of the frame operator $S = \Theta^*\Theta$. Composing the analysis and synthesis operators in the other order $G = \Theta\Theta^*$ gives an operator called the *Grammian operator* on the Hilbert space $\mathbb{C}^k$. The Grammian also plays an important role in frame theory. The entries of the Grammian matrix are the inner products between the frame elements:

$$G = \Theta\Theta^* = \begin{bmatrix} \langle x_1, x_1 \rangle & \langle x_2, x_1 \rangle & \cdots & \langle x_k, x_1 \rangle \\ \langle x_1, x_2 \rangle & \langle x_2, x_2 \rangle & \cdots & \langle x_k, x_2 \rangle \\ \vdots & \vdots & \ddots & \vdots \\ \langle x_1, x_k \rangle & \langle x_2, x_k \rangle & \cdots & \langle x_k, x_k \rangle \end{bmatrix}.$$

The diagonal entries of the Grammian are $\|x_i\|^2, i = 1, 2, \ldots, k$, the squares of the norms of the frame elements.

Proposition 3.28. *A collection of vectors $\{x_i\}_{i=1}^k \subset \mathcal{H}$, where $\mathcal{H}$ is a Hilbert space of dimension n, is a Parseval frame for $\mathcal{H}$ if and only if the associated Grammian operator G is an orthogonal projection of rank n.*

Proof. This follows from Remark 3.23. $\{x_i\}_{i=1}^k$ is a Parseval frame if and only if the frame operator $\Theta^*\Theta$ is the identity operator. Let G be the associated Grammian operator $\Theta\Theta^*$. It is easily verified that G is self-adjoint, and we also find $G^2 = (\Theta\Theta^*)(\Theta\Theta^*) = \Theta(\Theta^*\Theta)\Theta^*$, which by Exercise 7 will equal $\Theta(I_n)\Theta^* = G$ if and only if $\{x_i\}_{i=1}^k$ is a Parseval frame. □

3.5. Similarity and Unitary Equivalence of Frames

There are several commonly used notions of equivalence among frames. In other words, there are frames which, although they are technically different, are considered to be the "same". Below are some natural notions of equivalent frames in $\mathbb{R}^n$. These equivalences are described more precisely in Section 4.2.

- Frames which contain the same vectors, but given in a different order.
- Frames which only differ in that some of the vectors x_i have been replaced with the additive inverse $-x_i$.
- Frames which are rotations of each other, in the sense that a fixed rotation is applied to each vector of one frame to create the other frame.

There are more general notions of equivalence called the similarity of frames and the unitary equivalence of frames. To begin this discussion, observe the following result. We have left the proof for the reader in the exercises.

Lemma 3.29. *Given $\{x_i\}_{i=1}^k \subset \mathcal{H}$ and T any invertible (bijective) operator from $\mathcal{H}$ to $\mathcal{K}$, $\{x_i\}_{i=1}^k$ is a frame for $\mathcal{H}$ if and only if $\{Tx_i\}_{i=1}^k$ is a frame for $\mathcal{K}$.*

Proof. Exercise 1. □

This lemma motivates our definition of two types of equivalence of frames:

Definition 3.30. Two frames $\{x_i\}_{i=1}^k$ and $\{y_i\}_{i=1}^k$ for Hilbert spaces $\mathcal{H}$ and $\mathcal{K}$ respectively are said to be *similar* if there exists an invertible operator $T : \mathcal{H} \to \mathcal{K}$ such that $Tx_i = y_i$ for $i = 1, 2, \ldots, k$. The frames are called *unitarily equivalent* if we require T to be a unitary operator from $\mathcal{H}$ to $\mathcal{K}$.

We remark that similarity is an equivalence relation which is order dependent. For example, if $\{e_i\}_{i=1}^n$ is an orthonormal basis for $\mathcal{H}$, then $\{0, e_1, \ldots, e_n\}$ and $\{e_1, 0, e_2, \ldots, e_n\}$ are two nonsimilar frames, although they are the same set. An equivalence relation which does equate permutations of the vectors was described at the beginning of this section, and will be introduced more carefully in Section 4.2.

The following result tells us the rather interesting fact that every frame is similar to a Parseval frame. Recall that the frame operator S for a frame is always a positive invertible operator, and therefore has a positive square root operator $S^{\frac{1}{2}}$. The inverse of S is also a positive operator, and hence also has a square root. The proposition below will make use of this square root of the inverse, which we denote $S^{-\frac{1}{2}}$.

Proposition 3.31. *Let $\{x_i\}_{i=1}^k$ be a frame for $\mathcal{H}$ with frame operator S. Then $\{S^{-\frac{1}{2}}x_i\}_{i=1}^k$ is a Parseval frame for $\mathcal{H}$.*

Proof. We will show that $\{S^{-\frac{1}{2}}x_i\}_{i=1}^k$ satisfies Equation (3.4), the reconstruction formula, which proves that it is a Parseval frame for $\mathcal{H}$ by Proposition 3.11. The computation below uses the definition of the frame operator S and that $S^{-\frac{1}{2}}$ is both linear and self-adjoint.

$$\begin{aligned} x = S^{-\frac{1}{2}}SS^{-\frac{1}{2}}x &= S^{-\frac{1}{2}}\sum_{i=1}^k \left\langle S^{-\frac{1}{2}}x, x_i \right\rangle x_i \\ &= S^{-\frac{1}{2}}\sum_{i=1}^k \left\langle x, S^{-\frac{1}{2}}x_i \right\rangle x_i \\ &= \sum_{i=1}^k \left\langle x, S^{-\frac{1}{2}}x_i \right\rangle S^{-\frac{1}{2}}x_i. \end{aligned}$$

The last line is the frame operator for $\{S^{-\frac{1}{2}}x_i\}_{i=1}^k$ applied to the vector x. Since this always is equal to x, we have proved the Parseval reconstruction formula from Proposition 3.11. Therefore, $\{S^{-\frac{1}{2}}x_i\}_{i=1}^k$ is a Parseval frame. □

If we apply the above proposition to a Parseval frame, we get that the Parseval frame is similar to itself since S is the identity operator. It is possible, though, for a frame to be similar to more than one Parseval frame. Proposition 3.31 provides an example, but does not claim the uniqueness of the example. The following lemma describes similarity between two different Parseval frames.

Lemma 3.32. *If two Parseval frames are similar, then they must also be unitarily equivalent.*

Proof. Let $\{x_i\}_{i=1}^k$ and $\{y_i\}_{i=1}^k$ be two Parseval frames such that $Tx_i = y_i$ for $i = 1, 2, \ldots, k$ for some invertible operator T from $\mathcal{H}$ onto $\mathcal{K}$. Then for each $y \in \mathcal{K}$, we have

$$\begin{aligned} \|T^*y\|^2 &= \sum_{i=1}^{k} |\langle T^*y, x_i \rangle|^2 \\ &= \sum_{i=1}^{k} |\langle y, Tx_i \rangle|^2 \\ &= \sum_{i=1}^{k} |\langle y, y_i \rangle|^2 = \|y\|^2. \end{aligned}$$

This proves that the operator T^* is an isometry. From Proposition 2.16, this means that $TT^* = I_{\mathcal{K}}$. We also know, however, that T is an invertible operator. Therefore, $T^* = T^{-1}$, which proves that T is unitary by Theorem 2.17. □

We point out that if a frame $\{x_i\}_{i=1}^k$ is unitarily equivalent to a Parseval frame, then $\{x_i\}_{i=1}^k$ is also a Parseval frame. The next result gives us a characterization of similar frames:

Theorem 3.33. *Let $\{x_i\}_{i=1}^k$ and $\{y_i\}_{i=1}^k$ be two frames for $\mathcal{H}$ and $\mathcal{K}$, respectively. Then they are similar if and only if their analysis operators have the same range.*

Proof. Let Θ_1 and Θ_2 be the analysis operators for $\{x_i\}_{i=1}^k$ and $\{y_i\}_{i=1}^k$, respectively. First assume that $Tx_i = y_i$ for some invertible operator $T : \mathcal{H} \to \mathcal{K}$. Then

$$\begin{aligned} \Theta_2(y) &= \sum_{i=1}^{k} \langle y, y_i \rangle e_i \\ &= \sum_{i=1}^{k} \langle y, Tx_i \rangle e_i \\ &= \sum_{i=1}^{k} \langle T^* y, x_i \rangle e_i \\ &= \Theta_1(T^* y). \end{aligned}$$

Thus $\Theta_2(\mathcal{K}) = \Theta_1(T^*\mathcal{K}) = \Theta_1(\mathcal{H})$.

To show the converse, assume that $\Theta_1(\mathcal{H}) = \Theta_2(\mathcal{K}) = M$. Note that Θ_1^* and Θ_2^* are invertible when restricted to M, and so $T = \Theta_2^*(\Theta_1\Theta_1^*)^{-1}\Theta_1$ is an invertible operator from $\mathcal{H}$ onto $\mathcal{K}$. Let P be the orthogonal projection from $\mathbb{C}^k$ onto M. Then by the definition of the orthogonal complement, we have that $\Theta_1^*(M^\perp) = \Theta_2^*(M^\perp) = \{0\}$. Thus $x_i = \Theta_1^* e_i = \Theta_1^* P e_i$, and similarly $y_i = \Theta_2^* e_i = \Theta_2^* P e_i$. Therefore

$$\begin{aligned} Tx_i &= T\Theta_1^* P e_i \\ &= \Theta_2^*(\Theta_1\Theta_1^*)^{-1}\Theta_1\Theta_1^* P e_i \\ &= \Theta_2^* P e_i = y_i, \end{aligned}$$

which implies that $\{x_i\}_{i=1}^k$ and $\{y_i\}_{i=1}^k$ are similar. □

The following result is left to the reader to prove in Exercise 3.

Corollary 3.34. *A frame $\{x_i\}_{i=1}^k$ for a finite-dimensional Hilbert space $\mathcal{H}$ is also a basis if and only if the range of its analysis operator is the whole space $\mathbb{C}^k$.*

Theorem 3.33 induces a classification of all the frames having k vectors, according to the range of their analysis operators.

Corollary 3.35. *Let $\mathbb{J} = \{1, 2, \ldots, k\}$. Then the set of the equivalence classes (by similarity) of all the frames indexed by $\mathbb{J}$ is in one-to-one correspondence with the set of all subspaces of $\mathbb{C}^k$.*

3.6. Frame Potential

In physics, potential energy is a scalar quantity assigned to a system of physical objects operating under a force. Freely moving objects will change position in order to minimize the potential energy of the system. For example, extended springs retract, electrons move away from each other, and dropped objects fall to the ground. Equilibrium is a configuration such that every possible change in position will increase the potential energy. In other words, an equilibrium configuration is one at which the potential energy achieves a local minimum.

In 2001, John Benedetto and Matthew Fickus developed a theoretical notion of *frame potential*, which is an analog of a potential energy in the physical world. It is a function which can be computed for a set of vectors in $\mathbb{R}^n$, and which is minimized exactly when the vectors form a tight frame [**9**]. We will see in the exercises for Chapter 4, that all collections of $k > 2$ unit vectors in $\mathbb{R}^2$ which are spaced at the angle multiples of $\frac{2\pi}{k}$ form tight frames. (Example 3.9 demonstrates this for $\frac{2\pi}{3}$, but the vectors have been scaled to make a Parseval frame.) The example of unit vectors in $\mathbb{R}^2$ motivates us to consider k electrons placed on a wire circle, as in Figure 3.2. The electrons will reach equilibrium when they are equally positioned on the circle. In this situation, it seems like electromagnetic potential yields equilibrium for configurations that correspond to tight frames. In a more general setting and higher dimensions, however, will the equilibrium positions of electrons on a metal sphere always correspond to vectors of a tight frame?

We can realize readily that the electron comparison is not perfect. If only two electrons are placed on the wire circle, they immediately move to opposing poles to maximize the distance between them. A tight frame for $\mathbb{R}^2$ with only two unit vectors must, in fact, be an orthonormal basis, and such vectors are not positioned as the electrons would be. Tight frames seem to occur when vectors are as close to orthogonal as they can be. If $k \geq n$ unit vectors in $\mathbb{R}^n$ are considered to be subject to a repellant force when they are at an angle less than $\frac{\pi}{2}$ with a neighboring vector and an attractive force when the angle is

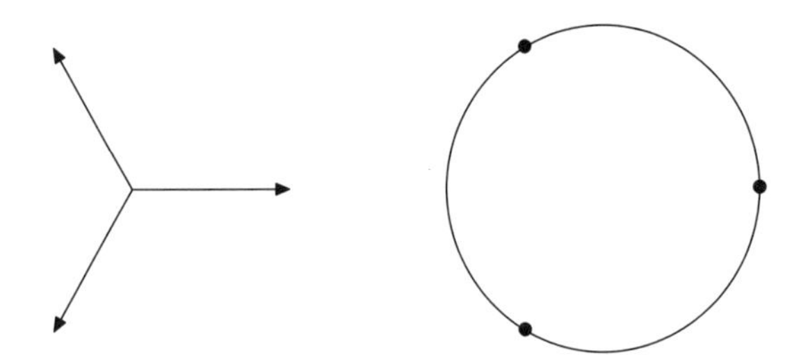

Figure 3.2. The 3-vector uniform Parseval frame and three electrons in equilibrium on a circular metal wire.

greater than $\frac{\pi}{2}$, then the configurations which minimize the potential energy under this force are exactly the tight frames.

In this section, we give the formula for the frame potential. Even though the frame potential does not correspond to an actual physical force, it does give an intuitive idea of the configurations of vectors which can possibly form tight frames. Although we begin by defining the frame potential for collections of unit vectors, there is a natural extension to collections of vectors with varied norms ([**17**]).

The inner product between vectors in a Hilbert space gives a quantity describing the orthogonality of the vectors. It is natural to expect, then, that the frame potential of a collection of vectors must be a scalar quantity derived from the inner products between the vectors.

Definition 3.36. Let $\mathcal{H}$ be a Hilbert space with dimension n and let $F = \{x_i\}_{i=1}^{k}$ be a collection of (unit) vectors from $\mathcal{H}$. The *frame potential* for F is the quantity

$$P_F = \sum_{i=1}^{k} \sum_{j=1}^{k} |\langle x_i, x_j \rangle|^2. \tag{3.10}$$

If a tight frame occurs when a set of vectors is collectively as orthogonal as possible, then we have an idea that this frame potential will attain some kind of minimal value when the vectors form a tight frame. We must state this minimization carefully, but it turns out that this is the right idea.

One question to ask is whether every tight frame has the same frame potential. It is not surprising that the potential will depend on k, the number of vectors in the collection. If we fix k, then we do have that every tight frame consisting of $k \geq n$ unit vectors in an n-dimensional Hilbert space has the same frame potential.

Lemma 3.37. *Let $F = \{x_i\}_{i=1}^k$ be a tight frame of unit vectors in $\mathbb{R}^n$. Then the frame potential P_F of F is $\frac{k^2}{n}$.*

Proof. Since F is a tight frame of unit vectors, the frame bound must be $A = \frac{k}{n}$ (see Exercise 10). Then, by the definition of a tight frame, we have

$$\sum_{i=1}^{k} \left(\sum_{j=1}^{k} |\langle x_i, x_j \rangle|^2 \right) = \sum_{i=1}^{k} A\|x_i\|^2 = \frac{k^2}{n}. \qquad \square$$

We next prove that, if a collection F contains at least as many vectors as the dimension of the Hilbert space, the frame potential is minimized precisely when F is a tight frame.

Proposition 3.38. [9] *The minimum value of the frame potential for a set of $k \geq n$ unit vectors $F = \{x_i\}_{i=1}^k$ in an n-dimensional Hilbert space is $\frac{k^2}{n}$. This minimum is attained exactly when the vectors form a tight frame for $\mathcal{H}$.*

Proof. From the preceding lemma, we know that if F is a tight frame, then its associated frame potential is $\frac{k^2}{n}$. It remains to be shown that $\frac{k^2}{n}$ is a lower bound on the set of achievable frame potentials among such collections F, and that every collection attaining this lower bound is a tight frame.

Let S be the frame operator for $F = \{x_i\}_{i=1}^k$, and let $\lambda_1, \lambda_2, \ldots, \lambda_n$ be the n eigenvalues of S, counting multiplicity. Since S is a positive operator, its eigenvalues are real and nonnegative. The trace of S is the sum $\lambda_1 + \lambda_2 + \cdots + \lambda_k$ and the trace of S^2 is $\lambda_1^2 + \lambda_2^2 + \cdots + \lambda_k^2$.

Given Θ the analysis operator of F, the frame operator is $S = \Theta^*\Theta$ and the Grammian operator is $G = \Theta\Theta^*$. From Proposition 2.67, this implies that $\operatorname{tr}(S) = \operatorname{tr}(G)$. The matrix G^2 has diagonal entries $d_{ii} = \sum_{j=1}^k \langle x_i, x_j \rangle \langle x_j, x_i \rangle = \sum_{j=1}^k |\langle x_i, x_j \rangle|^2$. Using the definition of the frame potential from Equation (3.10), we see that the frame potential is equal to the trace of the matrix G^2. (The frame potential is also the square of the Hilbert-Schmidt norm of the Grammian G; see Exercise 16.)

$$\begin{aligned} P_F &= \sum_{i=1}^{k}\sum_{j=1}^{k} |\langle x_i, x_j \rangle|^2 \\ &= \sum_{i=1}^{k}\sum_{j=1}^{k} |G_{i,j}|^2 \\ &= \operatorname{tr}(G^2). \end{aligned}$$

This then implies that the frame potential is equal to the trace of S^2, which is $\sum_{i=1}^{n} \lambda_i^2$. We can consider the minimization of the frame potential as a minimization problem with n variables, $\lambda_1, \lambda_2, \ldots, \lambda_n$. These variables are constrained, however. The diagonal elements of the Grammian matrix for $\{x_i\}_{i=1}^{k}$ are the squared norms $\|x_i\|^2$, which are all equal to 1. The trace of the Grammian is therefore k, and since it is equal to the trace of S, we have $\sum_{i=1}^{n} \lambda_i = k$.

There are a couple of ways to complete the proof. One way is a straightforward Lagrange multiplier computation, to minimize the quantity $\sum_{i=1}^{n} \lambda_i^2$ subject to the constraint $\sum_{i=1}^{n} \lambda_i = k$. We leave this version of the proof to Exercise 4. Another is to use the Cauchy-Schwarz inequality, Proposition 1.64. Let x be the vector in $\mathbb{R}^n$ containing the eigenvalues of S, $x = \begin{bmatrix} \lambda_1 \\ \lambda_2 \\ \vdots \\ \lambda_n \end{bmatrix}$, and let $y \in \mathbb{R}^n$ be $y = \begin{bmatrix} 1 \\ 1 \\ \vdots \\ 1 \end{bmatrix}$. From our computations above, we know that $\|x\|^2 = P_F$ and $\langle x, y \rangle = \sum_{i=1}^{n} \lambda_i = k$. By the Cauchy-Schwarz inequality,

$$k = |\langle x, y \rangle| \leq \|x\|\|y\| = \sqrt{P_F}\sqrt{n},$$

where equality holds if and only if x is in the span of y. Therefore, the frame potential P_F has minimal value $\frac{k^2}{n}$ which is attained if and only if the eigenvalues of S are all equal, $\lambda_i = \frac{k}{n}$. This is equivalent to $S = \frac{k}{n} I$; hence F is a tight frame for $\mathcal{H}$. □

This proposition confirms our previous intuition that the frame potential is minimized when the vectors are as orthogonal as possible, and these configurations are precisely the tight frames when tight frames exist. It is possible to run computer simulations to demonstrate how a set of random vectors moves toward minimum frame potential, and their equilibrium position can be numerically verified to be a tight frame.

So far, we have only described the frame potential for a set of unit vectors, but there is a natural extension to sets of vectors with nonuniform norms. In our analog to physical potential energy, we find that vectors of greater norm must exert a greater force. Consequently, there are collections of vectors with norms such that they can never be positioned into a tight frame. This topic will be addressed in more detail in Section 7.3.

Let $F = \{x_i\}_{i=1}^k$, $k \geq n$, be a set of vectors in $\mathcal{H}$, where $\mathcal{H}$ has dimension n. Let $\{a_i\}_{i=1}^k$ be the respective norms of each vector. We define the frame potential of F as before, $P_F = \sum_{i=1}^k \sum_{j=1}^k |\langle x_i, x_j \rangle|^2$, and also define $L = \sum_{i=1}^k a_i^2$. We want to find the configurations of vectors which have this given sequence of norms and which will minimize the frame potential.

If S is the frame operator for F, we still have $\sum_{i=1}^k \|x_i\|^2 = \operatorname{tr}(S) = L$. A similar argument to that used above in Proposition 3.38 shows that the frame potential is minimized exactly when the frame is a tight frame, if such a tight frame exists, and the minimum value for the frame potential is $\frac{L^2}{n}$. This is the result stated in the following proposition.

Proposition 3.39. [17] *Let $\mathcal{H}$ be a Hilbert space with dimension n. The minimum value of the frame potential for a collection $\{x_i\}_{i=1}^k$ of $k \geq n$ vectors in $\mathcal{H}$, under the constraint that $\sum_{i=1}^k \|x_i\|^2 = L$, is $\frac{L^2}{n}$, and the minimum value is attained exactly when F is a tight frame with frame bound $\frac{L}{n}$.*

The proof of Proposition 3.39 is left for the reader to complete in Exercise 5.

There are sequences of positive numbers $\{a_i\}_{i=1}^k$ for which there cannot exist a tight frame $\{x_i\}_{i=1}^k$ with $\|x_i\| = a_i$, $i = 1, 2, \ldots, k$. The condition under which a tight frame exists with vectors of specified norms is given in the following proposition. This result is proven in [**17**] using an argument which evolved from Proposition 3.39. It is a technical proof which we will not include here, but the interested reader is encouraged to refer to this article. We remark that Proposition 3.40 is a consequence of Theorem 7.16 from Section 7.3, so we will in fact have a proof of this condition later in the text.

Proposition 3.40. [**17**] *There is a tight frame for an n-dimensional Hilbert space $\mathcal{H}$ with k vectors having norms $\|x_i\| = a_i$, $i = 1, 2, \ldots, k$ if and only if the following inequality is satisfied:*

$$\max_i \{a_i^2\} \leq \frac{1}{n} \sum_{i=1}^k a_i^2. \tag{3.11}$$

The inequality in this result is called the *fundamental inequality* by the authors of [**17**]. It gives the important intuition that a vector cannot have a norm too much greater than those of the remaining vectors in order to possibly form a tight frame. As an example, there is no tight frame of four vectors for $\mathbb{R}^3$ having respective norms $3, 2, 1, 1$ since $3^2 > \frac{1}{3}(3^2 + 2^2 + 1^2 + 1^2)$.

3.7. Numerical Algorithms

Let $\{x_i\}_{i=1}^k$ be a frame for a Hilbert space $\mathcal{H}$ with frame operator S. Suppose that the frame coefficients $\{\langle x, x_i \rangle\}_{i=1}^k$ are known. We want to reconstruct x by using these coefficients and the frame vectors $\{x_i\}_{i=1}^k$. Recall that we can do this by computing the canonical dual frame $\{S^{-1}x_i\}_{i=1}^k$ and using the reconstruction formula

$$x = \sum_{i=1}^n \langle x, x_i \rangle S^{-1} x_i.$$

In order to do this, however, we need to invert the frame operator S. The speed of convergence in the numerical procedure of finding

S^{-1} depends heavily on the condition number of S. (Recall that the condition number is the ratio between the optimal upper frame bound and the optimal lower frame bound.) Therefore, inverting the frame operator by computer could be unacceptably time consuming if the dimension of $\mathcal{H}$ and the condition number are large.

An alternative to exactly reconstructing x is to use an algorithm which will produce increasingly accurate approximations of $x \in \mathcal{H}$ using the frame vectors and coefficients. The purpose of this section is to very briefly introduce three such algorithms: *the frame algorithm, the Chebyshev algorithm, and the conjugate gradient algorithm* ([**22**]). The frame algorithm is the simplest. However, the other two were showed by Gröchenig [**38**] to provide faster convergence when the condition number of S is very large.

We encourage the interested reader to consult [**22**] and [**38**] for more details about the numerical approach to reconstruction.

(1) **The frame algorithm:** *Let* $\{x_i\}_{i=1}^n$ *be a frame for* $\mathcal{H}$ *with frame bounds* A *and* B. *Given* $x \in \mathcal{H}$, *we describe the following recursive algorithm:*

$$\begin{aligned} u_0 &= 0, \\ u_k &= u_{k-1} + \frac{2}{A+B} S(x - u_{k-1}), \quad k \geq 1. \end{aligned}$$

Note that the values

$$S(x - u_{k-1}) = \sum_{i=1}^{n} (\langle x, x_i \rangle + \langle u_{k-1}, x_i \rangle) x_k$$

can be easily calculated since $\{\langle x, x_i \rangle\}_{i=1}^n$ and $\{x_i\}_{i=1}^n$ are already given. The convergence speed of this algorithm is given by

$$\|x - u_i\| \leq \left(\frac{B - A}{A + B} \right)^i \|x\|.$$

(2) **The Chebyshev algorithm:** *Let* $\{x_i\}_{i=1}^n$ *be a frame for* $\mathcal{H}$ *with frame bounds* A *and* B. *Given* $x \in \mathcal{H}$, *define*

$$\rho = \frac{B - A}{B + A}, \qquad \sigma = \frac{\sqrt{B} - \sqrt{A}}{\sqrt{B} + \sqrt{A}}.$$

Define the sequence $\{u_k\}_{k=0}^{\infty}$ *in* $\mathcal{H}$ *and corresponding numbers* $\{\lambda_k\}_{k=1}^{\infty}$ *by*

$$u_0 = 0, \quad u_1 = \frac{2}{B+A} Sx, \quad \lambda_1 = 2,$$

and for $k \geq 2$,

$$\lambda_k = \frac{1}{1 - \frac{\rho^2}{4}\lambda_{k-1}}$$

and

$$u_k = \lambda_k \left(u_{k-1} - u_{k-2} + \frac{2}{B+A} S(f - u_{k-1})\right) + u_{k-2}.$$

Then the sequence $\{u_k\}$ converges to x in $\mathcal{H}$, and the speed of convergence for the Chebyshev algorithm is:

$$\|x - u_k\| \leq \frac{2\sigma^k}{1+\sigma^{2k}} \|x\|.$$

(3) **The conjugate gradient algorithm:** Unlike the previous two algorithms, the conjugate gradient algorithm works without the knowledge of the frame bounds (but the speed of convergence does depend on the frame bounds).

Let $\{x_i\}_{i=1}^n$ *be a frame for* $\mathcal{H}$ *with frame bounds* A *and* B. *Let* $x \in \mathcal{H}$ *be a nonzero vector. Define three sequences* $\{u_k\}_{k=0}^{\infty}$, $\{r_k\}_{k=0}^{\infty}$, *and* $\{p_k\}_{k=1}^{\infty}$ *in* $\mathcal{H}$, *and corresponding scalars* $\{\lambda_k\}_{k=-1}^{\infty}$ *by*

$$u_0 = 0, \quad r_0 = p_0 = Sx, \quad p_{-1} = 0$$

and for $k \geq 0$,

$$\lambda_k = \frac{\langle r_k, p_k \rangle}{\langle p_k, Sp_k \rangle},$$

$$u_{k+1} = u_k + \lambda_k p_k,$$

$$r_{k+1} = r_k - \lambda_k S p_k,$$

$$p_{k+1} = Sp_k - \frac{\langle Sp_k, Sp_k \rangle}{\langle p_k, Sp_k \rangle} p_k - \frac{\langle Sp_k, Sp_{k-1} \rangle}{\langle p_{k-1}, Sp_{k-1} \rangle} p_{k-1}.$$

The sequence u_k converges in $\mathcal{H}$ to the vector x.

3.8. Exercises from the Text

Exercise 1. Prove Lemma 3.29.

Exercise 2. Given a sequence of vectors $\{x_i\}_{i=1}^k$ in a Hilbert space, prove that the frame operator S from Definition 3.22 is a positive operator.

Exercise 3. Prove Corollary 3.34.

Exercise 4. Complete the proof of Proposition 3.38 using the Lagrange multiplier method to minimize the frame potential under the given eigenvalue constraint $\sum_{i=1}^n \lambda_i = k$.

Exercise 5. Complete the proof of Proposition 3.39, using either a Lagrange multiplier argument or the technique from Proposition 3.38.

3.9. Additional Exercises

Exercise 6. Show that a Parseval sequence for $\mathbb{R}^n$ is necessarily an $\mathbb{R}^n$-frame. *Hint*: Show that a Parseval sequence must span $\mathbb{R}^n$.

Exercise 7. Let A and B be $n \times n$ positive self-adjoint matrices such that for all $x \in \mathbb{C}^n$, $x^*Ax = x^*Bx$. Prove that $A = B$. Equivalently, prove that if A, B are positive operators on $\mathcal{H}$ such that $\langle Ax, x \rangle = \langle Bx, x \rangle$ $\forall x \in \mathcal{H}$, then $A = B$. *Hint*: See Lemma 2.12.

Exercise 8. Verify that the vectors in Example 3.9 are an example of a Parseval sequence for $\mathbb{R}^2$ by showing that they satisfy Equation (3.1).

Exercise 9. Prove that if $\mathcal{H}$ is a finite-dimensional Hilbert space, then every finite sequence has an upper frame bound.

Exercise 10. Prove that if $\{x_i\}_{i=1}^k$ is a tight frame of unit vectors for an n-dimensional Hilbert space, then the frame bound is $A = \frac{k}{n}$. More generally, if $\{x_i\}_{i=1}^k$ is a tight frame for $\mathcal{H}$, then the frame bound is given by: $A = \frac{1}{n}\sum_{i=1}^k \|x_i\|^2$.

Exercise 11. Verify that the matrix of the Grammian operator is $[G]_{i,j} = \langle x_j, x_i \rangle$.

Exercise 12. Prove that if $\{x_i\}_{i=1}^k$ is a frame with upper frame bound B, then $\|x_i\|^2 \le B$ for all $i = \{1, 2, \ldots, k\}$.

Exercise 13. Let $\{x_i\}_{i=1}^k$ be any sequence of vectors in $\mathcal{H}$ with $k \ge n$ and let S be the associated frame operator. (Note that a sequence need not be a frame to form the frame operator.) Let $b_1 \le b_2 \le \cdots \le b_n$ be the eigenvalues of S. If $b_1 > 0$, prove that the sequence is a frame for $\mathcal{H}$ with optimal frame bounds b_1 and b_n. *Hint*: Since S is a positive operator, the Spectral Theorem implies that there is an orthonormal basis $\{u_i\}_{i=1}^n$ of eigenvectors of S.

Exercise 14. Let $\{x_i\}_{i=1}^k$ be a frame with lower and upper frame bounds A and B respectively, and let S be the associated frame operator. Prove that $\{S^{-1}x_i\}_{i=1}^k$ is also a frame with lower frame bound $\frac{1}{B}$ and upper frame bound $\frac{1}{A}$. *Hint*: Find the frame operator for $\{S^{-1}x_i\}_{i=1}^k$ and use Exercise 13.

Exercise 15. Let G be the Grammian operator for a frame $\{x_i\}_{i=1}^k$ in $\mathbb{R}^n$. Prove that G is invertible if and only if $k = n$.

Exercise 16. Let $\mathcal{H}$ be a finite-dimensional Hilbert space. For $A \in \mathcal{B}(\mathcal{H})$, the *Hilbert-Schmidt norm* of A is defined by $\|A\|_2 = [\text{tr}(A^*A)]^{\frac{1}{2}}$.

(i) Prove that $\|\cdot\|_2$ is, in fact, a norm on the vector space $\mathcal{B}(\mathcal{H})$.

(ii) Prove that $\|\cdot\|_2$ is *submultiplicative*, which means that for all $A, B \in \mathcal{B}(\mathcal{H})$, $\|AB\|_2 \le \|A\|_2\|B\|_2$.

(iii) More generally, for any fixed p, $1 \le p \le \infty$, we can define a norm on $\mathcal{B}(\mathcal{H})$ called the Shatten p-norm, given by $\|A\|_p = [\text{tr}(|A|^p)]^{\frac{1}{p}}$. Prove that $\|\cdot\|_p$ is, in fact, a norm on $\mathcal{B}(\mathcal{H})$.

Chapter 4

Frames in $\mathbb{R}^2$

This chapter develops a geometric description of tight frames in the plane $\mathbb{R}^2$. While this characterization of tight frames does not extend to higher-dimensional spaces, we can use it to develop some intuition about the types of tight frames that exist. We will discover some properties of $\mathbb{R}^2$ frames, and these properties will generate a variety of questions, some still unanswered, about frames in $\mathbb{R}^n$.

4.1. Diagram Vectors

We begin by using polar coordinates to express any vector x in $\mathbb{R}^2$ in the form $x = \begin{bmatrix} a\cos\theta \\ a\sin\theta \end{bmatrix}$, where θ is the angle the vector makes with the positive x-axis. From Remark 3.23, a collection of vectors $\{x_i\}_{i=1}^k$, where $x_i = \begin{bmatrix} a_i\cos\theta_i \\ a_i\sin\theta_i \end{bmatrix}$, is a tight frame with frame bound A if and only if the frame operator S is equal to A times the identity operator. The frame operator for a collection of vectors $\left\{\begin{bmatrix} a_i\cos\theta_i \\ a_i\sin\theta_i \end{bmatrix}\right\}_{i=1}^k$ in $\mathbb{R}^2$ will be the 2×2 matrix:

$$S = \Theta^*\Theta = \begin{bmatrix} \sum_{i=1}^k a_i^2\cos^2\theta_i & \sum_{i=1}^k a_i^2\cos\theta_i\sin\theta_i \\ \sum_{i=1}^k a_i^2\cos\theta_i\sin\theta_i & \sum_{i=1}^k a_i^2\sin^2\theta_i \end{bmatrix}.$$

Using trigonometric double-angle formulas, we see that the frame operator S is a scalar multiple of the identity operator if and only if the following vector equation holds:

$$\sum_{i=1}^{k} \begin{bmatrix} a_i^2 \cos 2\theta_i \\ a_i^2 \sin 2\theta_i \end{bmatrix} = \begin{bmatrix} 0 \\ 0 \end{bmatrix}.$$

This establishes an exact correspondence between tight frames for $\mathbb{R}^2$ and collections of vectors obtained from the tight frame vectors by squaring the length and doubling the angle of each vector; the original collection is a tight frame exactly when the new collection of vectors sums to zero. Using the tip-to-tail method to sum vectors, the construction of tight frames for $\mathbb{R}^2$ becomes a problem in plane geometry.

To establish some terminology and notation for this chapter, if $x = \begin{bmatrix} a\cos\theta \\ a\sin\theta \end{bmatrix}$ is a vector in $\mathbb{R}^2$, let $\tilde{x} = \begin{bmatrix} a^2\cos 2\theta \\ a^2\sin 2\theta \end{bmatrix}$ be this associated vector which we will call the *diagram vector*, because we will be drawing diagrams in which we discuss the sum of such vectors. Our computation of the frame operator above results in the following lemma.

Lemma 4.1. *A collection $\{x_i\}_{i=1}^k$ of vectors in $\mathbb{R}^2$, where $k \geq 2$, is a tight frame for $\mathbb{R}^2$ if the diagram vectors $\{\tilde{x}_i\}_{i=1}^k$ sum to zero in $\mathbb{R}^2$.*

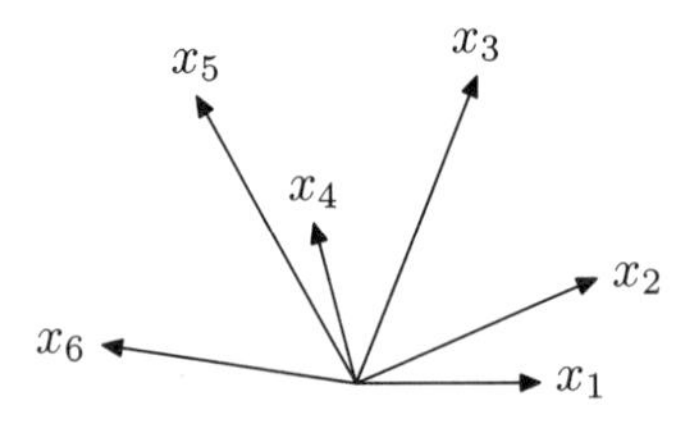

Figure 4.1. These vectors form a tight frame for $\mathbb{R}^2$. This isn't evident upon initial observation, but is demonstrated by their diagram vectors, shown in Figure 4.2.

The diagram of the sum of vectors $\{\tilde{x}_i\}_{i=1}^k$ provides a visual representation of the tight frames in $\mathbb{R}^2$, and provides very intuitive

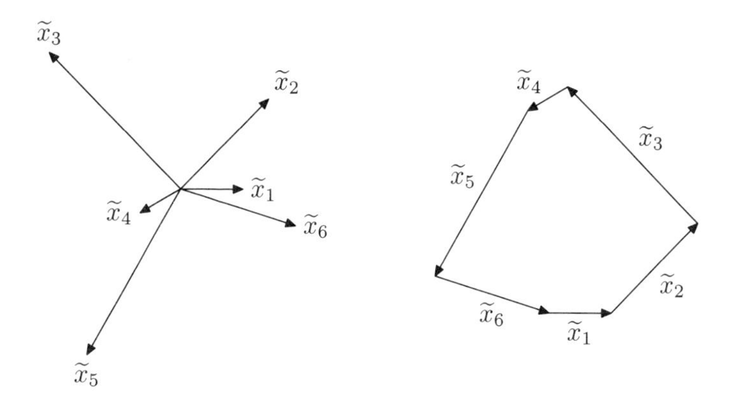

Figure 4.2. The diagram vectors here are shown first in standard position, and then placed tip-to-tail to demonstrate that they sum to zero.

answers to questions we may ask about frames. As an example, consider the collection of tight frames for $\mathbb{R}^2$ which consist of exactly three unit vectors. For convenience, we will call a tight frame consisting of unit vectors a *unit tight frame.* One example of a unit tight frame with three vectors in $\mathbb{R}^2$ can be formed by rescaling the vectors from Example 3.9 to unit vectors:

$$\left\{ \begin{bmatrix} 1 \\ 0 \end{bmatrix}, \begin{bmatrix} -\frac{1}{2} \\ \frac{\sqrt{3}}{2} \end{bmatrix}, \begin{bmatrix} -\frac{1}{2} \\ -\frac{\sqrt{3}}{2} \end{bmatrix} \right\}.$$

These vectors and their diagram vectors are shown in Figure 4.3, and we see that indeed the diagram vectors sum to zero.

If we want to consider all the unit tight frames having three vectors, we can consider the possible diagrams of unit vectors which can sum to zero. Since we are restricted to unit vectors in this case, we realize that the only possible diagrams will be equilateral triangles, which fixes the angles between the diagram vectors (see Figure 4.3).

4.2. Equivalence of Frames

Suppose that a collection of vectors $\{x_i\}_{i=1}^k$ is a frame or a tight frame. There are certain other collections which we would consider

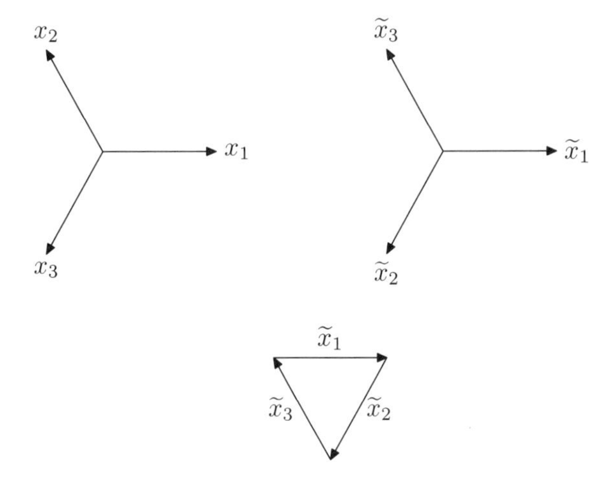

Figure 4.3. Here is the unit frame of three vectors given by scaling the vectors in Example 3.9, followed by the associated diagram vectors. In this special example, the set of diagram vectors is simply a rearrangement of the original set of vectors. Observe that the diagram vectors sum to zero, which proves that this frame is a tight frame for $\mathbb{R}^2$.

to be in some sense the *same* frame. We can carefully define an equivalence relation among such frames, so that we can talk about these frames collectively as a single frame. There are a variety of ways to do this, and each could legitimately be called a notion of equivalence of frames. Examples were presented in Section 3.5, in which we defined similarity and unitary equivalence of frames.

We recall from our discussion in Section 3.5 that similarity is an order-dependent relation. In other words, if we rearrange the vectors in a collection, the reordered collection is not necessarily similar to the original one. Since we would like to consider such reorderings to actually be the same frame, we will describe a new equivalence relation in which frames containing the same vectors in different orders are equivalent. We will also consider collections for which some vectors x_i are replaced with $-x_i$ and collections which are a uniform rotation from the original one to be equivalent to the original one. This equivalence we are describing here is *not* the one most commonly called frame equivalence, so we will use the term *PRR-equivalence* (permutation-rotation-reflection equivalence) to avoid any confusion.

PRR-equivalence will equate two frames which contain the same elements, only permuted. The order in which the vectors are listed may change the analysis, synthesis, and frame operators we defined in the previous chapter, but in this section, we will consider these frames to be equivalent. In the same way, if we replace x_i with $-x_i$, we can verify from the definitions given in Chapter 3 that the frame bound and frame operator do not change. So the act of replacing a subset of frame vectors with their additive inverse should not change the frame, in our description of different frames. We also recognize by looking at the figures in this section that if each vector is rotated by a fixed angle θ, the resulting collection is also a frame, with the same properties as the original frame. It seems natural that we would consider such rigid rotations to produce the same frame as the original.

The three equivalences – permutation, reflection, rotation – are naturally seen to give rise to diagrams that are also, in some sense, the same. If the order of the vectors in an $\mathbb{R}^2$ frame is altered, the diagram vectors are the same, but also permuted in order. Because there are a finite number of diagram vectors, the sum of these diagram vectors is certainly unchanged by the rearrangement. If the vectors are placed tip-to-tail as in Figure 4.2, the resulting plane figure will look different, but will begin and end at the same points as the original figure. If the frame was originally a tight frame, both diagrams will be closed polygons.

To demonstrate permutation equivalence, let's examine a permutation of the frame depicted in Figures 4.1 and 4.2.

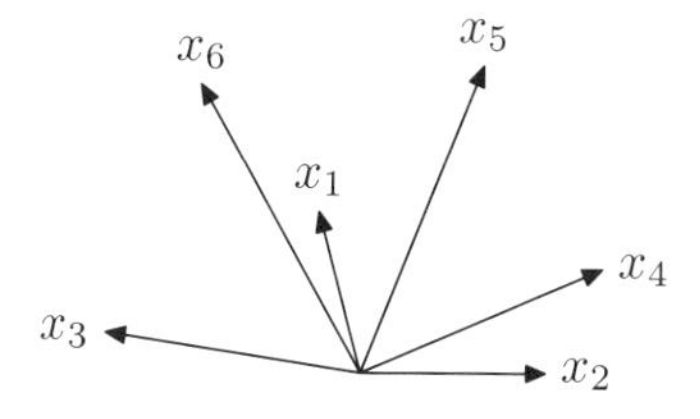

Figure 4.4. A permutation of the frame shown in Figure 4.1.

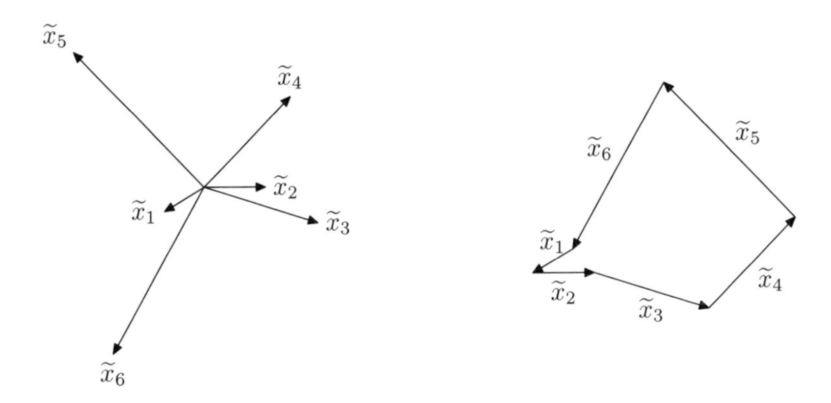

Figure 4.5. Here are the permuted diagram vectors from the frame in Figure 4.4. When we sum them in the order they are listed, the diagram looks different from the one in Figure 4.2, but of course, the vectors will have the same sum.

If each vector in an $\mathbb{R}^2$ frame is rotated by an angle θ, the resulting diagram vectors will each be rotated by 2θ, and the tip-to-tail figure will just be a rotation of the original figure (see Figure 4.6).

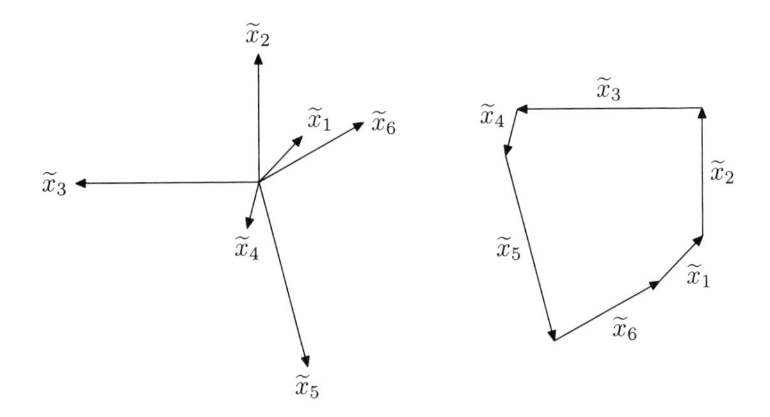

Figure 4.6. Here are the diagram vectors from the frame in Figure 4.4 after being rotated by an angle 2θ. The diagram is naturally just a rotation of the one in Figure 4.2, which does not affect whether or not the diagram vectors sum to zero.

Next, observe that the additive inverse $-x_i$ of a vector x_i in an $\mathbb{R}^2$ frame has exactly the same diagram vector as x_i, since $2(\theta+\pi) = 2\theta + 2\pi$. Therefore, the tip-to-tail diagram is completely unchanged when some of the frame vectors are replaced with their additive inverses (see Figure 4.7).

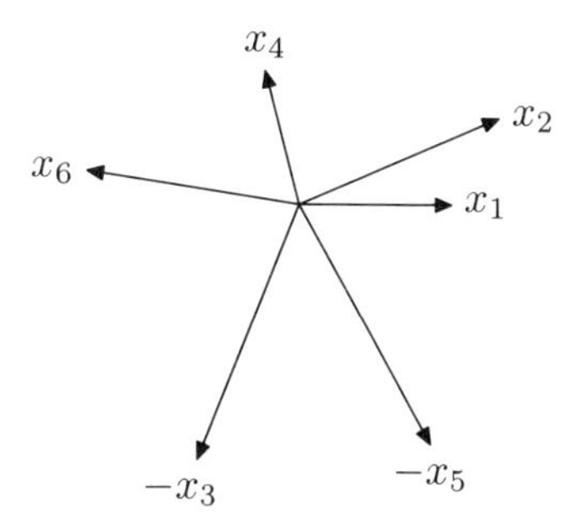

Figure 4.7. The vectors x_3 and x_5 from the frame shown in Figure 4.1 have been replaced with $-x_3$ and $-x_5$. Despite these reflections, the diagram vectors will be the same as those shown in Figure 4.2.

With the definition of PRR-equivalence at hand, we can now classify all of the unit tight frames for $\mathbb{R}^2$ which have exactly three vectors. Since the only possible tip-to-tail diagram of three unit vectors which sum to zero forms an equilateral triangle, every tight frame must have this diagram. Therefore, there is only one PRR-equivalence class of unit tight frames for $\mathbb{R}^2$ with three vectors, and that equivalence class can be represented with the frame given in Example 3.9. The diagram vectors must be equally spaced at angles of $\frac{2\pi}{3}$ when in standard position so that they form an equilateral triangle when placed tip-to-tail (see Figure 4.3).

4.3. Unit Tight Frames with Four Vectors

The diagram vectors also allow us to characterize the unit tight frames for $\mathbb{R}^2$ having exactly four vectors. The tip-to-tail diagram of such a frame would be a quadrilateral with equal sides (a rhombus), which must necessarily be a parallelogram as well. In other words, the diagram consists of two pairs of vectors which are additive inverses of each other. This implies that the original frame must contain two pairs of orthonormal vectors. An example is given below in Figure 4.8.

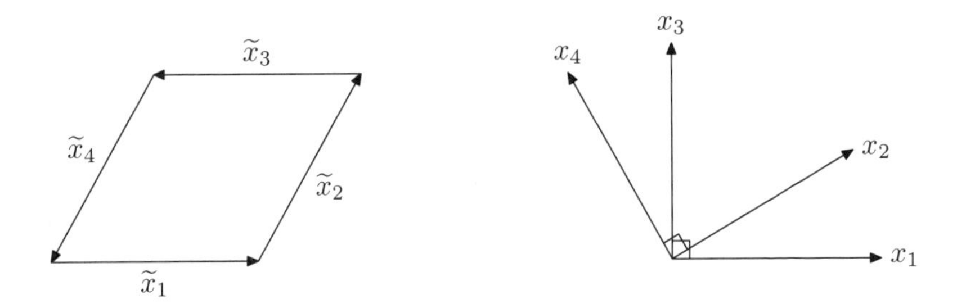

Figure 4.8. The diagram for a 4-vector unit tight frame for $\mathbb{R}^2$ must be a parallelogram, so the original frame must have two pairs of orthogonal vectors.

This discussion leads to the following proposition.

Proposition 4.2. *Every unit tight frame for $\mathbb{R}^2$ having exactly four vectors must be the union of two orthonormal bases for $\mathbb{R}^2$ (see Figure 4.8).*

From this proposition, the set of all nonPRR-equivalent unit tight frames with four vectors can be characterized by the angle between nonorthogonal vectors. In other words, there is a one-parameter family of unit tight frames with four vectors in $\mathbb{R}^2$, where the parameter is the angle between two nonorthogonal vectors.

Proposition 4.3. *Given any θ, $0 \leq \theta < \frac{\pi}{2}$, there exists a unit tight frame F_θ with four vectors for $\mathbb{R}^2$ such that if $\theta_1 \neq \theta_2$, then F_{θ_1} is not PRR-equivalent to F_{θ_2}.*

Proof. This follows from the previous discussion, where we let θ be the angle between two nonorthogonal vectors in the frame F_θ (see Figure 4.9). □

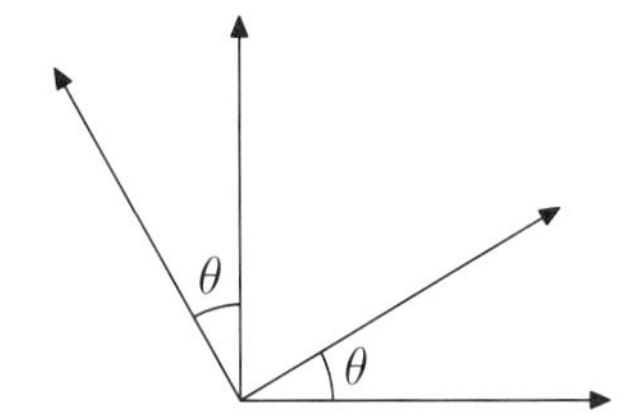

Figure 4.9. The angle θ characterizes all the nonPRR-equivalent unit tight frames for $\mathbb{R}^2$ with four vectors.

4.4. Unit Tight Frames with k Vectors

The tip-to-tail diagrams are useful in describing the possibilities of general unit tight frames for $\mathbb{R}^2$, and we can answer a wide variety of questions just using plane geometry. (The authors found that manipulating straws which have been strung on a piece of wire or yarn gives a very helpful model of the possible tip-to-tail diagrams.)

For example, we see that given any $k \geq 2$, there always exists a way to arrange k unit vectors so that they sum to zero. This proves that for each such k, there exists at least one unit tight frame for $\mathbb{R}^2$. As we've seen above, there are restrictions on how many nonequivalent frames there are when $k = 2, 3, 4$. We can also make statements about larger k.

One natural question one may ask is whether k unit vectors that are spaced at regular $\frac{2\pi}{k}$ angular intervals will form a tight frame for $\mathbb{R}^2$. This will not happen when $k = 2$, since these two vectors would be $\{x, -x\}$ and therefore would only span a single dimension. We have seen in the previous two sections, however, that the answer is affirmative for $k = 3, 4$. What happens for larger k? We find in the following proposition that we will have a tight frame for all $k \geq 3$.

Proposition 4.4. *Given $k \geq 3$, the sequence* $\mathcal{F} = \left\{ \begin{bmatrix} \cos \frac{2\pi j}{k} \\ \sin \frac{2\pi j}{k} \end{bmatrix} \right\}_{j=0}^{k-1}$ *is a tight frame for $\mathbb{R}^2$ (see Figure 4.10).*

Proof. The diagram vectors for the frame $\mathcal{F}$ are $\left\{\begin{bmatrix}\cos\frac{4\pi j}{k}\\ \sin\frac{4\pi j}{k}\end{bmatrix}\right\}_{j=0}^{k-1}$.

We can write complex numbers of modulus 1 as

$$z = e^{i\theta} = \cos\theta + i\sin\theta.$$

We then have the well-known result that the sum of the kth roots of unity is zero, which we prove here using a geometric series identity.

$$\begin{aligned}\sum_{j=0}^{k-1}\left(\cos\frac{4\pi j}{k} + i\sin\frac{2\pi j}{k}\right) &= \sum_{j=0}^{k-1} e^{\frac{4\pi i j}{k}}\\ &= \frac{1-e^{\frac{4\pi i k}{k}}}{1-e^{\frac{4\pi i}{k}}}\\ &= \frac{1-1}{1-e^{\frac{4\pi i}{k}}}\\ &= 0.\end{aligned}$$

Writing this result in the corresponding $\mathbb{R}^2$ form, we have

$$\sum_{j=0}^{k-1}\begin{bmatrix}\cos\frac{4\pi j}{k}\\ \sin\frac{4\pi j}{k}\end{bmatrix} = \begin{bmatrix}0\\0\end{bmatrix}.$$ □

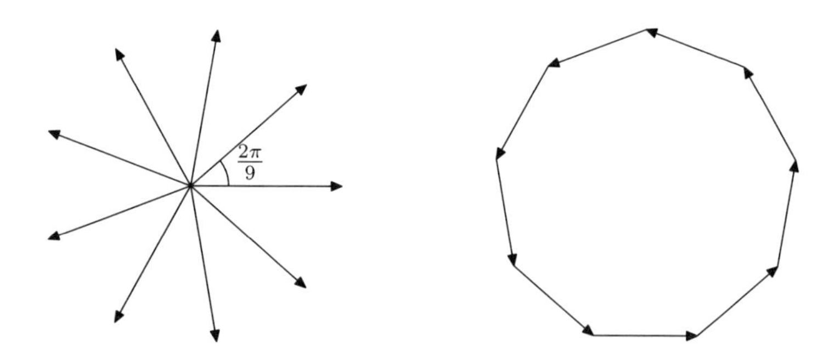

Figure 4.10. This shows a $k = 9$ tight frame for $\mathbb{R}^2$, where the vectors are spaced at regular $\frac{2\pi}{9}$ angular intervals. The diagram vectors form a permutation of the original sequence, and are shown here summing to zero.

Another property we could examine is whether a tight frame for $\mathbb{R}^2$ can be decomposed into two other tight frames. For example, we showed above that a unit tight frame with four vectors for $\mathbb{R}^2$ is *always* a union of two orthonormal bases, but clearly a unit tight frame with three vectors does not contain enough vectors to be decomposed into two spanning sets for $\mathbb{R}^2$.

Let us consider the case of five unit vectors. It is certainly possible to form a unit tight frame with five vectors by combining an orthonormal basis with a unit tight frame of three vectors. The tip-to-tail diagram in Figure 4.11 is an example which looks like a martini glass (at least to the authors!). As an exercise, explore the collection of nonPRR-equivalent tight frames of five unit vectors which can also be decomposed into a 2-frame and a 3-frame. To do this, consider variations of the tip-to-tail diagram in Figure 4.11 which maintain tightness of both the frame as a whole and the separate components to guide you.

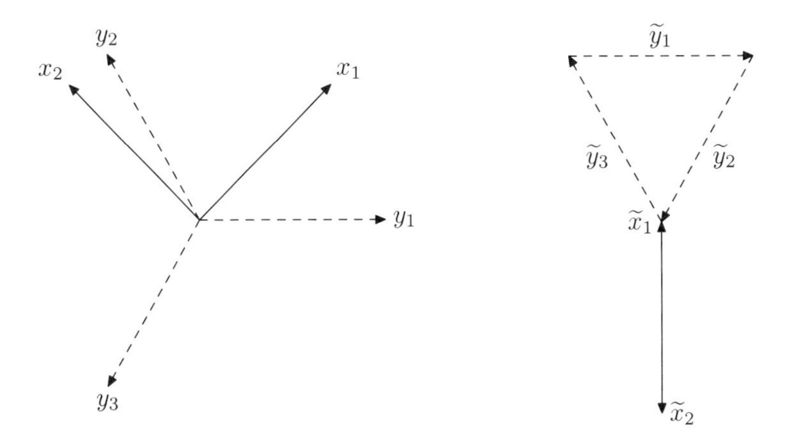

Figure 4.11. The tip-to-tail diagram of the union of an orthonormal basis and a unit tight frame for $\mathbb{R}^2$ having three vectors.

There are also certainly unit tight frames having five vectors which are *not* decomposable into an orthonormal basis and a three-vector tight frame. For example, the "stem" of the martini glass above consists of two vertical vectors. These can be separated to increase the angle θ between them, as in Figure 4.12.

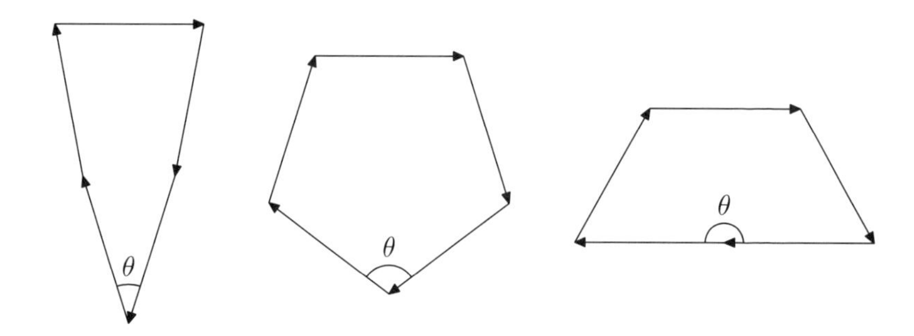

Figure 4.12. Tip-to-tail diagrams of unit tight frames for $\mathbb{R}^2$ having five vectors. These are obtained by increasing the angle θ, which is zero in the martini glass example above.

This discussion leads us to the two statements in the following proposition. The proofs are left to the reader as an exercise.

Proposition 4.5. (i) *For every $k \geq 2$, there exists a unit tight frame for $\mathbb{R}^2$ having k vectors.*

(ii) *For $k \neq 4$, there exists a unit tight frame for $\mathbb{R}^2$ which is not the union of two or more existing tight frames for $\mathbb{R}^2$.*

Proof. See Exercises 1 and 2. □

4.5. Frame Surgery: Removals and Replacements

Given a collection of vectors $\{x_i\}_{i=1}^k$ from a Hilbert space $\mathcal{H}$, we are interested in describing when vectors can be added to the collection and/or removed from the collection while making the resulting set a frame or tight frame. We have listed some properties below, and left others to the exercises. There are certainly a wide range of questions to ask on this topic, and we certainly have not addressed them all here.

Remark 4.6. This section deals exclusively with vectors in $\mathbb{R}^2$, but the questions have natural analogs in higher-dimensional space. Often, an easily answered question in $\mathbb{R}^2$ will be much more difficult in the general case. The reader is encouraged to think about how to approach these questions for higher-dimensional spaces.

Definition 4.7. A frame *surgery* is an operation on a finite sequence of vectors in which a finite number of vectors (perhaps zero) are removed from the collection and a finite number of vectors (perhaps zero) are added to the collection. More specifically, an (m, n)*-surgery* on a sequence $\mathcal{F}$ removes m vectors from $\mathcal{F}$ and replaces them with n vectors.

We are interested particularly in two types of surgeries: those in which tight frames remain tight under frame surgery and those in which a sequence is made into a tight frame by the addition of vectors.

Proposition 4.8. *Let $\mathcal{F} = \{x_i\}_{i=1}^k$ be a unit tight frame for $\mathbb{R}^2$, with $k > 2$. If we restrict surgeries on $\mathcal{F}$ to only add unit vectors, then the only $(2, 2)$-surgery on $\mathcal{F}$ such that the two vectors removed are not orthogonal and which results in a tight frame is the identity surgery, in which the vectors are replaced with themselves (with a possible permutation).*

Proof. We can reorder $\mathcal{F}$ so that the vectors removed by the surgery are x_{k-1} and x_k. We see that if these are orthogonal vectors, they form themselves a tight frame for $\mathbb{R}^2$, and therefore the remaining vectors also form a tight frame. In this special case, we could add back in any two orthonormal vectors and have the new collection be a tight frame. In the case where x_{k-1} and x_k are not orthogonal, let $y = \sum_{i=1}^{k-2} \tilde{x}_i$ be the sum of the remaining diagram vectors. We know $y \neq 0$ now since the removed vectors are not orthogonal. Since $\mathcal{F}$ is a unit tight frame, we know that $\tilde{x}_{k-1} + \tilde{x}_k = -y$. Therefore, the tip-to-tail diagram of the vectors $\tilde{x}_{k-1}, \tilde{x}_k$, and y forms a triangle with side lengths $1, 1$, and $\|y\|$. But if all three side lengths of a triangle are given, the angles of the triangle are fixed. Therefore, the only way to get a tight frame back using two unit vectors is to return x_{k-1} and x_k to the collection (see Figure 4.13). □

Proposition 4.9. *Let $\mathcal{F}$ be a unit tight frame for $\mathbb{R}^2$ with five vectors. Given any two vectors x, y in F, there exists a $(3, 2)$-surgery on F*

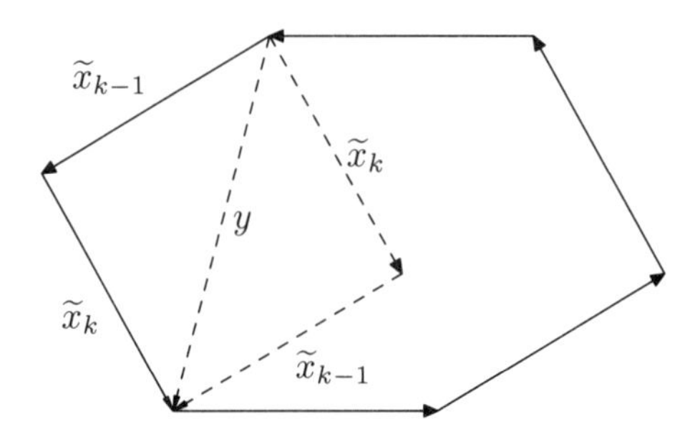

Figure 4.13. There is only one (2,2)-surgery (using PRR-equivalence), which is the identity surgery.

which leaves x and y in F, adds two unit vectors to the sequence $\{x, y\}$, and yields a unit tight frame for $\mathbb{R}^2$. Moreover, since this new frame has exactly four unit vectors, if x is not orthogonal to y, this surgery is unique up to PRR-equivalence.

Proof. This proof is an immediate consequence of Proposition 4.2. We replace the three removed vectors with one unit vector which is orthogonal to x and one which is orthogonal to y. The result is a unit tight frame of four vectors containing x and y. □

The following addresses $(0, p)$-surgeries. We start with a collection of vectors which may or may not be a frame, and discover conditions under which vectors can be added to make a tight frame.

We leave the proof of the following proposition to Exercise 4.

Proposition 4.10. *Given $\{x_i\}_{i=1}^k$ a nonempty collection of vectors in $\mathbb{R}^2$, there exists a vector $y \in \mathbb{R}^2$ such that $\{x_i\}_{i=1}^k \cup \{y\}$ is a tight frame for $\mathbb{R}^2$. In other words, a $(0, 1)$-surgery is always possible which will make a sequence into a tight frame.*

If we restrict our vectors to unit vectors, the $(0, p)$-surgery question becomes a little different. Given an arbitrary sequence of unit vectors, we can ask whether we can always add unit vectors to the sequence which will make the new sequence a unit tight frame. This question, too, can be answered almost trivially using diagram vectors.

Proposition 4.11. *Given a finite sequence $\mathcal{E} = \{x_i\}_{i=1}^k$ of k unit vectors in $\mathbb{R}^2$, there exists a finite sequence $\mathcal{F} \subset \mathbb{R}^2$ of unit vectors with cardinality at most k such that the sequence formed by appending $\mathcal{F}$ to $\mathcal{E}$ is a unit tight frame for $\mathbb{R}^2$. The minimum cardinality of $\mathcal{F}$ needed to make a tight frame depends on the quantity $\alpha = \| \sum_{i=1}^k \tilde{x}_i \|$.*

If $\alpha \in \mathbb{N}$, then $\mathcal{F}$ can contain as few as α unit vectors. If $\alpha \leq 2, \alpha \neq 1$, then $\mathcal{F}$ may contain as few as two unit vectors. Given p a natural number greater than 2, if $p - 1 < \alpha < p$, then $\mathcal{F}$ can contain as few as p unit vectors to make a unit tight frame.

Proof. Let $\{\tilde{x_i}\}_{i=1}^k$ be the diagram vectors for E, and let $y = \sum_{i=1}^k \tilde{x}_i$. Now, of course, we could always just include the vector $-y$ with the set of diagram vectors and thereby build a tight frame. But $-y$ is not in general a unit vector, so this does not prove this result. We are required to find unit vectors to comprise F whose sum is $-y$. This will be possible so long as the Triangle Inequality is not violated:

$$\| - y\| \leq \sum_{z_j \in F} \|z_j\| = \#F(\text{ the cardinality of } F).$$

The triangle inequality on the k diagram vectors from E also forces $\|y\| \leq k$, so we need at most k unit vectors in F to make up a tight frame from the vectors in both E and F. If $p - 1 \leq \|y\| \leq p$, then there will always be a set of p vectors which can be added to y to get zero (see Figure 4.14). $\square$

4.6. Fundamental Inequality in $\mathbb{R}^2$

We can state here the two-dimensional version of the fundamental inequality, which we will describe generally for finite dimensions in Chapter 7. Given a finite sequence of positive numbers, we can determine a necessary and sufficient condition under which there exists a tight frame for $\mathbb{R}^2$ with vectors having norms given by the sequence.

Proposition 4.12. *Let $\{a_i\}_{i=1}^k \subset \mathbb{R}^+$, with $k \geq 2$ and $a_1 \geq a_2 \geq \cdots \geq a_k > 0$. Then there exists a tight frame $\{x_i\}_{i=1}^k$ for $\mathbb{R}^2$ such*

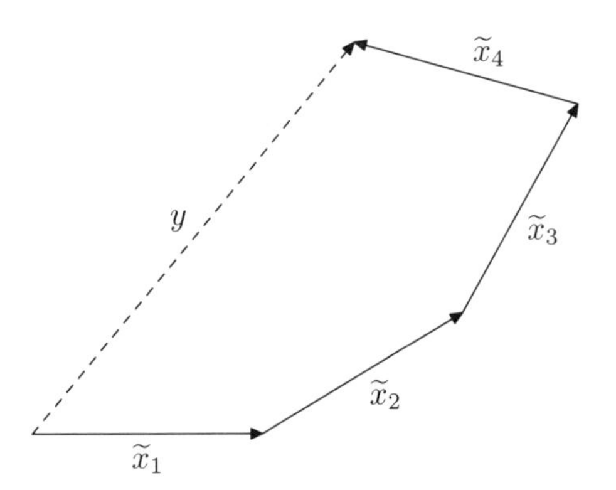

Figure 4.14. If we wish to find p unit vectors to include with the sequence $\{x_1, x_2, x_3, x_4\}$ in order to create a tight frame, we need the sum of their diagram vectors to be $-y$. Therefore, the number of additional unit vectors must be greater than or equal to the norm of y.

that $\|x_i\|^2 = a_i, i = 1, 2, \ldots, k$ *if and only if*

$$a_1 \leq \sum_{i=2}^{k} a_i.$$

Proof. If $\{x_i\}_{i=1}^k$ is a tight frame for $\mathbb{R}^2$ with $\|x_i\| = \sqrt{a_i}$, then the diagram vectors will have norms $\|\tilde{x_i}\| = a_i, i = 1, 2, \ldots, k$. Since the diagram vectors sum to zero, it must be true that the longest one is not as long as the sum of the lengths of the remaining vectors. Therefore, $a_1 \leq a_2 + \cdots + a_k$, which is what we needed to show.

We can use diagram vectors to show the converse statement as well. So long as we have at least two diagram vectors, and the longest one is not longer than the sum of the remaining ones, we can orient the diagram vectors in such a way that they sum to zero. These will correspond to a tight frame for $\mathbb{R}^2$. □

4.7. Exercises from the Text

Exercise 1. Prove the first part of Proposition 4.5: For every $k \geq 2$, there exists a unit tight frame for $\mathbb{R}^2$ having k vectors.

Exercise 2. Prove the second part of Proposition 4.5: For $k \neq 4$, there exists a unit tight frame for $\mathbb{R}^2$ which is not the union of two or more existing tight frames for $\mathbb{R}^2$.

4.8. Additional Exercises

Exercise 3. Describe the set of all unit tight frames with exactly five vectors, up to PRR-equivalence.

Exercise 4. Show that, given any nonempty collection $\{x_i\}_{i=1}^k$ of nonzero vectors in $\mathbb{R}^2$, there exists a single vector v such that $\{x_i\}_{i=1}^k \cup \{v\}$ is a tight frame for $\mathbb{R}^2$.

Exercise 5. Prove that the tip-to-tail diagram for the k angularly spaced unit vectors from Proposition 4.4 always gives a regular polygon. Is it always the regular k-gon? Explain.

Exercise 6. Prove that the only $(1,1)$-surgery on a tight frame in $\mathbb{R}^n$ is the identity surgery.

Exercise 7. Given a finite set of k unit vectors in $\mathbb{R}^2$, with $k \geq 3$, use diagram vectors to show that they can be scaled by positive constants to form a tight frame so long as their corresponding "double-angle vectors" $\begin{bmatrix} \cos 2\theta_i \\ \sin 2\theta_i \end{bmatrix}$ are not all contained in any open half-plane of $\mathbb{R}^2$.

Chapter 5

The Dilation Property of Frames

There is a very natural geometric way to interpret Parseval frames, as well as more general frames, by relating them to bases of Hilbert spaces. Parseval frames turn out to correspond in some way with orthonormal bases, while frames in general will be associated with general bases. In this chapter we specifically describe this connection. Roughly speaking, the idea is that Parseval frames are exactly the orthogonal compressions of orthonormal bases. Likewise, general frames are exactly the orthogonal compressions of linearly independent bases.

In this chapter, we define these orthogonal compressions of bases, and also examine compressions which are not necessarily orthogonal. We will characterize all the frames which are compressions (not necessarily orthogonal compressions) of orthonormal bases.

5.1. Orthogonal Compressions of Bases

Let P be an orthogonal projection from a Hilbert space $\mathcal{H}$ onto a subspace M, and let $\{u_i\}_{i=1}^k$ be a sequence in $\mathcal{H}$. Then we call $\{Pu_i\}_{i=1}^k$ the *orthogonal compression* of $\{u_i\}_{i=1}^k$ under P, and correspondingly $\{u_i\}_{i=1}^k$ is called an *orthogonal dilation* of $\{Pu_i\}_{i=1}^k$. We first observe the following useful fact:

Proposition 5.1. *Let P be an orthogonal projection from $\mathcal{H}$ onto a subspace M and let $\{x_i\}_{i=1}^k$ be a frame for $\mathcal{H}$. Then $\{Px_i\}_{i=1}^k$ is a frame for M with the same frame bounds. In particular, if $\{x_i\}_{i=1}^k$ is an orthonormal basis for $\mathcal{H}$, then $\{Px_i\}_{i=1}^k$ is a Parseval frame for M.*

In the language of compression, this proposition implies that every orthogonal compression of a linearly independent basis is a frame for the range of the projection, and every orthogonal compression of an orthonormal basis is a Parseval frame for the range space.

Proof. Let $x \in M$. Then we have $Px = x$. Since $\{x_i\}_{i=1}^k$ is a frame for $\mathcal{H}$, there exist two positive constants $A, B > 0$ such that

$$A\|x\|^2 \leq \sum_{i=1}^k |\langle x, x_i \rangle|^2 \leq B\|x\|^2 \qquad \text{for all } x \in \mathcal{H}.$$

We know that for all $x \in M$,

$$\langle x, x_i \rangle = \langle Px, x_i \rangle = \langle x, Px_i \rangle$$

since $Px = x$ and $P^* = P$. Thus we have

$$A\|x\|^2 \leq \sum_{i=1}^k |\langle x, Px_i \rangle|^2 \leq B\|x\|^2, \qquad \text{for all } x \in M,$$

which implies that $\{Px_i\}_{i=1}^k$ is a frame for M with frame bounds A and B. □

Example 5.2. Let $E = \{e_1, e_2, e_3\}$ be the standard orthonormal basis for $\mathbb{R}^3$. The orthogonal projection of E onto any plane through the origin will yield a Parseval frame for that two-dimensional subspace. The projection onto the plane which has normal vector $\begin{bmatrix} 1 \\ 1 \\ 1 \end{bmatrix}$ yields the uniform Parseval frame of three vectors for a 2-dimensional space, as we first saw in Example 3.9. This is illustrated in Figure 5.1.

Remark 5.3. From the above example, it is clear that there are infinitely many Parseval frames of three vectors for two-dimensional space, parameterized by the normal vectors to the subspace planes

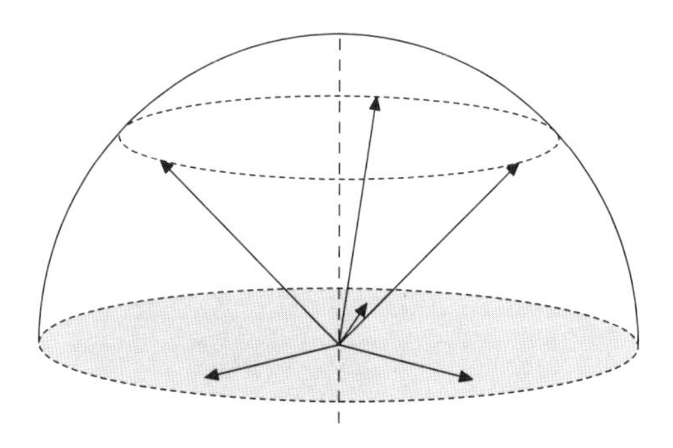

Figure 5.1. A projection of the standard orthonormal basis for $\mathbb{R}^3$ which yields the uniform 3-vector Parseval frame for the plane.

in $\mathbb{R}^3$. For the same reason, for any $k \geq n$, there will exist infinitely many Parseval frames having k vectors for $\mathbb{R}^n$ or $\mathbb{C}^n$. When $n = k$, we still have infinitely many Parseval frames (which are exactly the orthonormal bases), but we have shown that they are all unitarily equivalent.

Let $\mathcal{H}$ be a Hilbert space with dimension n. Recall that a uniform frame for $\mathcal{H}$ is a frame whose vectors are all of equal norm. Most of the frames with three vectors described in Remark 5.3 are not uniform, but the particular frame from Example 5.2 is a uniform frame. More generally, for each $k \geq n$, there always exists a Parseval frame which is uniform. We describe here one class of such frames called the *harmonic frames*, which will be further investigated in Chapters 8 and 9.

Example 5.4. We begin in $\mathbb{C}^n$ with the matrix representation of the *discrete Fourier transform* (*DFT*) on $\mathbb{C}^k$ for $k \geq n$. (You do *not* need to be familiar with the DFT to understand this example. Just take as the definition the matrix A below.) Given a vector $x \in \mathbb{C}^k$, the discrete Fourier transform of x is given by $\mathcal{F}_k(x) = Ax$, where A is the $k \times k$ matrix:

$$\frac{1}{\sqrt{k}}\begin{bmatrix} 1 & 1 & 1 & \cdots & 1 \\ 1 & e^{-i\frac{2\pi}{k}\cdot 1} & e^{-i\frac{2\pi}{k}\cdot 2} & \cdots & e^{-i\frac{2\pi}{k}\cdot (k-1)} \\ 1 & e^{-i\frac{2\pi}{k}\cdot 2} & e^{-i\frac{2\pi}{k}\cdot 4} & \cdots & e^{-i\frac{2\pi}{k}\cdot 2(k-1)} \\ \vdots & \vdots & \vdots & \ddots & \vdots \\ 1 & e^{-i\frac{2\pi}{k}\cdot (k-1)} & e^{-i\frac{2\pi}{k}\cdot 2(k-1)} & \cdots & e^{-i\frac{2\pi}{k}\cdot (k-1)(k-1)} \end{bmatrix}.$$

The matrix A is an orthogonal matrix, so the columns form an orthonormal basis for $\mathbb{C}^k$. (Exercise 2 asks you to verify this fact.) By Proposition 5.1, any projection of the column vectors will form a Parseval frame for the range of the projection. In particular, we project to the n-dimensional subspace spanned by the first n standard orthonormal basis elements. If we form an $n \times k$ matrix B consisting of the first n rows of A, then the columns of B are the image of the columns of A under this projection. The columns of B all have the same norm, since the modulus of each entry is 1, so they form a uniform Parseval frame for $\mathbb{C}^n$. This works on $\mathbb{C}^n$, and in fact, there is a similar construction using the real form of the DFT which yields Parseval frames for $\mathbb{R}^n$.

The Fourier basis is widely used and we will discuss it again in Chapter 9.

5.2. Dilations of Frames

In connection to Proposition 5.1, it is natural to ask whether every Parseval frame is an orthogonal compression of an orthonormal basis for a bigger Hilbert space, and respectively whether every general frame is an orthogonal compression of a linearly independent basis for a bigger Hilbert space. Or, from the other point of view, can we always dilate a Parseval frame to an orthonormal basis? As a motivating example, let us consider the frame in Example 3.9 for $\mathbb{R}^2$. In Example 5.2, we found that this frame (or more precisely a PRR-equivalent copy) can be seen as a compression of an orthonormal basis for $\mathbb{R}^3$. Even more directly, observe that the frame in that example in fact is the compression of the following three elements in $\mathbb{R}^3$ onto the first two coordinates:

$$\left\{ \sqrt{\frac{2}{3}} \begin{bmatrix} 1 \\ 0 \\ \frac{1}{\sqrt{2}} \end{bmatrix}, \sqrt{\frac{2}{3}} \begin{bmatrix} -\frac{1}{2} \\ \frac{\sqrt{3}}{2} \\ \frac{1}{\sqrt{2}} \end{bmatrix}, \sqrt{\frac{2}{3}} \begin{bmatrix} -\frac{1}{2} \\ -\frac{\sqrt{3}}{2} \\ \frac{1}{\sqrt{2}} \end{bmatrix} \right\}.$$

We leave it to the reader (Exercise 1) to check that the above set is an orthonormal basis for $\mathbb{R}^3$. In fact, we see that Figure 5.1 could be viewed (by rotation-equivalence) to depict these vectors and their compression to the xy-plane.

It turns out that, in fact, this example is generic and serves as a model for arbitrary Parseval frames. In other words, given any Parseval frame, we can indeed always dilate such a frame to an orthonormal basis for a larger Hilbert space. This dilation is specified in the following proposition.

Proposition 5.5. (i) *Suppose that $\{x_i\}_{i=1}^k$ is a Parseval frame for a Hilbert space $\mathcal{H}$. Then there exists a Hilbert space $\mathcal{K} \supseteq \mathcal{H}$ and an orthonormal basis $\{u_i\}_{i=1}^k$ for $\mathcal{K}$ such that $x_i = Pu_i$, where P is the orthogonal projection from $\mathcal{K}$ onto $\mathcal{H}$.*

(ii) *Suppose that $\{x_i\}_{i=1}^k$ is a frame for a Hilbert space $\mathcal{H}$. Then there exists a Hilbert space $\mathcal{K} \supseteq \mathcal{H}$ and a basis $\{v_i\}_{i=1}^k$ for $\mathcal{K}$ such that $x_i = Pv_i$, where P again is the orthogonal projection from $\mathcal{K}$ onto $\mathcal{H}$.*

Proof. We only prove (i). The proof of (ii) is similar and we leave it as Exercise 3.

Let Θ be the analysis operator of $\{x_i\}_{i=1}^k$, and let Q be the orthogonal projection from $\mathbb{C}^k$ onto $\Theta(\mathcal{H})$, and therefore $Q^\perp = I - Q$ will be the projection onto $\Theta(\mathcal{H})^\perp$. Construct the Hilbert space $\mathcal{K} = \mathcal{H} \oplus \Theta(\mathcal{H})^\perp$ with the operations and inner product for the direct sum space we described in Section 1.7. Recall that we can identify $\mathcal{H}$ with $\mathcal{H} \oplus \{0\}$. Let $u_i = x_i \oplus Q^\perp e_i$, where $\{e_i\}_{i=1}^k$ is the standard orthonormal basis for $\mathbb{C}^k$. Then clearly $Pu_i = x_i$ where P is the orthogonal projection from $\mathcal{K}$ onto $\mathcal{H}$.

It remains to be shown that $\{u_i\}_{i=1}^k$ is an orthonormal basis for $\mathcal{K}$, which we accomplish by showing that there is a unitary operator which takes the standard orthonormal basis $\{e_i\}_{i=1}^k$ for $\mathbb{C}^k$ to $\{u_i\}_{i=1}^k$. To start, we first show the useful fact that the analysis operators of $\{x_i\}_{i=1}^k$ and $\{Qe_i\}_{i=1}^k$ have the same range space $\Theta(\mathcal{H})$. Let Γ be the analysis operator for $\{Qe_i\}_{i=1}^k$. Since the span of $\{Qe_i\}_{i=1}^k$ is $\Theta(\mathcal{H})$, Γ will map $\Theta(\mathcal{H})$ to $\mathbb{C}^k$. Given $y \in \Theta(\mathcal{H})$, we have

$$\Gamma y = \sum_{i=1}^{k} \langle x, Qe_i \rangle e_i = \sum_{i=1}^{k} \langle Qy, e_i \rangle e_i = \sum_{i=1}^{k} \langle y, e_i \rangle e_i = y.$$

Therefore, the range space of Γ is $\Theta(\mathcal{H})$.

Using this fact, we know from Lemma 3.32 and Theorem 3.33 that the sequences $\{x_i\}_{i=1}^k$ and $\{Qe_i\}_{i=1}^k$ are unitarily equivalent. Let T be the unitary operator such that $x_i = TQe_i$ for $i = 1, 2, \ldots, k$. Then we have for each i,

$$u_i = TQe_i \oplus Q^{\perp}e_i = U(Qe_i \oplus Q^{\perp}e_i) = Ue_i,$$

where $U = T \oplus I$ is a unitary operator from $\mathbb{C}^k$ onto $\mathcal{K}$. Since $\{e_i\}_{i=1}^k$ is an orthonormal basis for $\mathbb{C}^k$ and unitary operators preserve orthonormal bases, we obtain that $\{u_i\}_{i=1}^k$ is an orthonormal basis for $\mathcal{K}$, as claimed. □

Let us interpret the results in Proposition 5.5 using matrix completion language. In finite dimensions, Proposition 5.5 implies that the synthesis operator Θ^*, which is the $n \times k$ matrix (with respect to given bases) with the vectors $x_i \in \mathbb{C}^n$ as its columns, can be extended by adding rows to a $k \times k$ orthogonal (unitary) matrix A, so that the columns of A are orthonormal, and thereby form an orthonormal basis for $\mathbb{C}^k$. If A is orthogonal, however, it is also true that the rows of A are orthonormal. As long as the n rows of Θ^* are orthonormal, then there is always an extension to an orthogonal matrix. The Gram-Schmidt algorithm, for example, could be used to find an orthonormal basis for $\mathbb{C}^k$ containing the n rows of Θ^*.

These results combine to justify our original definition of $\mathbb{R}^n$-frames and Parseval sequences in Section 3.1. Frames for $\mathbb{R}^n$ are exactly the sequences which can be dilated to bases, and Parseval frames for $\mathbb{R}^n$ are exactly the sequences which can be dilated to orthonormal bases. We summarize these notions in the following corollary, written from the matrix-completion point of view. Note that the results from Section 3.1 hold in $\mathbb{C}^n$ as well.

Corollary 5.6. (i) *Let T be an $n \times k$ Parseval matrix. Then the rows of T are orthonormal and T can be extended to a $k \times k$ unitary matrix by appending $(k-n)$ rows to T.*

(ii) *Let T be an $n \times k$ frame matrix. Then the rows of T are linearly independent and T can be extended to a $k \times k$ invertible matrix by appending $(k-n)$ rows to T.*

Let $\{u_i\}_{i=1}^k$ and P be as in Proposition 5.5, part (i), and let $y_i = (I-P)u_i$ for $i = 1, 2, \ldots, k$. Then $\{y_i\}_{i=1}^k$ is a frame for the subspace $(I-P)\mathcal{K}$ and $\{x_i \oplus y_i\}_{i=1}^k$ is an orthonormal basis for $\mathcal{K}$. Such a frame $\{y_i\}_{i=1}^k$ is referred to as an *orthogonal complementary frame* of $\{x_i\}_{i=1}^k$ to an orthonormal basis.

Proposition 5.7. *The orthogonal complementary frame of a Parseval frame to an orthonormal basis is unique up to unitary equivalence. That is, if $\mathcal{N}$ is another Hilbert space and $\{z_i\}_{i=1}^k$ is a Parseval frame for $\mathcal{N}$ such that $\{x_i \oplus z_i\}_{i=1}^k$ is an orthonormal basis for $\mathcal{H} \oplus \mathcal{N}$, then there is a unitary transformation U mapping $\mathcal{M} = (I-P)\mathcal{K}$ onto $\mathcal{N}$ such that $Uy_i = z_i$ for all $i = 1, 2, \ldots, k$, where $y_i = (I-P)u_i$.*

Proof. Write $u_i = x_i \oplus y_i$ and $v_i = x_i \oplus z_i$ for $i = 1, 2, \ldots, k$. By hypothesis, both $\{u_i\}_{i=1}^k$ and $\{v_i\}_{i=1}^k$ are orthonormal bases for k-dimensional Hilbert spaces, so there must exist a unitary operator $\widetilde{U} : \mathcal{K} = \mathcal{H} \oplus \mathcal{M} \to \mathcal{H} \oplus \mathcal{N}$ such that $\widetilde{U}u_i = v_i$ for each $i = 1, 2, \ldots, k$.

Fix $x \in \mathcal{H}$, and write $0_{\mathcal{M}}, 0_{\mathcal{N}}$ for the zero vectors in $\mathcal{M}$ and $\mathcal{N}$, respectively. We can then use the appropriate inner products to find:

$$\langle x, x_i \rangle_{\mathcal{H}} = \langle x \oplus 0_{\mathcal{M}}, u_i \rangle_{\mathcal{H} \oplus \mathcal{M}} = \langle x \oplus 0_{\mathcal{N}}, v_i \rangle_{\mathcal{H} \oplus \mathcal{N}}.$$

Thus, we find that $x \oplus 0_{\mathcal{M}} = \sum_{i=1}^k \langle x \oplus 0_{\mathcal{M}}, u_i \rangle u_i = \sum_{i=1}^k \langle x, x_i \rangle u_i$, and similarly, $x \oplus 0_{\mathcal{N}} = \sum_{i=1}^k \langle x, x_i \rangle v_i$. Therefore, we can now conclude that any such map $\widetilde{U}$ must act like the identity on $\mathcal{H} \oplus 0_M$ in the sense that it will map $x \oplus 0_{\mathcal{M}}$ to $x \oplus 0_{\mathcal{N}}$:

$$\widetilde{U}(x \oplus 0_{\mathcal{M}}) = \sum_{i=1}^k \langle x, x_i \rangle \widetilde{U}u_i = \sum_{i=1}^k \langle x, x_i \rangle v_i = x \oplus 0_{\mathcal{N}}.$$

Another way to say this is that if we identify $\mathcal{H}\oplus 0_{\mathcal{M}}$ and $\mathcal{H}\oplus 0_{\mathcal{N}}$, we can write $\widetilde{U} = I \oplus U$, where U is a unitary operator which maps $\mathcal{M}$ to $\mathcal{N}$. Once we have this, applying $\widetilde{U}$ to the vectors $x_i \oplus y_i$ immediately shows that $Uy_i = z_i$ for $i = 1, 2, \ldots, k$. This is what we were required to show. $\square$

There is a similar result for general frames which we leave for the reader to prove in Exercise 5.

We have seen that a compression of a Parseval frame by an orthogonal projection is always Parseval. Let's look at the converse question. If we compute the orthogonal compression of a sequence of vectors, and see that this compression is a Parseval frame for its span, does this always mean the original sequence is a Parseval frame? It is pretty easy to decide that this is not the case. One counterexample would be the single vector $e_1 = \begin{bmatrix} 1 \\ 0 \end{bmatrix}$ in $\mathbb{R}^2$. If we project e_1 onto its span (the x-axis), then it is naturally a Parseval frame (in fact, an orthonormal basis) for that subspace. But $\{e_1\}$ does not span $\mathbb{R}^2$, so is not itself a Parseval frame for $\mathbb{R}^2$.

Therefore, if we know that just a single orthogonal projection of a finite sequence of vectors is a Parseval frame for its span, this is insufficient to conclude that the sequence is a Parseval frame. In finite dimensions, we might wish to describe a sufficient set of projections which will ensure a frame is Parseval. The following is one such example.

Proposition 5.8. *Let $\{x_i\}_{i=1}^k \subset \mathbb{C}^n$, with $k \geq n \geq 2$. Then $\{x_i\}_{i=1}^k$ is a Parseval frame for $\mathbb{C}^n$ if and only if each of the $\binom{n}{2}$ projections of the vectors $\{x_i\}_{i=1}^k$ onto the coordinate planes in $\mathbb{C}^n$ is a Parseval frame for its two-dimensional span.*

Proof. Let $\{e_j\}_{j=1}^n$ be the standard orthonormal basis for $\mathbb{C}^n$. Define the two-dimensional coordinate projections to have matrix form P_{lm}, $i \neq j$, where P_{lm} is the diagonal matrix with 1 in the lth and m^{th} diagonal entries and zero elsewhere. It is easily verified that each P_{lm} is a projection which maps a vector $v \in \mathbb{C}^n$ to the $\mathbb{C}^2$ vector containing the lth and m^{th} entries of v. We can also now see that there are $\binom{n}{2}$ different projections P_{lm}.

The forward direction follows immediately from Proposition 5.1. The reverse direction is proved using Corollary 5.6. If each $\{P_{lm}x_i\}_{i=1}^k$ is a Parseval frame, then if we construct the matrix with columns $\{P_{lm}x_i\}_{i=1}^k$, this matrix will have orthonormal rows. If we then consider the matrix with columns $\{x_i\}_{i=1}^k$, we have just shown that the rows are pairwise orthogonal. Therefore, $\{x_i\}_{i=1}^k$ forms a Parseval frame for $\mathbb{C}^n$ by Corollary 5.6. □

5.3. Frames and Oblique Projections

This section generalizes some of the results in the previous section to more general compressions and dilations. We begin by defining an oblique projection.

Definition 5.9. An *oblique projection* on a Hilbert space $\mathcal{H}$ is a linear operator P on $\mathcal{H}$ such that $P^2 = P$. Unlike an orthogonal projection, P need not be self-adjoint. Oblique projections may also be called *idempotents.*

To make the terminology very clear, an idempotent or oblique projection P is an orthogonal projection if and only if P is self-adjoint. The matrix form of this distinction is demonstrated in Section 10.4.

Example 5.10. The matrix $P = \begin{bmatrix} 1 & c \\ 0 & 0 \end{bmatrix}$ is an oblique projection of $\mathbb{R}^2$ for any $c \in \mathbb{R}$ (see Figure 5.2). The range of the projection is the x-axis. It is straightforward to verify that $P^2 = P$, and we can tell by observation that P is not self-adjoint unless $c = 0$. Therefore, P is an orthogonal projection if and only if $c = 0$.

The following proposition is the analog to Proposition 5.1 when the projection is oblique.

Proposition 5.11. *Let P be an oblique projection of $\mathcal{H}$ onto a subspace $\mathcal{M}$, and let $\{u_i\}_{i=1}^k$ be an orthonormal basis for $\mathcal{H}$. Then $\{Pu_i\}_{i=1}^k$ is a frame of $\mathcal{M}$ with the lower frame bound greater than or equal to one.*

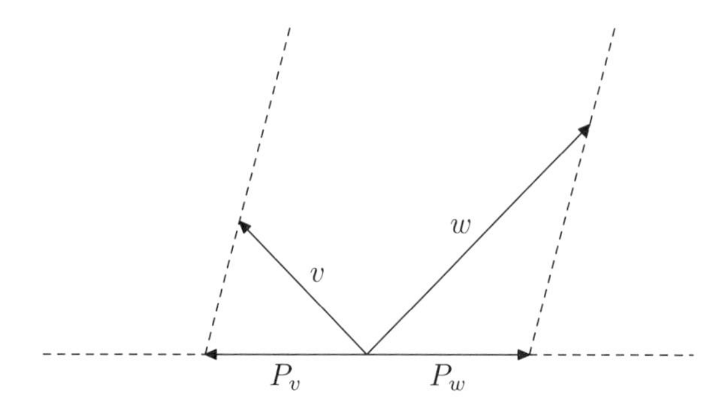

Figure 5.2. An oblique projection P on $\mathbb{R}^2$ acts on vectors v and w. In this particular diagram, the constant c defined in Example 5.10 is a negative number. In fact, you should be able to verify that the slope of the dotted lines is $-\frac{1}{c}$.

Proof. Let $x \in \mathcal{M}$, so that we have $Px = x$. Since $\{u_i\}_{i=1}^k$, we have

$$x = \sum_{i=1}^{k} \langle x, u_i \rangle u_i,$$

which then gives

$$x = Px = \sum_{i=1}^{k} \langle x, u_i \rangle Pu_i.$$

Therefore, for all $x \in \mathcal{M}$, we have

$$\|x\|^2 = \sum_{i=1}^{k} \langle x, u_i \rangle \langle Pu_i, x \rangle.$$

Next, using the Cauchy-Schwarz inequality in $\mathbb{C}^k$ followed by Parseval's Identity, we find that

$$\begin{aligned} \|x\|^2 &= \sum_{i=1}^{k} \langle x, u_i \rangle \langle Pu_i, x \rangle \\ &\leq \left(\sum_{i=1}^{k} | \langle x, u_i \rangle |^2 \right)^{\frac{1}{2}} \cdot \left(\sum_{i=1}^{k} | \langle Pu_i, x \rangle |^2 \right)^{\frac{1}{2}} \\ &= \|x\| \cdot \left(\sum_{i=1}^{k} | \langle x, Pu_i \rangle |^2 \right)^{\frac{1}{2}}. \end{aligned}$$

This implies that for all $x \in \mathcal{M}$,

$$\|x\|^2 \leq \sum_{i=1}^{k} |\langle x, Pu_i \rangle|^2,$$

and hence $\{Pu_i\}_{i=1}^k$ is a frame for $\mathcal{M}$ having lower frame bound greater than or equal to one. □

It is natural to wonder next about the converse of this proposition. Does every frame with lower frame bound greater than or equal to one appear as the oblique projection of an orthonormal basis? It turns out that the answer is negative, as demonstrated by the next example.

Example 5.12. Let $\{x_i\}_{i=1}^k$ be a linearly independent frame (hence, a basis) for $\mathcal{H}$. Assume that $\mathcal{K} \supset \mathcal{H}$ and $x_i = Pu_i$, where $\{u_i\}_{i=1}^k$ is an orthonormal basis for $\mathcal{K}$ and P is an oblique projection such that $P\mathcal{K} = \mathcal{H}$. Note that $\dim \mathcal{H} = k$ since $\{x_i\}_{i=1}^k$ is a linearly independent basis for $\mathcal{H}$. So $\dim \mathcal{H} = \dim \mathcal{K}$ which implies that $\mathcal{K} = \mathcal{H}$. Since $Px = x$ on $\mathcal{H}$, we now have $P = I$. The above argument tells us that if $\{x_i\}_{i=1}^k$ is a basis for $\mathcal{H}$ which is not an orthonormal basis, then it can never be the compression of an orthonormal basis under an oblique projection.

We follow up with another question. Under which conditions is a frame the compression of an orthonormal basis by an oblique projection? There is a complete answer to this question.

Theorem 5.13. *Let $\{x_i\}_{i=1}^k$ be a frame for $\mathcal{H}$ with lower frame bound ≥ 1, and let Θ be its analysis operator. Then the following are equivalent:*

(i) *There exists a Hilbert space $\mathcal{K} \supseteq \mathcal{H}$, an orthonormal basis $\{u_i\}_{i=1}^k$ for $\mathcal{K}$, and an oblique projection P of $\mathcal{K}$ onto $\mathcal{H}$ such that $x_i = Pu_i$ for all $i = 1, 2, \ldots, k$.*

(ii) *The dimension of the range of $\Theta^*\Theta - I_{\mathcal{H}}$ is less than or equal to the dimension of the orthogonal complement of $\Theta(\mathcal{H})$; i.e.,*

$$\dim \operatorname{range}(\Theta^*\Theta - I_{\mathcal{H}}) \leq \dim \Theta(\mathcal{H})^{\perp}.$$

Proof. The proof of this result requires some careful technical details. It is presented in detail as a student presentation in Section 10.4. □

There are some simple situations in which we can automatically conclude that every frame with large enough lower frame bound must be the oblique projection of an orthonormal basis. For example, we have the following corollary.

Corollary 5.14. *Let* $\dim \mathcal{H} = n$ *and* $k \geq 2n$. *Then for every frame* $\{x_i\}_{i=1}^k$ *of* $\mathcal{H}$ *with lower frame bound* $A \geq 1$, *there exists a Hilbert space* $\mathcal{K} \supseteq \mathcal{H}$, *an orthonormal basis* $\{u_i\}_{i=1}^k$ *for* $\mathcal{K}$, *and an oblique projection* P *from* $\mathcal{K}$ *onto* $\mathcal{H}$ *such that* $x_i = Pu_i$ *for all* i *and* $P\mathcal{K} = \mathcal{H}$.

Proof. Let Θ be the analysis operator of $\{x_i\}_{i=1}^k$ for $\mathcal{H}$ and $\dim \mathcal{H} = n$. Since $k \geq 2n$ and $\mathbb{C}^k = \Theta(\mathcal{H}) \oplus \Theta(\mathcal{H})^\perp$, it follows that

$$\dim \Theta(\mathcal{H})^\perp \geq n \geq \dim \operatorname{range}(\Theta^*\Theta - I_{\mathcal{H}}).$$

Hence, the proposition follows immediately from Theorem 5.13. □

5.4. Exercises from the Text

Exercise 1. Prove that

$$\left\{ \sqrt{\frac{2}{3}} \begin{bmatrix} 1 \\ 0 \\ \frac{1}{\sqrt{2}} \end{bmatrix}, \sqrt{\frac{2}{3}} \begin{bmatrix} -\frac{1}{2} \\ \frac{\sqrt{3}}{2} \\ \frac{1}{\sqrt{2}} \end{bmatrix}, \sqrt{\frac{2}{3}} \begin{bmatrix} -\frac{1}{2} \\ -\frac{\sqrt{3}}{2} \\ \frac{1}{\sqrt{2}} \end{bmatrix} \right\}$$

is an orthonormal basis for for $\mathbb{R}^3$.

Exercise 2. Prove that the matrix for the discrete Fourier transform described in Example 5.4 has orthonormal columns.

Exercise 3. Prove part (ii) of Proposition 5.5.

5.5. Additional Exercises

Exercise 4. Let $\{x_i\}_{i=1}^k$ be a frame for $\mathcal{H}$ and let S be its frame operator.

(i) Prove that there exists another Hilbert space M and a Parseval frame $\{y_i\}_{i=1}^k$ such that $\{S^{-\frac{1}{2}}x_i \oplus y_i\}_{i=1}^k$ is an orthonormal basis for $\mathcal{H} \oplus M$.

(ii) Let $\{y_i\}_{i=1}^k$ be as in (i). Prove that $\{x_i \oplus y_i\}_{i=1}^k$ is a basis for $\mathcal{H} \oplus M$ and

$$\sum_{i=1}^{k} \langle x, x_i \rangle y_i = \sum_{i=1}^{k} \langle y, y_i \rangle x_i = 0$$

holds for all $x \in \mathcal{H}$ and all $y \in M$.

Exercise 5. Let $\{x_i\}_{i=1}^k$ be a frame for a Hilbert space $\mathcal{H}$, and let $\{y_i\}_{i=1}^k$ and $\{z_i\}_{i=1}^k$ be two frames for Hilbert spaces $\mathcal{M}$ and $\mathcal{N}$, respectively, satisfying the following two conditions:

(i) $\{x_i \oplus y_i\}_{i=1}^k$ is a basis for $\mathcal{H} \oplus \mathcal{M}$, and $\{x_i \oplus z_i\}_{i=1}^k$ is a basis for $\mathcal{H} \oplus \mathcal{N}$.

(ii) $\sum_{i=1}^{k} \langle x, x_i \rangle y_i = \sum_{i=1}^{k} \langle x, x_i \rangle z_i = 0$ for all $x \in \mathcal{H}$.

Prove that there exists an invertible linear operator A mapping $\mathcal{M}$ to $\mathcal{N}$ such that $z_n = Ay_n$ for all n.

Note: The frames $\{y_i\}$ and $\{z_i\}$ satisfying the two conditions in this exercise are called *orthogonal complementary frames* of $\{x_i\}$ to a basis (not an orthonormal basis as in Proposition 5.7). This exercise shows that these complementary frames are unique up to similarity.

Exercise 6. Use the dilation and compression results to show that a three-element set

$$\left\{ \begin{bmatrix} a_1 \\ b_1 \end{bmatrix}, \begin{bmatrix} a_2 \\ b_2 \end{bmatrix}, \begin{bmatrix} a_3 \\ b_3 \end{bmatrix} \right\}$$

is a Parseval frame for $\mathbb{C}^2$ if and only if there exist $c_1, c_2, c_3 \in \mathbb{C}$ such that

$$\left\{ \begin{bmatrix} a_1 \\ b_1 \\ c_1 \end{bmatrix}, \begin{bmatrix} a_2 \\ b_2 \\ c_2 \end{bmatrix}, \begin{bmatrix} a_3 \\ b_3 \\ c_3 \end{bmatrix} \right\}$$

is an orthonormal basis for $\mathbb{C}^3$.

Exercise 7. Let $\{u_i\}_{i=1}^k$ be an orthonormal basis for a Hilbert space $\mathcal{K}$ and let P be an oblique projection of $\mathcal{K}$ onto a subspace M. Show that $\{Pu_i\}_{i=1}^k$ is an orthonormal basis for the subspace M if and only if $P = I$.

Exercise 8. Let $\{x_i\}_{i=1}^k$ and $\{y_i\}_{i=1}^k$ be two Parseval frames for Hilbert spaces $\mathcal{H}$ and $\mathcal{K}$, respectively. Prove that they are unitarily equivalent if and only if they have a common orthogonal complementary frame $\{w_i\}_{i=1}^k$ (which is a Parseval frame for its span) to an orthonormal basis.

Exercise 9. Let $\mathcal{H}$ be the not-necessarily orthogonal direct sum $M \dot{+} N$. Recall that this means any $x \in \mathcal{H}$ can be expressed uniquely as $x = m+n$, where $m \in M$ and $n \in N$. Let P be a linear operator on $\mathcal{H}$. We can write P in a matrix form with respect to the decomposition $M \dot{+} N$:

$$P = \begin{bmatrix} A & B \\ C & D \end{bmatrix},$$

where A maps $M \to M$, B maps $N \to M$, C maps $N \to M$, and D maps $N \to N$. Show that the following are equivalent:

(i) P is an oblique projection on $\mathcal{H}$ such that $P\mathcal{H} = M$.

(ii) P has the following matrix form with respect to the decomposition $\mathcal{H} = M \dot{+} N$:

$$P = \begin{bmatrix} I_M & B \\ 0 & 0 \end{bmatrix}.$$

for some linear operator B mapping N to M.

Exercise 10. If P is an oblique projection on $\mathcal{H}$, show that $\text{range}(P) \cap \ker(P) = \{0\}$, which means we have $\mathcal{H} = \text{range}(P) \dot{+} \ker(P)$.

Chapter 6

Dual and Orthogonal Frames

In this chapter we further explore the reconstruction formula introduced in Proposition 3.19, and investigate its connections with dual frames, orthogonal or disjoint sequences, and multiplexing. In addition, we also consider the question of whether a frame has a tight dual frame.

6.1. Reconstruction Formula Revisited

One of the most important properties of a frame is the ability to recover every element in the Hilbert space as a combination of frame vectors. The utility of a frame is therefore highly dependent on how readily such a combination can be computed. Recall that if $\{x_i\}_{i=1}^k$ is a Parseval frame for a Hilbert space $\mathcal{H}$, we have the following very simple and easily computed reconstruction formula:

$$x = \sum_{i=1}^{k} \langle x, x_i \rangle x_i, \qquad \forall x \in \mathcal{H}.$$

However, in the case that $\{x_i\}_{i=1}^k$ is a general frame for a Hilbert space $\mathcal{H}$, the situation is a little bit more complicated. Let S be the frame operator, which we recall is given by the formula:

$$Sx = \sum_{i=1}^{k} \langle x, x_i \rangle x_i, \qquad \forall x \in \mathcal{H}. \tag{6.1}$$

Since S is a positive and invertible operator on $\mathcal{H}$, we can replace x in the above formula by $S^{-1}x$, which then gives the reconstruction formula:

$$x = \sum_{i=1}^{k} \langle S^{-1}x, x_i \rangle x_i = \sum_{i=1}^{k} \langle x, S^{-1}x_i \rangle x_i, \qquad \forall x \in \mathcal{H}.$$

If we apply S^{-1} to both sides of Equation (6.1), we also have a dual version of the above reconstruction formula:

$$x = \sum_{i=1}^{k} \langle x, x_i \rangle S^{-1}x_i, \qquad \forall x \in \mathcal{H}.$$

Combining these results, we have an example of a reconstruction such as given in Proposition 3.19.

$$x = \sum_{i=1}^{k} \langle x, S^{-1}x_i \rangle x_i = \sum_{i=1}^{k} \langle x, x_i \rangle S^{-1}x_i, \qquad \forall x \in \mathcal{H}. \tag{6.2}$$

The collection of vectors $\{S^{-1}x_i\}_{i=1}^k$ is called the *canonical dual frame* of $\{x_i\}_{i=1}^k$. It will be a frame since S^{-1} is an invertible operator and therefore $\{S^{-1}x_i\}_{i=1}^k$ will span $\mathcal{H}$. It is also easily verified that $\{x_i\}_{i=1}^k$ will be the canonical dual frame of $\{S^{-1}x_i\}_{i=1}^k$.

However, because of the redundancy which frames may have, there can be other collections of vectors $\{y_i\}_{i=1}^k$ in $\mathcal{H}$ that satisfy such a reconstruction formula:

$$x = \sum_{i=1}^{k} \langle x, y_i \rangle x_i \qquad \forall x \in \mathcal{H}.$$

This leads to the definition of an alternate dual frame.

6.2. Dual Frames

Definition 6.1. Let $\{x_i\}_{i=1}^k$ be a frame for a Hilbert space $\mathcal{H}$. A sequence $\{y_i\}_{i=1}^k$ in $\mathcal{H}$ is called a *dual frame* for $\{x_i\}_{i=1}^k$ if $\{y_i\}_{i=1}^k$

satisfies the reconstruction formula:

$$x = \sum_{i=1}^{k} \langle x, y_i \rangle x_i, \quad \forall x \in \mathcal{H}.$$

If $y_i = S^{-1}x_i, i = 1, 2, \ldots, k$, then it is called the *canonical dual frame.* If $\{y_i\}_{i=1}^k$ is not the canonical dual frame, it is called an *alternate dual frame.*

In Exercise 9, the reader is asked to prove that if $\{x_i\}_{i=1}^k$ and $\{y_i\}_{i=1}^k$ satisfy the equation $x = \sum_{i=1}^k \langle x, y_i \rangle x_i \; \forall x \in \mathcal{H}$, then they also satisfy the equation $x = \sum_{i=1}^k \langle x, x_i \rangle y_i \; \forall x \in \mathcal{H}$. In other words, the vectors $\{y_i\}_{i=1}^k$ will span $\mathcal{H}$ whenever $\{x_i\}_{i=1}^k$ spans. Since $\mathcal{H}$ is a finite-dimensional space, this implies that if $\{x_i\}_{i=1}^k$ is a frame for $\mathcal{H}$, then so are any of its dual frames. This does not hold, in general, in an infinite-dimensional setting.

Some frames will have only the canonical dual frame while others may have alternate duals. We examine conditions under which a frame may have alternate duals, and then move on to consider when there may be a tight or Parseval dual frame.

Proposition 6.2. *Let $\{x_i\}_{i=1}^k$ be a basis for $\mathcal{H}$. Then its dual frame is unique.*

Proof. Assume that $\{y_i\}_{i=1}^k$ and $\{z_i\}_{i=1}^k$ are both dual frames of $\{x_i\}_{i=1}^k$. We need to show that they are the same frame.

By the definition of dual frames, we have for each $x \in \mathcal{H}$ that

$$\begin{aligned} \sum_{i=1}^{k} (\langle x, y_i \rangle - \langle x, z_i \rangle) x_i &= \sum_{i=1}^{k} \langle x, y_i \rangle x_i - \sum_{i=1}^{k} \langle x, z_i \rangle x_i \\ &= x - x = 0. \end{aligned}$$

Since $\{x_i\}_{i=1}^k$ are linearly independent, it follows from

$$\sum_{i=1}^{k} (\langle x, y_i \rangle - \langle x, z_i \rangle) x_i = 0$$

that $\langle x, y_i - z_i \rangle = 0$ for all $i = 1, 2, \ldots, k$. Therefore, each $y_i - z_i$ is orthogonal to x. Since $x \in \mathcal{H}$ is arbitrary, we have that each $y_i - z_i = 0$, so $y_i = z_i$ for $i = 1, 2, \ldots, k$. Therefore, $\{x_i\}_{i=1}^k$ has a unique dual frame. □

Proposition 6.2 tells us that the canonical dual frame $\{S^{-1}x_i\}_{i=1}^k$ is the only dual frame when $\{x_i\}_{i=1}^k$ is a basis for $\mathcal{H}$. Moreover, in this case, we also have that $\{S^{-1}x_i\}_{i=1}^k$ is *bi-orthogonal* to $\{x_i\}_{i=1}^k$ in the sense that

$$\left\langle x_i, S^{-1}x_i \right\rangle = 1 \quad \text{and} \quad \left\langle x_i, S^{-1}x_j \right\rangle = 0 \quad \text{if } i \neq j.$$

We leave this fact to be shown in Exercise 1.

It turns out that the uniqueness of the dual frame is a characteristic which distinguishes bases from general frames. In other words, the converse of Proposition 6.2 is also true.

Proposition 6.3. *Let $\{x_i\}_{i=1}^k$ be a frame for $\mathcal{H}$. Then $\{x_i\}_{i=1}^k$ has a unique dual frame if and only if $\{x_i\}_{i=1}^k$ is a basis.*

Proof. The reverse direction was proven in Proposition 6.2.

To prove the forward direction, we will use the contrapositive. Assume that $\{x_i\}_{i=1}^k$ is not a basis. Then $\Theta(\mathcal{H}) \neq \mathbb{C}^k$, where Θ is the analysis operator of $\{x_i\}_{i=1}^k$. Define P to be the orthogonal projection onto $\Theta(\mathcal{H})^\perp$ and let $T : \Theta(\mathcal{H})^\perp \to \mathcal{H}$ be any nonzero linear operator. Then $TPe_i \neq 0$ for some i, where $\{e_i\}_{i=1}^k$ is the standard orthonormal basis for $\mathbb{C}^k$. If we let $y_i = S^{-1}x_i + TPe_i$, then $\{y_i\}_{i=1}^k$ is different from $\{S^{-1}x_i\}_{i=1}^k$. Note that, for all $x, y \in \mathcal{H}$, we have

$$\begin{aligned}
\left\langle \sum_{i=1}^k \langle x, TPe_i \rangle x_i, y \right\rangle &= \sum_{i=1}^k \langle PT^*x, e_i \rangle \langle x_i, y \rangle \\
&= \left\langle PT^*x, \sum_{i=1}^k \langle y, x_i \rangle e_i \right\rangle \\
&= \langle PT^*x, \Theta(y) \rangle \\
&= 0.
\end{aligned}$$

Thus $\sum_{i=1}^k \langle x, TPx_i \rangle x_i = 0$ for all $x \in \mathcal{H}$. Therefore, we have

$$\begin{aligned}
\sum_{i=1}^k \langle x, y_i \rangle x_i &= \sum_{i=1}^k \left\langle x, S^{-\frac{1}{2}}x_i + TPe_i \right\rangle x_i \\
&= \sum_{i=1}^k \left\langle x, S^{-\frac{1}{2}}x_i \right\rangle x_i + \sum_{i=1}^k \langle x, TPe_i \rangle x_i \\
&= x + 0 = x,
\end{aligned}$$

which implies that $\{y_i\}_{i=1}^k$ is also a dual frame for $\{x_i\}_{i=1}^k$. Therefore $\{x_i\}_{i=1}^k$ has more than one dual frame. □

The following proposition gives a characterization of all the dual frames for any given frame, making use of the analysis operator.

Proposition 6.4. *Let $\{x_i\}_{i=1}^k$ be a frame for $\mathcal{H}$ and let S be its frame operator. Then $\{y_i\}_{i=1}^k$ is a dual frame of $\{x_i\}_{i=1}^k$ if and only there exists a sequence $\{z_i\}_{i=1}^k$ such that $y_i = S^{-1}x_i + z_i$ and for which $\Theta_z(\mathcal{H}) \perp \Theta_x(\mathcal{H})$, where Θ_x and Θ_z are the respective analysis operators of $\{x_i\}_{i=1}^k$ and $\{z_i\}_{i=1}^k$.*

Proof. First assume that $\{y_i\}_{i=1}^k$ is a dual frame of $\{x_i\}_{i=1}^k$. Let $z_i = y_i - S^{-1}x_i$. Then for any $u \in \mathcal{H}$ we have

$$\begin{aligned}\sum_{i=1}^k \langle u, z_i \rangle x_i &= \sum_{i=1}^k \langle u, y_i - S^{-1}x_i \rangle x_i \\ &= \sum_{i=1}^k \langle u, y_i \rangle x_i - \sum_{i=1}^k \langle u, S^{-1}x_i \rangle x_i \\ &= u - u = 0.\end{aligned}$$

This implies that

$$\langle \Theta_z(u), \Theta_x(v) \rangle = \sum_{i=1}^k \langle u, z_i \rangle \langle x_i, v \rangle = 0$$

holds for all $u, v \in \mathcal{H}$. Therefore, $\Theta_z(\mathcal{H}) \perp \Theta_x(\mathcal{H})$.

To show the converse, assume that there exists a sequence $\{z_i\}_{i=1}^k$ such that $y_i = S^{-1}x_i + z_i$ with $\Theta_z(\mathcal{H}) \perp \Theta_x(\mathcal{H})$. Then we have

$$\sum_{i=1}^k \langle u, z_i \rangle \langle x_i, v \rangle = 0 \qquad \forall u, v \in \mathcal{H}$$

which implies that

$$\sum_{i=1}^k \langle u, z_i \rangle x_i = 0 \qquad \forall u \in \mathcal{H}.$$

This results in the following for every $u \in \mathcal{H}$:

$$\begin{aligned}\sum_{i=1}^{k} \langle u, y_i \rangle x_i &= \sum_{i=1}^{k} \langle u, S^{-1}x_i \rangle x_i + \sum_{i=1}^{k} \langle u, z_i \rangle x_i \\ &= u + 0 = u.\end{aligned}$$

Therefore $\{y_i\}_{i=1}^k$ is a dual of $\{x_i\}_{i=1}^k$. □

It should be noted here that the sequence $\{z_i\}_{i=1}^k$ from Proposition 6.4 need not be a frame for the Hilbert space $\mathcal{H}$. We can also interpret the above result in terms of synthesis operators. We leave the proof to Exercise 2.

Theorem 6.5. *Let $\{x_i\}_{i=1}^k$ and $\{y_i\}_{i=1}^k$ be two frames for $\mathcal{H}$ and let Θ_x and Θ_y be their respective analysis operators. Then $\{y_i\}_{i=1}^k$ is a dual frame of $\{x_i\}_{i=1}^k$ if and only if Θ_y^* is a left inverse of Θ_x, so that $\Theta_y^*\Theta_x = I_{\mathcal{H}}$.*

Theorem 6.5 tells us that finding an alternate dual for $\{x_i\}_{i=1}^k$ is the same as finding an $n \times k$ matrix which is a left inverse for the matrix representation of Θ. To make this statement precise, let $\{x_i\}_{i=1}^k$ be a frame for a Hilbert space $\mathcal{H}$ with $\dim \mathcal{H} = n$. Fix an orthonormal basis $\{e_j\}_{j=1}^n$ for $\mathcal{H}$. Suppose that the coordinate representation of each x_i is denoted

$$x_i = \begin{bmatrix} x_{i1} \\ x_{i2} \\ \vdots \\ x_{in} \end{bmatrix}$$

with respect to the fixed orthonormal basis. Then the matrix form of the analysis operator Θ is the $k \times n$ matrix with row vectors $x_i^* = \overline{x_i}^T$, where we know that $k \geq n$. Suppose that T is an $n \times k$ matrix such that

$$T\Theta = I_n.$$

Then it can be checked (see Exercise 12) that $\{y_1, y_2, \ldots, y_k\}$ is a dual frame for $\{x_i\}_{i=1}^k$, where $\{y_i\}_{i=1}^k$ are the column vectors of T.

It is now possible to actually describe in matrix terms the possible left inverses of a $k \times n$ analysis operator matrix Θ, when we impose the restriction that $k \geq n$. We just use elementary row operations to find an invertible matrix P (the product of the matrices for the row operations) such that $P\Theta$ has the form of:

$$P\Theta = \begin{bmatrix} I_n \\ 0 \end{bmatrix},$$

where 0 is the $(k-n) \times n$ zero matrix. Let $T = \begin{bmatrix} I_n & A \end{bmatrix} P$ for any $n \times (k-n)$ matrix A. Then we see that

$$\begin{aligned} T\Theta &= \begin{bmatrix} I_n & A \end{bmatrix} P\Theta \\ &= \begin{bmatrix} I_n & A \end{bmatrix} \begin{bmatrix} I_n \\ 0 \end{bmatrix} \\ &= I_n. \end{aligned}$$

Thus, the sequence of the column vectors of T is a dual frame of $\{x_i\}_{i=1}^k$. If $k > n$, then we will have infinitely many choices for A and hence can produce many different dual frames.

Recall from Section 3.4 that if a frame $\{x_i\}_{i=1}^k$ is a Parseval frame, then the Grammian operator is a self-adjoint projection onto the range of the analysis operator. There is a corresponding result for pairs of dual frames. Given dual frames $\{x_i\}_{i=1}^k$ and $\{y_i\}_{i=1}^k$ with analysis operators Θ_x and Θ_y respectively, we define the *cross-Grammian matrices* for this pair to be the $k \times k$ matrices $\Theta_x\Theta_y^*$ and $\Theta_y\Theta_x^*$. These matrices have entries $\langle y_i, x_j \rangle$ or $\langle x_i, y_j \rangle$.

Corollary 6.6. *If $\{x_i\}_{i=1}^k$ and $\{y_i\}_{i=1}^k$ are dual frames with analysis operators Θ_x and Θ_y respectively, then the cross-Grammian operators are oblique projections, with $\Theta_x\Theta_y^*$ projecting onto $\Theta_x(\mathcal{H})$ and $\Theta_y\Theta_x^*$ projecting onto $\Theta_y(\mathcal{H})$.*

Proof. We leave the proof of this result to Exercise 3. □

The next two results characterize the canonical dual frame among all the dual frames.

Proposition 6.7. *Let $\{x_i\}_{i=1}^k$ be a frame for $\mathcal{H}$ and let S be its frame operator. Then the canonical dual $\{S^{-1}x_i\}_{i=1}^k$ is the only dual frame that is similar to $\{x_i\}_{i=1}^k$.*

Proof. Let $\{y_i\}$ be a dual frame of $\{x_i\}$ which is similar to the canonical dual frame $\{S^{-1}x_i\}_{i=1}^k$. Recall from Section 3.5 that this means there exists an invertible operator T on $\mathcal{H}$ such that $y_i = TS^{-1}x_i$ for $i = 1, 2, \ldots, k$. But, this will give for every $x \in \mathcal{H}$:

$$\begin{aligned} T^*x &= \sum_{i=1}^k \langle T^*x, S^{-1}x_i \rangle x_i \\ &= \sum_{i=1}^k \langle x, TS^{-1}x_i \rangle x_i \\ &= \sum_{i=1}^k \langle x, y_i \rangle x_i \\ &= x. \end{aligned}$$

This means that $T^* = I$, which implies that $T = I$, so we actually do not have such an alternate dual frame. □

The above result suggests that the canonical dual frame has some special properties which tie it back to the original frame. The next result shows that the canonical dual is the dual frame which minimizes a particular norm.

Proposition 6.8. *Let $\{x_i\}_{i=1}^k$ be a frame for $\mathcal{H}$ and let $\{y_i\}_{i=1}^k$ be a dual frame of $\{x_i\}_{i=1}^k$. Then $\{y_i\}_{i=1}^k$ is the canonical dual if and only if*

$$\sum_{i=1}^k |\langle x, y_i \rangle|^2 \leq \sum_{i=1}^k |\langle x, w_i \rangle|^2 \qquad \forall x \in \mathcal{H}$$

for all frames $\{w_i\}_{i=1}^k$ which are duals of $\{x_i\}_{i=1}^k$.

Proof. From Proposition 6.4, we have that there exists a sequence $\{z_i\}_{i=1}^k$ such that $w_i = S^{-1}x_i + z_i$ and $\Theta_x(\mathcal{H}) \perp \Theta_z(\mathcal{H})$, where Θ_x and Θ_z are the analysis operators of $\{x_i\}_{i=1}^k$ and $\{z_i\}_{i=1}^k$, respectively. Therefore, we can do the following computation, using the definition of the analysis operator to write $\langle x, x_i \rangle = \langle \Theta_x x, e_i \rangle$ where $x \in \mathcal{H}$

and e_i is the ith standard basis element in $\mathbb{C}^k$.

$$\begin{aligned}
\sum_{i=1}^{k} |\langle x, w_i \rangle|^2 &= \sum_{i=1}^{k} \left|\left\langle x, S^{-1}x_i \right\rangle + \langle x, z_i \rangle\right|^2 \\
&= \sum_{i=1}^{k} \left|\left\langle S^{-1}x, x_i \right\rangle + \langle x, z_i \rangle\right|^2 \\
&= \sum_{i=1}^{k} \left|\left\langle \Theta_x(S^{-1}x), e_i \right\rangle + \langle \Theta_z(x), e_i \rangle\right|^2 \\
&= \sum_{i=1}^{k} \left|\left\langle \Theta_x(S^{-1}x) + \Theta_z(x), e_i \right\rangle\right|^2 \\
&= \|\Theta_x(S^{-1}x) + \Theta_z(x)\|^2 \quad \text{Parseval's Identity} \\
&= \|\Theta_x(S^{-1}x)\|^2 + \|\Theta_z(x)\|^2 \quad \text{Pythagorean Theorem} \\
&= \sum_{i=1}^{k} |\left\langle x, S^{-1}x_i \right\rangle|^2 + \sum_{i=1}^{k} |\langle x, z_i \rangle|^2.
\end{aligned}$$

In the last line above, the term $\sum_{i=1}^{k} |\langle x, z_i \rangle|^2$ is strictly greater than zero for some choice of $x \in \mathcal{H}$ unless each z_i is zero, in which case $\{w_i\}_{i=1}^{k}$ is the canonical dual frame. This proves the result. $\square$

In matrix language, the above result tells us that for a given analysis operator Θ (where we view Θ in its $k \times n$ matrix form), the left inverse matrix M of Θ obtained by the canonical dual frame will minimize the quantity $\|M^*x\|$ for every x among all the left inverses of Θ. Thus, the canonical dual frame also minimizes the operator norm of the analysis operator.

6.3. Orthogonality of Frames

We have seen in the previous section that the orthogonality of the range spaces of the analysis operators for two sequences indicates some nice properties about the sum of the two sequences. This motivates the concept of orthogonal and disjoint frames.

Definition 6.9. Let $\{x_i\}_{i=1}^{k} \subset \mathcal{H}$ and let $\{y_i\}_{i=1}^{k} \subset \mathcal{K}$, and Θ_x and Θ_y be their respective analysis operators. Then we say that $\{x_i\}_{i=1}^{k}$

and $\{y_i\}_{i=1}^k$ are *orthogonal sequences* if $\Theta_x(\mathcal{H}) \perp \Theta_y(\mathcal{K})$. If these sequences are also frames for their respective spaces, then they are called *orthogonal frames*.

The following lemma is a fairly immediate result of the definition of orthogonal sequences or frames. We leave the proof to Exercise 5.

Lemma 6.10. *Two sequences $\{x_i\}_{i=1}^k$ and $\{y_i\}_{i=1}^k$ are orthogonal if and only if $\Theta_x^*\Theta_y = 0$, where Θ_x and Θ_y are the analysis operators for $\{x_i\}_{i=1}^k$ and $\{y_i\}_{i=1}^k$, respectively.*

This notion of orthogonal frames (also called strongly disjoint frames in [**42**]) was first formally introduced and systematically studied by R. Balan in [**5**], D. Han and D.R. Larson in [**42**], and has been used in the investigation of orthogonal Weyl-Heisenberg frames, super-wavelets, and sampling. In this section we will summarize some basic properties of orthogonal frames, which will be used in the later chapters.

Theorem 6.11. *Let $\{x_i\}_{i=1}^k$ and $\{y_i\}_{i=1}^k$ be two Parseval frames for Hilbert spaces $\mathcal{H}$ and $\mathcal{K}$ respectively. Then $\{x_i\}_{i=1}^k$ and $\{y_i\}_{i=1}^k$ are orthogonal if and only if $\{x_i \oplus y_i\}_{i=1}^k$ is a Parseval frame for $\mathcal{H} \oplus \mathcal{K}$.*

Proof. First note that for every $x \in \mathcal{H}$ and $y \in \mathcal{K}$ we have:

$$\begin{aligned}
\sum_{i=1}^k |\langle x \oplus y, x_i \oplus y_i \rangle|^2 &= \sum_{i=1}^k |\langle x, x_i \rangle + \langle y, y_i \rangle|^2 \\
&= \sum_{i=1}^k |\langle x, x_i \rangle|^2 + \sum_{i=1}^k |\langle y, y_i \rangle|^2 \\
&\quad +2\,\mathrm{Re}\sum_{i=1}^k \langle x, x_i \rangle \overline{\langle y, y_i \rangle} \\
&= \|x\|^2 + \|y\|^2 + 2\,\mathrm{Re}\sum_{i=1}^k \langle x, x_i \rangle \overline{\langle y, y_i \rangle} \\
&= \|x \oplus y\|^2 + 2\,\mathrm{Re}\sum_{i=1}^k \langle x, x_i \rangle \overline{\langle y, y_i \rangle}.
\end{aligned}$$

Thus the equality

$$\sum_{i=1}^{k} |\langle x \oplus y, x_i \oplus y_i \rangle|^2 = \|x \oplus y\|^2$$

holds for all $x \in \mathcal{H}$ and $y \in \mathcal{K}$ if and only if $\sum_{i=1}^{k} \langle x, x_i \rangle \overline{\langle y, y_i \rangle} = 0$ for all $x \in \mathcal{H}$ and $y \in \mathcal{K}$. Since $\sum_{i=1}^{k} \langle x, x_i \rangle \overline{\langle y, y_i \rangle} = \langle \Theta_x x, \Theta_y y \rangle$, we have the equality if and only if $\{x_i\}_{i=1}^k$ and $\{y_i\}_{i=1}^k$ are orthogonal frames. □

In the case of a general frame, the following corollary is the analog of Theorem 6.11.

Corollary 6.12. *If $\{x_i\}_{i=1}^k$ and $\{y_i\}_{i=1}^k$ are two orthogonal frames for $\mathcal{H}$ and $\mathcal{K}$, respectively, then $\{x_i \oplus y_i\}_{i=1}^k$ is a frame for $\mathcal{H} \oplus \mathcal{K}$.*

Proof. Let S_1 and S_2 be the frame operators for $\{x_i\}_{i=1}^k$ and $\{y_i\}_{i=1}^k$, respectively. Then the sequences $\{S_1^{-\frac{1}{2}} x_i\}_{i=1}^k$ and $\{S_2^{-\frac{1}{2}} y_i\}_{i=1}^k$ are Parseval frames for the appropriate Hilbert spaces, by Proposition 3.31. We will use the fact that the analysis operators of $\{S_1^{-\frac{1}{2}} x_i\}_{i=1}^k$ and $\{x_i\}_{i=1}^k$ have the same range space (see Exercise 11), and naturally the same holds for the frames $\{S_2^{-\frac{1}{2}} y_i\}_{i=1}^k$ and $\{y_i\}_{i=1}^k$. Therefore, using the definition of orthogonal frames, $\{S_1^{-\frac{1}{2}} x_i\}_{i=1}^k$ and $\{S_2^{-\frac{1}{2}} y_i\}_{i=1}^k$ are orthogonal Parseval frames.

By Theorem 6.11 we now have that $\{S_1^{-\frac{1}{2}} x_i \oplus S_2^{-\frac{1}{2}} y_i\}_{i=1}^k$ is a Parseval frame for $\mathcal{H} \oplus \mathcal{K}$. Note that $x_i \oplus y_i = T(S_1^{-\frac{1}{2}} x_i \oplus S_2^{-\frac{1}{2}} y_i)$ where $T = S_1^{\frac{1}{2}} \oplus S_2^{\frac{1}{2}}$ is the invertible operator on $\mathcal{H} \oplus \mathcal{K}$ defined by

$$T(x \oplus y) = S_1^{\frac{1}{2}} x \oplus S_2^{\frac{1}{2}} y$$

for $x \in \mathcal{H}$ and $y \in \mathcal{K}$. Since $\{x_i \oplus y_i\}_{i=1}^k$ is the image of a Parseval frame under an invertible operator, it will span the Hilbert space and (since the spaces are finite-dimensional) will be a frame for $\mathcal{H} \oplus \mathcal{K}$. □

We remark that for general frames, the condition that $\{x_i \oplus y_i\}_{i=1}^k$ is a frame for $\mathcal{H} \oplus \mathcal{K}$ does not imply the orthogonality of the two frames. We will explore this issue in more detail in the next section.

The following corollary is useful in applications such as the multiplexing technique described in Section 6.5. It is also interesting mathematically that orthogonal frames have a common dual frame.

Corollary 6.13. *If $\{x_i\}_{i=1}^k$ and $\{y_i\}_{i=1}^k$ are two orthogonal frames for the same Hilbert space $\mathcal{H}$, then they have a common dual frame.*

Proof. Let $u_i = S_x^{-1}x_i + S_y^{-1}y_i$ for $1 \le i \le k$, where S_x and S_y are the frame operators for $\{x_i\}_{i=1}^k$ and $\{y_i\}_{i=1}^k$, respectively. Note that the orthogonality of the range spaces of the analysis operators Θ_x and Θ_y implies that $\langle \Theta_x u, \Theta_y v \rangle = 0$ for all $u, v \in \mathcal{H}$. This readily yields the following:

$$\sum_{i=1}^k \langle v, x_i \rangle y_i = 0 = \sum_{i=1}^k \langle v, y_i \rangle x_i \qquad \forall v \in \mathcal{H}.$$

Since we know (from Exercise 11) that the analysis operator of the set $\{S_x^{-1}x_i\}_{i=1}^k$ has the same range as Θ_x and the analysis operator of $\{S_y^{-1}y_i\}_{i=1}^k$ has the same range as Θ_y, we also have that $\{x_i\}_{i=1}^k$ is orthogonal to $\{S_y^{-1}y_i\}_{i=1}^k$ and that $\{y_i\}_{i=1}^k$ is orthogonal to $\{S_x^{-1}x_i\}_{i=1}^k$. Therefore,

$$\sum_{i=1}^k \langle v, S_x^{-1}x_i \rangle y_i = 0 = \sum_{i=1}^k \langle v, S_y^{-1}y_i \rangle x_i \qquad \forall v \in \mathcal{H}.$$

Therefore for each $v \in \mathcal{H}$ we have

$$\begin{aligned}
\sum_{i=1}^k \langle v, u_i \rangle x_i &= \sum_{i=1}^k \langle v, S_x^{-1}x_i + S_y^{-1}y_i \rangle x_i \\
&= \sum_{i=1}^k \langle v, S_x^{-1}x_i \rangle x_i + \sum_{i=1}^k \langle v, S_y^{-1}y_i \rangle x_i \\
&= \sum_{i=1}^k \langle v, S_x^{-1}x_i \rangle x_i + 0 \\
&= v
\end{aligned}$$

and similarly

$$\sum_{i=1}^k \langle v, u_i \rangle y_i = v.$$

Hence $\{u_i\}_{i=1}^k$ is a common dual frame for both $\{x_i\}_{i=1}^k$ and $\{y_i\}_{i=1}^k$. □

The following is an interpolation result for orthogonal Parseval frames. In other words, it describes how orthogonal Parseval frame sequences can be combined to form new Parseval frames.

Proposition 6.14. *Suppose that $\{x_i\}_{i=1}^k$ and $\{y_i\}_{i=1}^k$ are orthogonal Parseval frames for $\mathcal{H}$ and V_1 and V_2 are linear operators on $\mathcal{H}$ such that $V_1V_1^* + V_2V_2^* = I$. Then $\{V_1x_i + V_2y_i\}_{i=1}^k$ is a Parseval frame for $\mathcal{H}$. In particular $\{\alpha x_i + \beta y_i\}_{i=1}^k$ is a Parseval frame whenever α and β are scalars such that $|\alpha|^2 + |\beta|^2 = 1$.*

Proof. Let $\{e_i\}_{i=1}^k$ be the standard orthonormal basis for $\mathbb{C}^k$, and let Θ_x and Θ_y be the analysis operators for $\{x_i\}_{i=1}^k$ and $\{y_i\}_{i=1}^k$, respectively. Then Θ_x and Θ_y are isometries with orthogonal ranges such that $\Theta_x^*e_i = x_i$ and $\Theta_y^*e_i = y_i$. Let $T = V_1\Theta_x^* + V_2\Theta_y^*$. Then T is a linear operator from $\mathbb{C}^k$ to $\mathcal{H}$. Since $\Theta_x^*\Theta_y = \Theta_y^*\Theta_x = 0$, we have

$$TT^* = V_1\Theta_x^*\Theta_xV_1^* + V_2\Theta_y^*\Theta_yV_2^* = V_1V_2^* + V_1V_2^* = I.$$

Let Θ be the analysis operator for $\{V_1x_i + V_2y_i\}_{i=1}^k$. A direct calculation shows that $\Theta = T^*$. So $\Theta^*\Theta = I$ which implies both that T is a co-isometry operator and that $\{V_1x_i + V_2y_i\}_{i=1}^k$ is a Parseval frame for $\mathcal{H}$. □

Just as we can discuss a finite collection of orthogonal vectors in $\mathcal{H}$, we can extend the concept of two orthogonal frames to a collection of L orthogonal frames for $L > 2$. From this, it is possible to generalize the above orthogonality results to L-tuples of frames. The details are left to Exercise 6.

There is a restriction on the number of vectors that must be present in each frame within an L-tuple of orthogonal frames for a Hilbert space $\mathcal{H}$. This restriction comes from the dimension of $\mathbb{C}^k$.

Proposition 6.15. *Let $\mathcal{H}$ be a Hilbert space with* $\dim \mathcal{H} = n$. *If there exists an L-tuple of orthogonal frames $\{x_i^{(\ell)}\}_{i=1}^k$, $\ell = 1, 2, \ldots, L$ for $\mathcal{H}$, then $k \geq nL$.*

Proof. Let Θ_ℓ be the analysis operator for $\{x_i^{(\ell)}\}_{i=1}^k$ for each $\ell = 1, 2, \ldots, L$. Each $\{x_i^{(\ell)}\}_{i=1}^k$ is a frame, which means that $\dim \Theta_\ell(\mathcal{H}) = n$. Because the L subspaces $\Theta_1(\mathcal{H}), \Theta_2(\mathcal{H}), \ldots, \Theta_L(\mathcal{H})$ of $\mathbb{C}^k$ are orthogonal, we must have $k \geq \sum_{\ell=1}^L \dim \Theta_\ell(\mathcal{H}) = nL$. □

6.4. Disjoint Frames

From Corollary 6.12 we know that the orthogonal direct sum of two orthogonal frames must be a frame for the direct sum space. This property holds for a much weaker condition than orthogonality. We introduce the concept of disjoint frames.

Definition 6.16. Let $\{x_i\}_{i=1}^k \subset \mathcal{H}$ and $\{y_i\}_{i=1}^k \subset \mathcal{K}$, and let Θ_x and Θ_y be their respective analysis operators. Then the finite sequences $\{x_i\}_{i=1}^k$ and $\{y_i\}_{i=1}^k$ are called *disjoint* if $\Theta_x(\mathcal{H}) \cap \Theta_y(\mathcal{K}) = \{0\}$. If $\{x_i\}_{i=1}^k$ and $\{y_i\}_{i=1}^k$ are also frames for $\mathcal{H}$ and $\mathcal{K}$ respectively, then they are called *disjoint frames*.

Clearly, orthogonal frames are disjoint. We first prove that the sum of two disjoint frame sequences for the same Hilbert space $\mathcal{H}$ is again a frame for $\mathcal{H}$. As part of this proof, we will need the result from Exercise 13.

Proposition 6.17. *If $\{x_i\}_{i=1}^k$ and $\{y_i\}_{i=1}^k$ are disjoint frames for $\mathcal{H}$, then $\{x_i + y_i\}_{i=1}^k$ is also a frame for $\mathcal{H}$.*

Proof. Let Θ_x and Θ_y be the analysis operators for $\{x_i\}$ and $\{y_i\}$, respectively. Then $x_i = \Theta_x^* e_i$ and $y_i = \Theta_y^* e_i$ for $1 \leq i \leq k$, where $\{e_i\}$ is the standard orthonormal basis for $\mathbb{C}^k$. Thus for any $v \in \mathcal{H}$, we have

$$\begin{aligned}
\sum_{i=1}^k |\langle v,\ x_i + y_i \rangle|^2 &= \sum_{i=1}^k |\langle v, \Theta_x^* e_i + \Theta_y^* e_i \rangle|^2 \\
&= \sum_{i=1}^k |\langle \Theta_x v + \Theta_y v,\ e_i \rangle|^2 \\
&= \|\Theta_x v + \Theta_y v\|^2 .
\end{aligned}$$

Since $\Theta_1(\mathcal{H}) \cap \Theta_2(\mathcal{H}) = \{0\}$, by Exercise 13, there exists a positive constant A such that

$$\|\Theta_x u + \Theta_y v\|^2 \geq A\left(\|\Theta_x u\|^2 + \|\Theta_y v\|^2\right)$$

for all $u, v \in \mathcal{H}$. Also note that if A_1, B_1 and A_2, B_2 are frame bounds for $\{x_i\}_{i=1}^k$ and $\{y_i\}_{i=1}^k$, respectively, then

$$A_1\|x\|^2 \leq \|\Theta_x x\|^2 \leq B_1\|x\|^2$$

and

$$A_2\|x\|^2 \leq \|\Theta_y x\|^2 \leq B_2\|x\|^2$$

for all $x \in \mathcal{H}$. It can then be shown that for all $x \in \mathcal{H}$,

$$A(A_1 + A_2)\|x\|^2 \leq \sum_i |\langle x,\ x_i + y_i \rangle|^2 \leq (\sqrt{B_1} + \sqrt{B_2})^2\|x\|^2. \tag{6.3}$$

(The proof of Equation (6.3) is left to Exercise 4.) Therefore, $\{x_i + y_i\}_{i=1}^k$ is a frame for $\mathcal{H}$. □

The following theorem tells us that the difference between "disjoint" and "orthogonal" frames can be characterized by the canonical dual of the direct sum of the frames.

Remark 6.18. In the following theorem, we will use the notation $\{x_i^*\}_{i=1}^k$ to represent the canonical dual of a frame $\{x_i\}_{i=1}^k$, so that $x_i^* = S^{-1}x_i, i = 1, 2, \ldots, k$, where S is the frame operator of $\{x_i\}_{i=1}^k$. This is standard notation for the canonical dual frame. It should not be confused with our previous usage of the asterisk on a vector $x \in \mathbb{C}^n$ where we thought of x as an operator from $\mathbb{C}^1$ to $\mathbb{C}^k$, so that the asterisk indicated the adjoint. In other words, in that usage, $x^* = \overline{x}^T$. It should always be clear from the context which use of the asterisk is intended, but we will make a point of mentioning the definition when we are describing the canonical dual frame.

Theorem 6.19. *Let $\{x_i\}_{i=1}^k$ and $\{y_i\}_{i=1}^k$ be frames for $\mathcal{H}$ and $\mathcal{K}$, respectively. Also let $\{x_i^*\}_{i=1}^k$ and $\{y_i^*\}_{i=1}^k$ be their respective canonical dual frames. Then the following statements hold.*

(i) *$\{x_i\}_{i=1}^k$ and $\{y_i\}_{i=1}^k$ are disjoint if and only if $\{x_i \oplus y_i\}_{i=1}^k$ is a frame for $\mathcal{H} \oplus \mathcal{K}$.*

(ii) *$\{x_i\}_{i=1}^k$ and $\{y_i\}_{i=1}^k$ are orthogonal if and only if $\{x_i \oplus y_i\}_{i=1}^k$ is a frame for $\mathcal{H} \oplus \mathcal{K}$ and $(x_i \oplus y_i)^* = x_i^* \oplus y_i^*$ for each $i = 1, 2, \ldots, k$.*

Proof. Let Θ_x and Θ_y be the analysis operators for $\{x_i\}_{i=1}^k$ and $\{y_i\}_{i=1}^k$, respectively. Then $x_i = \Theta_x^* e_i$ and $y_i = \Theta_y^* e_i$ for $1 \le i \le k$, where $\{e_i\}_{i=1}^k$ is the standard orthonormal basis for $\mathbb{C}^k$.

First, we prove (i). For any $u \in \mathcal{H}$ and $v \in \mathcal{K}$, we have that

$$\begin{aligned}
\sum_{i=1}^k |\langle u \oplus v, x_i \oplus y_i \rangle|^2 &= \sum_{i=1}^k |\langle u, x_i \rangle + \langle v, y_i \rangle|^2 \\
&= \sum_{i=1}^k \left|\langle u, \Theta_x^* e_i \rangle + \langle v, \Theta_y^* e_i \rangle\right|^2 \\
&= \sum_{i=1}^k |\langle \Theta_x u, e_i \rangle + \langle \Theta_y v, e_i \rangle|^2 \\
&= \sum_{i=1}^k |\langle \Theta_x u + \Theta_y v, e_i \rangle|^2 \\
&= \|\Theta_x u + \Theta_y v\|^2.
\end{aligned}$$

From Exercise 13, we have that $\Theta_x(\mathcal{H}) \cap \Theta_y(\mathcal{K}) = \{0\}$ if and only if there exists a constant $K > 0$ such that

$$\|\Theta_x u + \Theta_y v\|^2 \ge K(\|\Theta_x u\|^2 + \|\Theta_y v\|^2)$$

for all $u \in \mathcal{H}$ and $v \in \mathcal{K}$.

A quick calculation using the inner product definition of the norm will show the Parallelogram Identity: for all $u, v \in \mathcal{H}$, $\|u + v\|^2 + \|u - v\|^2 = 2(\|u\|^2 + \|v\|^2)$. From this, we readily see that for all $u \in \mathcal{H}$, $v \in \mathcal{K}$,

$$\|\Theta_x u + \Theta_y v\|^2 \le 2(\|\Theta_x u\|^2 + \|\Theta_y v\|^2).$$

Therefore, if we assume that $\{x_i\}$ and $\{y_i\}$ are disjoint, we have for any $u \in \mathcal{H}$ and $v \in \mathcal{K}$,

$$\begin{aligned}\sum_{i=1}^{k} |\langle u \oplus v, x_i \oplus y_i \rangle|^2 &= \|\Theta_x u + \Theta_y v\|^2 \\ &\geq K(\|\Theta_x u\|^2 + \|\Theta_y v\|^2) \\ &\geq KA(\|u\|^2 + \|v\|^2)\| \\ &= KA\|u \oplus v\|^2,\end{aligned}$$

where A is the minimum of the lower frame bounds of $\{x_i\}_{i=1}^k$ and $\{y_i\}_{i=1}^k$. Similarly, we have

$$\begin{aligned}\sum_{i=1}^{k} |\langle u \oplus v, x_i \oplus y_i \rangle|^2 &= \|\Theta_x u + \Theta_y v\|^2 \\ &\leq 2(\|\Theta_x u\|^2 + \|\Theta_y v\|^2) \\ &\leq 2B(\|u\|^2 + \|v\|^2)\| \\ &= 2B\|u \oplus v\|^2,\end{aligned}$$

where B is the maximum of the upper frame bounds of $\{x_i\}_{i=1}^k$ and $\{y_i\}_{i=1}^k$. These combine to prove that $\{x_i \oplus y_i\}_{i=1}^k$ is a frame for $\mathcal{H} \oplus \mathcal{K}$.

To prove the converse, suppose that $\{x_i \oplus y_i\}_{i=1}^k$ is a frame for $\mathcal{H} \oplus \mathcal{K}$. Then there exist constants $C, D > 0$ such that for all $u \in \mathcal{H}, v \in \mathcal{K}$:

$$C\|u \oplus v\|^2 \leq \sum_{i=1}^{k} |\langle u \oplus v, x_i \oplus y_i \rangle|^2 = \|\Theta_x u + \Theta_y v\|^2 \leq D\|u \oplus v\|^2.$$

This inequality implies that $\{x_i\}_{i=1}^k$ and $\{y_i\}_{i=1}^k$ are disjoint, since otherwise there would exist some $u_0 \in \mathcal{H}$ and some $v_0 \in \mathcal{K}$ such that $\Theta_x u_0 = \Theta_y v_0 \neq 0$. This would imply

$$0 < C\|u_0 \oplus (-v_0)\|^2 \leq \|\Theta_x u_0 + \Theta_2(-v_0)\|^2 = 0,$$

which is a contradiction. This completes the proof of the first part of the theorem.

Next, we prove (ii). Assume that $\{x_i\}_{i=1}^k$ and $\{y_i\}_{i=1}^k$ are orthogonal frames. Let $S_x = \Theta_x^* \Theta_x$ and $S_y = \Theta_y^* \Theta_y$ be their respective frame operators. Then, let Θ and S be the analysis operator and frame operator for $\{x_i \oplus y_i\}_{i=1}^k$. Since the frames are orthogonal, they are disjoint and therefore by part (i) of this theorem, $\{x_i \oplus y_i\}_{i=1}^k$ is a frame for $\mathcal{H} \oplus \mathcal{K}$. From the orthogonality of the two frames, we also have that

$$\Theta_x^* \Theta_y = \Theta_y^* \Theta_x = 0.$$

Thus, for any $u \in \mathcal{H}$ and $v \in \mathcal{K}$, we have

$$\begin{aligned}
S(u \oplus v) &= \Theta^* \Theta(u \oplus v) \\
&= \sum_{i=1}^{k} \langle u \oplus v, x_i \oplus y_i \rangle (x_i \oplus y_i) \\
&= \sum_{i=1}^{k} (\langle u, x_i \rangle + \langle v, y_i \rangle)(x_i \oplus y_i) \\
&= \sum_{i=1}^{k} (\langle u, x_i \rangle + \langle v, y_i \rangle) x_i \oplus \sum_{i=1}^{k} (\langle u, x_i \rangle + \langle v, y_i \rangle) y_i \\
&= \Theta_x^* \Theta_x u + \Theta_x^* \Theta_y v \oplus \Theta_y^* \Theta_x u + \Theta_y^* \Theta_x v \\
&= S_x u \oplus S_y v.
\end{aligned}$$

Therefore $S = S_x \oplus S_y$, which implies that for each $i = 1, 2, \ldots, k$,

$$(x_i \oplus y_i)^* = S^{-1}(x_i \oplus y_i) = S_1^{-1} x_i \oplus S_2^{-1} y_i = x_i^* \oplus y_i^*,$$

which is what we needed to prove.

To show the converse direction, assume that $\{x_i \oplus y_i\}_{i=1}^k$ is a frame for $\mathcal{H} \oplus \mathcal{K}$, and that its canonical dual frame is given by $(x_i \oplus y_i)^* = x_i^* \oplus y_i^*$ for all $1 \leq i \leq k$. This implies that $S^{-1} = S_x^{-1} \oplus S_y^{-1}$. From this, we have that $\{S^{-\frac{1}{2}}(x_i \oplus y_i)\}_{i=1}^k = \{S_x^{-\frac{1}{2}} x_i \oplus S_y^{-\frac{1}{2}} y_i\}_{i=1}^k$ is a Parseval frame for $\mathcal{H} \oplus \mathcal{K}$. So, by Theorem 6.11, $\{S_x^{-\frac{1}{2}} x_i\}_{i=1}^k$ and $\{S_y^{-\frac{1}{2}} y_i\}_{i=1}^k$ are orthogonal Parseval frames, which is equivalent to the orthogonality of the frames $\{x_i\}_{i=1}^k$ and $\{y_i\}_{i=1}^k$ by Exercise 11. □

6.5. Super-Frames and Multiplexing

Orthogonal frames have potential applications to data transmission making use of a technique called multiplexing, which we introduce in this section. To demonstrate, suppose that $\{x_i\}_{i=1}^k$ is a Parseval frame for a Hilbert space $\mathcal{H}$ and we want to transmit L vectors $\{f_1, f_2, \ldots, f_L\}$ (which we could call "signals"). This really involves computing and transmitting the coefficients for constructing the signals in terms of the Parseval frame vectors. To do this we would need to send each coefficient $\langle f_l, x_i \rangle$, for a total of $L \cdot k$ transmissions.

Now, suppose that we don't just have a single Parseval frame, but we actually have an L-tuple of orthogonal Parseval frames $\{x_i^{(\ell)}\}_{i=1}^k$ where $\ell = 1, 2, \ldots, L$ for our Hilbert space $\mathcal{H}$, and we are planning to transmit those same L signals $f_1, f_2, \ldots, f_L$ from $\mathcal{H}$. By using the orthogonality of these frames, it turns out that we can actually send a single set of k coefficients which will reconstruct *each* of the signals. This is the idea behind multiplexing of data.

Specifically, we let $c_i = \sum_{\ell=1}^L \left\langle f_\ell, x_i^{(\ell)} \right\rangle$. Rather than transmitting all the $L{\cdot}k$ coefficients $\{\langle f_\ell, x_i \rangle\}$, we can just send the coefficients $\{c_j\}_{j=1}^k$. By the orthogonality of the frames, we have

$$\sum_{i=1}^k \left\langle f_j, x_i^{(j)} \right\rangle x_i^{(\ell)} = 0$$

when $j \neq \ell$. (This is exactly $\Theta_\ell^* \Theta_j f_j = 0$ for $j \neq \ell$ from Lemma 6.10.) Therefore, for each $\ell = 1, 2, \ldots, L$,

$$\begin{aligned}
f_\ell &= \sum_{i=1}^k \left\langle f_\ell, x_i^{(\ell)} \right\rangle x_i^{(\ell)} \\
&= \sum_{j=1}^L \sum_{i=1}^k \left\langle f_j, x_i^{(j)} \right\rangle x_i^{(\ell)} \\
&= \sum_{i=1}^k \left(\sum_{j=1}^L \left\langle f_j, x_i^{(j)} \right\rangle \right) x_i^{(\ell)} \\
&= \sum_{i=1}^k c_i x_i^{(\ell)}.
\end{aligned}$$

Thus, when we transmit the set of $\{c_i\}_{i=1}^k$, they can be used to reconstruct each of the signals $f_1, f_2, \ldots, f_L$.

The concept of multiplexing motivates the definition of a super-frame.

Definition 6.20. Let $\{x_i^{(\ell)}\}_{i=1}^k \subset \mathcal{H}_\ell$ for each $\ell = 1, 2, \ldots, L$. The L-tuple of sequences $(\{x_i^{(1)}\}_{i=1}^k, \{x_i^{(2)}\}_{i=1}^k, \ldots, \{x_i^{(L)}\}_{i=1}^k)$ is called a *Parseval super-frame* if $\{x_i^{(1)} \oplus x_i^{(2)} \oplus \cdots \oplus x_i^{(L)}\}_{i=1}^k$ is a Parseval frame for the super-space $\mathcal{H}_1 \oplus \mathcal{H}_2 \oplus \cdots \oplus \mathcal{H}_L$. It is called a *super orthonormal basis* if $\{x_i^{(1)} \oplus x_i^{(2)} \oplus \cdots \oplus x_i^{(L)}\}_{i=1}^k$ is an orthonormal basis for $\mathcal{H}_1 \oplus \mathcal{H}_2 \oplus \cdots \oplus \mathcal{H}_L$.

Using this definition, if $(\{x_i^{(1)}\}_{i=1}^k, \{x_i^{(2)}\}_{i=1}^k, \ldots, \{x_i^{(L)}\}_{i=1}^k)$ is a Parseval super-frame, then $\{x_i^{(1)} \oplus x_i^{(2)} \oplus \cdots \oplus x_i^{(L)}\}_{i=1}^k$ is a Parseval frame for $\mathcal{H}_1 \oplus \mathcal{H}_2 \oplus \cdots \oplus \mathcal{H}_L$. By taking orthogonal projections onto the component spaces $\mathcal{H}_\ell$, we get from Proposition 5.1 that each $\{x_i^{(\ell)}\}_{i=1}^k$ is a Parseval frame for $\mathcal{H}_\ell$, and moreover, we can show that these Parseval frames are orthogonal. This leads to the following proposition, whose proof is left to Exercise 7.

Proposition 6.21. *Let $\{x_i^{(\ell)}\}_{i=1}^k \subset \mathcal{H}_\ell$ for each $\ell = 1, 2, \ldots, L$ and let Θ_ℓ be the corresponding analysis operator. Then the following are equivalent:*

(i) *$(\{x_i^{(1)}\}_{i=1}^k, \{x_i^{(2)}\}_{i=1}^k, \ldots, \{x_i^{(L)}\}_{i=1}^k)$ is a Parseval super-frame.*

(ii) *$(\{x_i^{(1)}\}_{i=1}^k, \{x_i^{(2)}\}_{i=1}^k, \ldots, \{x_i^{(L)}\}_{i=1}^k)$ is an L-tuple of orthogonal Parseval frames.*

(iii) *$\Theta_\ell^*\Theta_\ell = I$ for each $\ell = 1, 2, \ldots, L$, and $\Theta_\ell^*\Theta_j = 0$ when $\ell \neq j$.*

6.6. Parseval Dual Frames

Parseval frames have many nice features useful for applications, including the clear computational advantage when computing reconstruction coefficients. If a frame $\{x_i\}_{i=1}^k$ is a basis which is not a tight frame, then we know from Proposition 6.2 that it has a unique dual frame which also fails to be a tight frame. However, if a frame $\{x_i\}_{i=1}^k$ is not a basis, then it has many alternate dual frames. This leads to a natural question: Given a frame $\{x_i\}_{i=1}^k$ which is not a basis, can we always find a dual frame which is a tight frame? We will address this question in this section.

Assume that a frame $\{x_i\}_{i=1}^k$ has a dual frame $\{y_i\}_{i=1}^k$ which is A-tight. Then $\{\frac{1}{\sqrt{A}}y_i\}_{i=1}^k$ will be a Parseval frame and is a dual frame for the re-scaled frame $\{\sqrt{A}x_i\}_{i=1}^k$. Therefore, we can focus on determining conditions under which a frame has a dual frame which is a Parseval frame.

Definition 6.22. A dual frame which is also Parseval is called a *Parseval dual* frame.

It turns out that the existence of a Parseval dual frame is related to the frame dilation result which we studied in Section 5.3.

Theorem 6.23. *Let $\{x_i\}_{i=1}^k$ be a frame for a Hilbert space $\mathcal{H}$. Then the following statements are equivalent:*

(i) *The frame $\{x_i\}_{i=1}^k$ has a Parseval dual frame.*

(ii) *There exists a Hilbert space $\mathcal{K} \supseteq \mathcal{H}$, an orthonormal basis $\{u_i\}_{i=1}^k$ for $\mathcal{K}$, and an oblique projection Q such that $Qu_i = x_i$ for each $i = 1, 2, \ldots, k$ and $Q(\mathcal{K}) = \mathcal{H}$.*

Recall that an *oblique projection* is an operator Q which is an idempotent; i.e., $Q^2 = Q$. It is not necessarily self-adjoint, and therefore it is not necessarily an orthogonal projection.

Proof. (i)$\rightarrow$(ii): Let $\{y_i\}_{i=1}^k$ be a Parseval dual frame for $\{x_i\}_{i=1}^k$. Then by the dilation result from Proposition 5.5 there exists a Hilbert space $\mathcal{K} \supseteq \mathcal{H}$ and an orthonormal basis $\{u_i\}_{i=1}^k$ for $\mathcal{K}$ such that $Pu_i = y_i$, $i = 1, 2, \ldots, k$, where P is the orthogonal projection from $\mathcal{K}$ onto $\mathcal{H}$. Define Q on $\mathcal{K}$ by

$$Qx = \sum_{i=1}^{k} \langle x, u_i \rangle x_i.$$

Then $Qu_j = \sum_{i=1}^k \langle u_j, u_i \rangle x_i = x_j$ since $\{u_i\}_{i=1}^k$ is an orthonormal basis for $\mathcal{K}$. Now we check that Q is an oblique projection with $Q(\mathcal{K}) = \mathcal{H}$. For any $x \in \mathcal{H}$, we have $Px = x$, and the following computation shows that we also have $Qx = x$.

$$\begin{aligned} Qx &= \sum_{i=1}^{k} \langle x, u_i \rangle x_i \\ &= \sum_{i=1}^{k} \langle Px, u_i \rangle x_i \\ &= \sum_{i=1}^{k} \langle x, Pu_i \rangle x_i \qquad \text{since } P \text{ is self-adjoint} \\ &= \sum_{i=1}^{k} \langle x, y_i \rangle x_i = x. \end{aligned}$$

The last line above holds since $\{y_i\}_{i=1}^k$ is a dual frame for $\{x_i\}_{i=1}^k$.

It is clear from the definition that $Q(\mathcal{K}) \subseteq \mathcal{H}$. Combining this with $Qx = x$ for all $x \in \mathcal{H}$, we get that $Q(\mathcal{K}) = \mathcal{H}$. Moreover, $Q^2u = Q(Qu) = Qu$ for all $u \in \mathcal{K}$ since $Qu \in \mathcal{H}$. Thus $Q^2 = Q$, as required.

(ii)$\rightarrow$(i): Let $y_i = PQ^*u_i$ for $i = 1, 2, \ldots, k$, where again P is the orthogonal projection from $\mathcal{K}$ onto $\mathcal{H}$. Then each $y_i \in \mathcal{H}$ and for each $x \in \mathcal{H}$ we have

$$\begin{aligned} x = Q(QPx) &= Q \sum_{i=1}^{k} \langle QPx, u_i \rangle u_i \\ &= \sum_{i=1}^{k} \langle x, PQ^*u_i \rangle Qu_i \\ &= \sum_{i=1}^{k} \langle x, y_i \rangle x_i. \end{aligned}$$

Therefore, we know that $\{y_i\}_{i=1}^k$ is a dual frame for $\{x_i\}_{i=1}^k$. Additionally, we have for all $x \in \mathcal{H}$,

$$\begin{aligned} \|x\|^2 &= \sum_{i=1}^{k} |\langle x, u_i \rangle|^2 \\ &= \sum_{i=1}^{k} |\langle Qx, u_i \rangle|^2 \end{aligned}$$

The last equality holds because for all $x \in \mathcal{H}$, we have $Qx = x$. We can then use the adjoint of Q and the fact that $Px = x$ to compute:

$$\begin{aligned}
\|x\|^2 &= \sum_{i=1}^{k} |\langle x, Q^* u_i \rangle|^2 \\
&= \sum_{i=1}^{k} |\langle Px, Q^* u_i \rangle|^2 \\
&= \sum_{i=1}^{k} |\langle x, PQ^* u_i \rangle|^2 \\
&= \sum_{i=1}^{k} |\langle x, y_i \rangle|^2.
\end{aligned}$$

This computation verifies that $\{y_i\}_{i=1}^k$ is a Parseval dual frame for $\{x_i\}_{i=1}^k$. □

Proposition 6.24. *Let $\{x_i\}_{i=1}^k$ be a frame for a Hilbert space $\mathcal{H}$, and let Θ be its analysis operator. If $\|(\Theta^*\Theta)^{-1}\| \leq 1$ and $\dim \Theta(\mathcal{H})^\perp \geq \dim \mathcal{H}$, then $\{x_i\}_{i=1}^k$ has a Parseval dual frame.*

Proof. Although this follows from Theorem 5.13 and Theorem 6.23, we include a direct proof for perspective. Let $S = \Theta^*\Theta$ be the frame operator for $\{x_i\}_{i=1}^k$. Since $\dim(\Theta(\mathcal{H})^\perp) \geq \dim \mathcal{H}$, we can choose a subspace N of $\Theta(\mathcal{H})^\perp$ such that $\dim N = \dim \mathcal{H}$. Let $W : N \to \mathcal{H}$ be a fixed unitary operator, and let $w_i = WPe_i$, $i = 1, 2, \ldots, k$, where P is the orthogonal projection from $\mathbb{C}^k$ onto N and $\{e_i\}_{i=1}^k$ is the standard orthonormal basis for $\mathbb{C}^k$. We can show that $\{w_i\}_{i=1}^k$ is a Parseval frame for $\mathcal{H}$ and is orthogonal to $\{x_i\}_{i=1}^k$. First, for every $x \in \mathcal{H}$, we have

$$\begin{aligned}
\sum_{i=1}^{k} |\langle x, w_i \rangle|^2 &= \sum_{i=1}^{k} |\langle x, WPe_i \rangle|^2 \\
&= \sum_{i=1}^{k} |\langle PW^* x, e_i \rangle|^2 \\
&= \|PW^* x\|^2 = \|x\|^2,
\end{aligned}$$

where we use the fact that $PW^*x = W^*x$ and W^* is unitary. Therefore, $\{w_i\}_{i=1}^k$ is a Parseval frame for $\mathcal{H}$.

For the orthogonality part, let Θ_w be the analysis operator for $\{w_i\}_{i=1}^k$. For any $x \in \mathcal{H}$, we have

$$\begin{aligned}\Theta_w x = \sum_{i=1}^{k} \langle x, w_i \rangle e_i &= \sum_{i=1}^{k} \langle PW^* x, e_i \rangle e_i \\ &= PW^* x \in N \subseteq \Theta(\mathcal{H})^{\perp}.\end{aligned}$$

Therefore $\Theta(\mathcal{H})$ and $\Theta_w(\mathcal{H})$ are orthogonal, which implies that $\{w_i\}_{i=1}^k$ and $\{x_i\}_{i=1}^k$ are orthogonal frames. We will use $\{w_i\}_{i=1}^k$ to construct a Parseval frame which is a dual frame to $\{x_i\}_{i=1}^k$.

Using the hypothesis that $\|S^{-1}\| \le 1$, we note that $I - S^{-1}$ is a positive operator. To verify this, we have

$$\langle (I - S^{-1})x, x \rangle = \|x\|^2 - \langle S^{-1}x, x \rangle \ge (1 - \|S^{-1}\|)\, \|x\|^2 \ge 0.$$

Therefore, we can define the operator $B = \sqrt{I - S^{-1}}$. Then $\{Bw_i\}_{i=1}^k$ is also orthogonal to $\{x_i\}_{i=1}^k$. (We leave the proof of this to Exercise 8.) Let T be the analysis operator for $\{S^{-1}x_i + Bw_i\}_{i=1}^k$. Then we have

$$\begin{aligned}T^*Tx &= \sum_{i=1}^{k} \langle x, S^{-1}x_i + Bw_i \rangle (S^{-1}x_i + Bw_i) \\ &= \sum_{i=1}^{k} \langle x, S^{-1}x_i \rangle S^{-1}x_i + \sum_{i=1}^{k} \langle x, Bw_i \rangle Bw_i \\ &= \sum_{i=1}^{k} \langle S^{-1}x, x_i \rangle S^{-1}x_i + B\left(\sum_{i=1}^{k} \langle Bx, w_i \rangle w_i\right) \\ &= S^{-1}x + B^2 x,\end{aligned}$$

where we use the orthogonality of the frames and the facts that $\{S^{-1}x_i\}_{i=1}^k$ is a dual frame for $\{x_i\}_{i=1}^k$ and that $\{w_i\}_{i=1}^k$ is a Parseval frame to prove this equation. Therefore, we have

$$T^*T = S^{-1} + B^2 = I.$$

This proves that $\{S^{-1}x_i + Bw_i\}_{i=1}^k$ is a Parseval frame for $\mathcal{H}$. Moreover, for every $x \in \mathcal{H}$, we have that

$$\begin{aligned}\sum_{i=1}^k \langle x, S^{-1}x_i + Bw_i \rangle x_i &= \sum_{i=1}^k \langle x, x_i \rangle x_i + \sum_{i=1}^k \langle x, Bw_i \rangle x_i \\ &= x + 0 = x.\end{aligned}$$

Therefore $\{S^{-1}x_i + Bw_i\}_{i=1}^k$ is also a dual frame, and thus is a Parseval dual frame for $\{x_i\}_{i=1}^k$. □

6.7. Exercises from the Text

Exercise 1. Let $\mathcal{H}$ be a Hilbert space and let $\{x_i\}_{i=1}^k$ be a basis for $\mathcal{H}$. Let S be the frame operator for $\{x_i\}_{i=1}^k$. Prove that the canonical dual frame $\{S^{-1}x_i\}_{i=1}^k$ is bi-orthogonal to $\{x_i\}_{i=1}^k$, which means that

$$\langle x_i, S^{-1}x_i \rangle = 1 \quad \text{and} \quad \langle x_i, S^{-1}x_j \rangle = 0 \quad \text{if } i \neq j.$$

Exercise 2. Prove Theorem 6.5.

Exercise 3. Prove Corollary 6.6.

Exercise 4. Complete the proof of Proposition 6.17 by demonstrating the inequality in Equation (6.3).

Exercise 5. Prove Lemma 6.10.

Exercise 6. Give the definition of orthogonality for an L-tuple of frames. (Use as a model the definition of orthogonality of L elements in a Hilbert space.) Then generalize Lemma 6.10, Theorem 6.11, Corollary 6.13, and Proposition 6.14 to the case of an L-tuple of frames.

Exercise 7. Prove Proposition 6.21.

Exercise 8. Let $\{x_i\}_{i=1}^k$ be a frame for a Hilbert space $\mathcal{H}$ with frame operator S. Suppose the hypotheses in Proposition 6.24 hold. Let $B = \sqrt{I - S^{-1}}$ and $\{w_i\}$ be as in the proof of Proposition 6.24. Prove that $\{Bw_i\}_{i=1}^k$ and $\{x_i\}_{i=1}^k$ are orthogonal sequences.

6.8. Additional Exercises

Exercise 9. Prove that if $\{y_i\}_{i=1}^k$ is a dual frame for a frame $\{x_i\}_{i=1}^k$ in a Hilbert space $\mathcal{H}$, then $\{x_i\}_{i=1}^k$ is a dual frame for $\{y_i\}_{i=1}^k$.

Exercise 10. Find all the dual frames for the Parseval frame

$$\left\{ \sqrt{\frac{2}{3}} \begin{bmatrix} 1 \\ 0 \end{bmatrix}, \sqrt{\frac{2}{3}} \begin{bmatrix} -\frac{1}{2} \\ \frac{\sqrt{3}}{2} \end{bmatrix}, \sqrt{\frac{2}{3}} \begin{bmatrix} -\frac{1}{2} \\ -\frac{\sqrt{3}}{2} \end{bmatrix} \right\}.$$

Exercise 11. Let $\{x_i\}_{i=1}^k$ be a frame for $\mathcal{H}$ with analysis operator Θ_x and frame operator S. Then we know that $\{S^{-1}x_i\}_{i=1}^k$ is the canonical dual frame for $\{x_i\}_{i=1}^k$ and that $\{S^{-\frac{1}{2}}x_i\}_{i=1}^k$ is a Parseval frame for $\mathcal{H}$. Prove that the analysis operators for both sequences $\{Sx_i\}_{i=1}^k$ and $\{S^{-\frac{1}{2}}x_i\}_{i=1}^k$ have the same range as Θ_x.

Exercise 12. Let $\{x_i\}_{i=1}^k$ be a frame for a Hilbert space $\mathcal{H}$ with $\dim \mathcal{H} = n$. Suppose that the coordinate representation of x_i is

$$x_i = \begin{bmatrix} x_{i1} & x_{i2} & \cdots & x_{in} \end{bmatrix}^T$$

with respect to a fixed orthonormal basis for $\mathcal{H}$. Then the matrix form of the analysis operator Θ has row vectors $x_i^* = \overline{x_i}^T$. Suppose that T is an $n \times k$ matrix such that $T\Theta = I_n$. Let $y_1, y_2, \ldots, y_k$ be the column vectors of T. Prove that $\{y_i\}_{i=1}^k$ is a dual frame for $\{x_i\}_{i=1}^k$.

Exercise 13. Suppose that M and N are two subspaces in a finite-dimensional Hilbert space $\mathcal{H}$. Prove that $M \cap N = \{0\}$ if and only if there exists a constant $A > 0$ such that the inequality

$$\|x+y\|^2 \geq A\left(\|x\|^2 + \|y\|^2\right)$$

holds for all $x \in M$, $y \in N$.

Hint: For the forward direction, define a linear operator $T : M + N \to M \oplus N$ such that $T(x+y) = x \oplus y$, where $x \in M, y \in N$. Why is T well defined? Use T to find the constant A.

Exercise 14. Give an example of two frames which are disjoint but not orthogonal.

Exercise 15. (i) Generalize (with extra caution) the concept of two disjoint frames to a finite L-tuple of disjoint frames. The following two parts describe why this may be more tricky than it appears at first.

(ii) Construct three subspaces M_1, M_2, M_3 in a Hilbert space such that pairwise, they have trivial intersection $\{0\}$, but $M_1 \cap (M_2 + M_3) \neq \{0\}$.

(iii) Use part (ii) to show that three pairwise disjoint frames are not necessarily disjoint.

Chapter 7

Frame Operator Decompositions

We've made the statement in previous chapters that frames are more general that orthonormal bases, with the implication that there are "more" frames in some sense, and that they can take on a wider variety of properties. In this chapter, we will examine some interesting varieties of frames and the properties that frames and tight frames can attain in finite dimensions. Frames are being utilized in industries including cellular phones, medical imaging, and recognition and identification software. They also turn up in a variety of mathematical contexts. If frames are going to be useful in solving mathematical and industrial problems, we'd like them to come in a variety of types, so they can be selected and adjusted to suit each particular application.

The results in this chapter indicate that there are indeed many types of frames, having a variety of properties. We will investigate which sorts of frames can exist by clarifying the connection between a frame and its frame operator, and then applying matrix techniques to the frame operator. Most of these results are very new, published within 3–5 years of the writing of this book. Certainly the list is growing, and many more types of frames have since been explored.

7.1. Continuity of Eigenvalues

Before we can use properties of operators to explore varieties of frames, we will need to develop the result that the eigenvalues of an $n \times n$ matrix are continuous with respect to the operator norm. In other words, small changes in the eigenvalues of an operator result in small changes in its norm. This is an important and useful theorem from finite-dimensional operator theory, and will play a big role in the constructions presented later in the chapter.

First, recall from Section 2.10 that the operator norm of an $n \times n$ matrix A is given by

$$\|A\|_{\text{op}} = \sup_{\|x\|=1} \|Ax\|.$$

We can define a variety of other norms on $\mathbb{M}_n(\mathbb{C})$, the space of $n \times n$ matrices with complex entries. Given $A \in \mathbb{M}_n(\mathbb{C})$ with entries $a_{j,k}$, we have the following:

$$(7.1) \quad \|A\|_1 = \sum_{j=1}^{n} \sum_{k=1}^{n} |a_{jk}|,$$

$$(7.2) \quad \|A\|_2 = \|A\|_{\text{hs}} = \Big(\sum_{j=1}^{n} \sum_{k=1}^{n} |a_{jk}|^2 \Big)^{\frac{1}{2}} \quad \text{Hilbert-Schmidt norm,}$$

$$(7.3) \quad \|A\|_{\max} = \max\{|a_{jk}| \ : \ j,k = 1,2,\ldots,n\} \quad \text{Maximum norm.}$$

The proof that each of these do indeed satisfy the norm properties (recall Definition 1.63) is left for Exercise 3.

Remark 7.1. Notice that we give the definitions of the norms here without associating an inner product with them. Remember that while every inner product generates a norm $\|x\|^2 = \langle x, x \rangle$, it is not true that every norm arises from an inner product. A space which has a norm defined on it and which is complete in that norm (i.e., every Cauchy sequence converges) is called a Banach space. The spaces $\mathbb{M}_n(\mathbb{C}, \|\cdot\|_1)$, $\mathbb{M}_n(\mathbb{C}, \|\cdot\|_{\text{hs}})$, and $\mathbb{M}_n(\mathbb{C}, \|\cdot\|_{\max})$ are each Banach spaces.

Definition 7.2. Two norms $\|\cdot\|_a, \|\cdot\|_b$ on a vector space V are *equivalent* if there exist positive constants α, β such that for every

$x \in V$,

$$\alpha \|x\|_a \leq \|x\|_b \leq \beta \|x\|_a.$$

Norm equivalence does induce an equivalence relation among norms on a given space. It turns out that each of these norms given above and the operator norm all reside in the same equivalence class on $\mathbb{M}_n(\mathbb{C})$.

Lemma 7.3. *Each of the norms in Equations* (7.1), (7.2), *and* (7.3) *are equivalent to the operator norm on* $M_n(\mathbb{C})$.

Proof. We show the proof that the operator norm is equivalent to the 2-norm, or Hilbert-Schmidt norm, defined in Equation (7.2). We leave the other equivalences to Exercise 4. Let $A \in M_n(\mathbb{C})$ have entries $\{a_{jk}\}_{j,k=1}^n$.

We obtain one inequality using the Cauchy-Schwarz Inequality from Proposition 1.64.

$$\begin{aligned}
\|A\|_{\text{op}}^2 &= \sup_{\|x\|=1} \|Ax\|^2 \\
&= \sup_{\|x\|=1} \sum_{j=1}^n |\langle x, a_j \rangle|^2 && \text{where } \{a_j\} \text{ are rows of } A \\
&\leq \sup_{\|x\|=1} \sum_{j=1}^n \|x\|^2 \|a_j\|^2 && \text{by Cauchy-Schwarz} \\
&\leq \sum_{j=1}^n \|a_j\|^2 \\
&= \sum_{j=1}^n \sum_{k=1}^n |a_{jk}|^2 = \|A\|_{\text{hs}}^2.
\end{aligned}$$

The other inequality follows from applying A to the standard orthonormal basis vectors $\{e_j\}$. Notice that Ae_j is the vector which is the jth column of the matrix A.

$$\begin{aligned} n\|A\|_{\text{op}}^2 &= n \sup_{\|x\|=1} \|Ax\|^2 \\ &\geq n \sup_j \|Ae_j\|^2 \\ &\geq \sum_{j=1}^n \|Ae_j\|^2 \\ &= \sum_{j=1}^n \sum_{k=1}^n |a_{jk}|^2 = \|A\|_{\text{hs}}^2. \end{aligned}$$

Together, these inequalities give

$$\|A\|_{\text{op}} \leq \|A\|_{\text{hs}} \leq \sqrt{n}\|A\|_{\text{op}}$$

which proves that the norms are equivalent. □

We are interested in the equivalence of these norms because of the topological implications. If a function with domain $M_n(\mathbb{C})$ is continuous with respect to one norm, it is also continuous with respect to any equivalent norm. We will use the maximum norm to establish the fact that the eigenvalues of a matrix vary continuously with the entries of the matrix. The equivalence of norms will then allow us to extend this result to say that the eigenvalues vary continuously with respect to the operator norm.

The proof will require the following technicality, that the roots of a complex polynomial vary continuously with the coefficients. This is an intuitively nice property which can be proven using a variety of techniques which are beyond the scope of this book. We will give a fairly convincing outline of a proof here, motivated by the paper [**52**], and encourage the reader to seek out proofs which fill in the details of convergence required for a rigorous argument. For instance, one might refer to [**23**] for a proof using the topology of metric spaces, [**51**] for a short proof using Banach space theory, or [**48**] for a proof using complex analysis techniques.

Lemma 7.4. *Let $p(x) = \sum_{i=0}^n a_i x^i$ with $a_n \neq 0$. Suppose λ is a root of $p(x)$ with multiplicity m. Given $\epsilon > 0$, there exists a $\delta > 0$ such* *that if* $q(x) = \sum_{i=0}^{n}(a_i + \delta_i)x^i$ *where* $\max_i |\delta_i| < \delta$, *then* $q(x)$ *has at least* m *roots within* ϵ *of* λ.

Outline of proof. Suppose that the conclusion is false. Then there is a sequence of polynomials $q_k(x)$ whose coefficients converge to the coefficients $a_0, a_1, \ldots, a_n$ of $p(x)$ such that each q_k has fewer than m roots within ϵ of λ. Since the coefficients of the polynomials q_k converge, they form bounded sequences.

By a result of Cauchy, given a polynomial

$$p(x) = \sum_{i=0}^{n} a_i x^i = x^n + \sum_{i=0}^{n-1}\left(\frac{a_i}{a_n}\right) x^i,$$

the roots of $p(x)$ are bounded in modulus:

$$p(\lambda) = 0 \Rightarrow |\lambda| < 1 + \max\{a_i \,:\, i = 0, 1, \ldots, n-1\}.$$

For each k, let the n roots of q_k be put in a vector $v_k \in \mathbb{C}^n$. By Cauchy's result, this sequence is bounded. Then, by completeness, there exists a convergent subsequence v_{k_i} converging to $\mu = \begin{bmatrix}\mu_1 & \mu_2 & \cdots & \mu_n\end{bmatrix}^T$, where at most $m-1$ of the entries of μ are equal to λ.

Since the coefficients of the polynomials $q_k(x)$ are converging to $p(x)$, we have that on one hand the subsequence q_{k_i} is converging to $p(x)$, but on the other it is converging to $a_n \prod_{i=1}^{n}(x - \mu_i)$ which is not equal to $p(x)$ since it has at most $m-1$ roots at λ. This is a contradiction. $\square$

Proposition 7.5. *Consider* $\mathbb{M}_n(\mathbb{C})$ *with the maximum norm, and let* $A \in \mathbb{M}_n(\mathbb{C})$ *have an eigenvalue* λ *with multiplicity* m. *Given* $\epsilon > 0$, *there exists a* $\delta > 0$ *such that if* $\|A - B\|_{\max} < \delta$, *then* B *has at least* m *eigenvalues (counting multiplicity) within* ϵ *of* λ.

Proof. Let $p_A(x) = \sum_{i=0}^{n} c_i x^i$ and $p_B(x) = \sum_{i=0}^{n} d_i x^i$ be the characteristic polynomials of A and B respectively. Recall that the characteristic polynomial $p_A(x)$ is the determinant of the matrix $A - xI$, and that the roots of $p_A(x)$ are the eigenvalues of A. The set of eigenvalues of A is called the spectrum of A, denoted $\sigma(A) = \{\lambda_i\}_{i=1}^{n}$.

Given $\epsilon > 0$, there exists by Lemma 7.4 a $\delta' > 0$ such that if $p_B(x)$ has coefficients d_i such that $\max_i |c_i - d_i| < \delta'$, then for $\lambda \in \sigma(A)$ with multiplicity m, $p_B(x)$ has at least m roots within ϵ of λ. We can think about the coefficients of $p_A(x)$ and $p_B(x)$ as polynomials in which the variables are the n^2 entries a_{jk}, b_{jk} of A and B respectively. For example, if A is a 2×2 matrix,

$$A = \begin{bmatrix} a_{11} & a_{12} \\ a_{21} & a_{22} \end{bmatrix},$$

here is the characteristic polynomial:

$$p_A(x) = (a_{11} - x)(a_{22} - x) - a_{12}a_{21} = x^2 - (a_{11} + a_{22})x - a_{12}a_{21}.$$

Polynomials are continuous functions, so for each i, we see that the difference between coefficients $|c_i - d_i|$ can be made arbitrarily small by selecting B such that $\|A - B\|_{\max} = \max_{j,k}\{|a_{jk} - b_{jk}|\}$ is small enough. Since there are only finitely many coefficients, we can find $\delta > 0$ such that if $\|A - B\|_{\max} < \delta$, then $\max_i\{|c_i - d_i| : 0 \leq i \leq n\} < \delta'$. This then ensures that $p_B(x)$ has at least m roots within ϵ of λ. □

This next proposition is the version of the continuity of eigenvalues which we will use in the following sections.

Proposition 7.6. *Let S_n be the vector space of self-adjoint $n \times n$ complex matrices with the operator norm. Let $f_i : S_n \to \mathbb{C}$ be the map from $A \in S_n$ to the ith largest eigenvalue of A, counting multiplicity. (We can order the eigenvalues since they are all real.) Then for each $i = 1, 2, \ldots, n$, f_i is continuous.*

Proof. Let $A \in S_n$. Given $\epsilon > 0$, there exists $\delta' > 0$ such that for $B \in S_n$ with $\|A - B\|_{\max} < \delta'$, we have for every eigenvalue λ of A having multiplicity m, the matrix B has at least m eigenvalues in $(\lambda - \epsilon, \lambda + \epsilon)$. If we select ϵ such that

$$\epsilon < \frac{1}{2} \min\{|\lambda_i - \lambda_j| \ : \ \lambda_i, \lambda_j \text{ distinct eigenvalues of } A\},$$

then for each i, $f_i(B)$ is within ϵ of $f_i(A)$. This is because each eigenvalue $f_i(B)$ belongs to at most one interval $(f_j(A) - \epsilon, f_i(A) + \epsilon)$, but the sum of the number of eigenvalues of B in these intervals must be at least n. Therefore, every eigenvalue of B is in exactly one of these ϵ intervals around the eigenvalues of A.

Since the operator norm and the maximum norm are equivalent, given $\delta' > 0$, there is a $\delta > 0$ such that if $\|A - B\|_{\text{op}} < \delta$, then $\|A-B\|_{\max} < \delta'$. By the preceding paragraph, then, if $\|A-B\|_{\text{op}} < \delta$, we have $|f_i(A) - f_i(B)| < \epsilon$. Therefore, for each $i = 1, 2, \ldots, n$, the function f_i is continuous. □

7.2. Ellipsoidal Tight Frames

Recall that a uniform frame is a frame in which all the vectors have the same norm. We can think of such a frame as spherical, in the sense that the vectors are all contained in a sphere $\{x : \|x\| = a\}$ within the given Hilbert space. We might ask the more general question whether we can find frames that are contained within an ellipsoid. First, we need to define what we mean by an ellipsoid in a Hilbert space.

Definition 7.7. Given a Hilbert space $\mathcal{H}$, an *ellipsoid* is the image of the unit sphere $S = \{x : \|x\| = 1\}$ under a positive invertible operator T. The ellipsoid determined by the operator T will be denoted $\mathcal{E}_T$. A tight frame $\{x_i\}_{i=1}^k$ for $\mathcal{H}$ which is contained in $\mathcal{E}_T$ will be called an *ellipsoidal tight frame* (ETF) for $\mathcal{H}$.

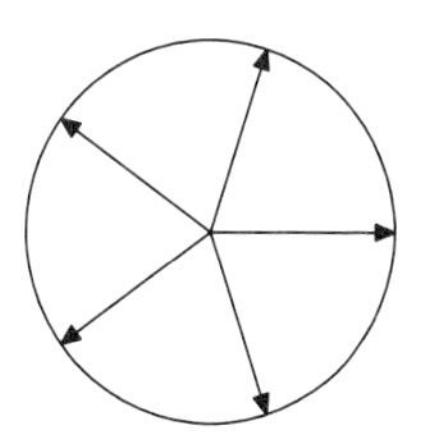
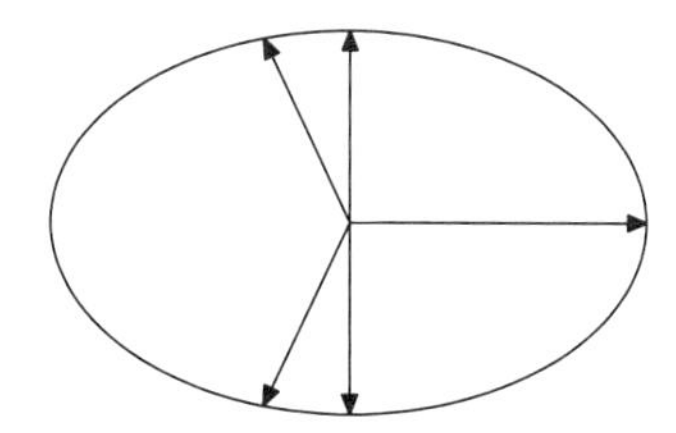

Figure 7.1. A uniform tight frame and an ellipsoidal tight frame for $\mathbb{R}^2$.

Remark 7.8. Another possible definition of an ellipsoid in $\mathcal{H}$ could be the image of the unit sphere under any *invertible* operator, without requiring it to have positive eigenvalues. But the polar decomposition of an operator from Theorem 2.64 shows that the positive operators are sufficient to see every possible ellipsoid up to unitary equivalence. Given T an invertible operator, let $T = U|T|$ be its polar decomposition, where $|T| = (T^*T)^{\frac{1}{2}}$ is a positive operator and U is a unitary operator (an isometry). There is a natural equivalence between $\mathcal{E}_T$ and $\mathcal{E}_{|T|}$ (think of the same ellipsoid, only rotated), so we can restrict the discussion of ellipsoids to the case where T is a positive operator.

Remark 7.9. If the Hilbert space is $\mathbb{R}^n$, one can readily verify that the equation we learned in high school for an ellipsoid centered at the origin

$$\frac{x_1^2}{a_1^2} + \frac{x_2^2}{a_2^2} + \cdots + \frac{x_n^2}{a_n^2} = 1$$

is consistent with Definition 7.7. We leave the proof of this to Exercise 1.

In order to figure out which ellipsoids contain tight frames, we need to introduce further properties and notation from linear algebra. We begin by giving a reminder of the tensor product notation for rank-one operators on $\mathcal{H}$, which we introduced in Example 2.62. Given $x, y \in \mathcal{H}$, we define the operator $x \otimes y$ by $(x \otimes y)w = \langle w, y \rangle x$ for all $w \in \mathcal{H}$. Since each image is a scalar multiple of x, this operator must have rank one.

It can be demonstrated that every rank-one operator on a Hilbert space $\mathcal{H}$ can be expressed in the form $x \otimes y$, for some choice of $x, y \in \mathcal{H}$. The proof is left to Exercise 2.

In the special case where the Hilbert space is $\mathbb{C}^n$, the matrix representation of the operator $x \otimes y$ is the $n \times n$ matrix xy^*, where y^* is the conjugate-transpose of the vector y.

$$x \otimes y = xy^* = \begin{bmatrix} x_1 \\ \vdots \\ x_n \end{bmatrix} \begin{bmatrix} \overline{y_1} & \cdots & \overline{y_n} \end{bmatrix} = \begin{bmatrix} x_1\overline{y_1} & \cdots & x_1\overline{y_n} \\ \vdots & \ddots & \vdots \\ x_n\overline{y_1} & \cdots & x_n\overline{y_n} \end{bmatrix}.$$

If $\|x\| = 1$, then the operator $x \otimes x$ is a projection onto the one-dimensional space spanned by x. To see this, recall that P is an orthogonal projection if it is self-adjoint and $P^2 = P$. We see from the definition that $x \otimes x$ is self-adjoint, and in fact positive. We also have:

$$\begin{aligned}(x \otimes x)^2 y &= (x \otimes x)(\langle y, x \rangle x) \\ &= \langle \langle y, x \rangle x, x \rangle x \\ &= \langle y, x \rangle \langle x, x \rangle x \\ &= (x \otimes x)\|x\|^2 y.\end{aligned}$$

Therefore, $x \otimes x$ is a projection exactly when $\|x\| = 1$.

Next, recall the definition of the frame operator of a frame $\{x_i\}_{i=1}^k$:

$$Sx = \Theta^* \Theta x = \sum_{i=1}^{k} \langle x, x_i \rangle x_i.$$

We see immediately that S can be expressed as a sum of k rank-one operators:

$$S = \sum_{i=1}^{k} x_i \otimes x_i. \tag{7.4}$$

We are going to study operators which are sums of rank-one operators (particularly projections) in some depth. In particular, we will determine some conditions under which a given operator S can be written as a sum of rank-one projections. We've already started to answer this question, of course. As we just stated above, if S is a frame operator for a frame in which the vectors are all unit vectors, then it can be expressed as a sum of rank-one projections. But what if we are just given an operator without an associated frame? We can observe one fact right away: since the sum of k rank-one operators can have rank at most k, if our operator S has rank n, it can only be written as a sum of n or more rank-one projections.

Proposition 7.10. *Let $\mathcal{H}$ be a Hilbert space with dimension n. A positive invertible operator T on $\mathcal{H}$ can be written as a sum of k rank-one projections if and only if $k \geq n$ and the trace of T is equal to k.*

Proof. The forward direction is proven easily using two facts about the trace of an operator, which were both shown in Chapter 1. The first is that the trace of a projection is equal to the dimension of the range, so that if x is a unit vector, the trace of the rank-one projection

$x \otimes x$ is 1. The second fact, which we recall from Proposition 1.56, is that the trace of an operator is additive: $\text{tr}(A + B) = \text{tr}(A) + \text{tr}(B)$.

Assume that $T = \sum_{i=1}^{k} x_i \otimes x_i$ with each $\|x_i\| = 1$. The collection $\{x_i\}_{i=1}^{k}$ must span the n-dimensional space because we assumed T to be invertible. Therefore, we must have $k \geq n$. By matching traces, the trace of T must be equal to the sum of the traces of the projections, which is k.

To prove the converse, assume that T has trace $k \geq n$. We use induction on k to find unit vectors $x_1, x_2, \ldots, x_k$ such that T is the sum of the operators $x_i \otimes x_i$. The base case is the case in which $k = n = 1$, in which T itself has rank one and is a projection since its trace is 1. We take x_k to be a unit vector in the range of T, so $T = x_k \otimes x_k$.

Let us begin with an outline of the induction step. Since T is a positive operator, we recall from the Spectral Theorem 2.74 that there exists an orthonormal basis for $\mathcal{H}$ such that T has a representation as a diagonal matrix with positive entries $a_1 \geq a_2 \geq \cdots \geq a_n > 0$, where these are the eigenvalues of T. We will demonstrate that if $k > n$, we can find a unit vector x_k such that $T - (x_k \otimes x_k)$ is still a positive operator with rank n, but now with trace $k - 1$. If $k = n$, then we show that there is a vector x_k which will reduce both the trace *and* the rank. In this case $T - x_k \otimes x_k$ is no longer invertible on $\mathcal{H}$, but is invertible on its range. In either case, we can repeat this process on the new operator $T - (x_k \otimes x_k)$ until we get to the base case of $n = k = 1$. At this point, we have written T as a sum of rank-one projections.

$$\begin{aligned}
T &= (T - x_k \otimes x_k) + (x_k \otimes x_k) \\
&\vdots \qquad \vdots \\
&= \left(T - \sum_{j=p}^{k} x_j \otimes x_j\right) + \left(\sum_{j=p}^{k} x_j \otimes x_j\right) \\
&\vdots \qquad \vdots \\
&= \sum_{j=1}^{k} x_j \otimes x_j.
\end{aligned}$$

Before we give the specific details of this part of the proof, we need a technical lemma which follows immediately from Proposition 7.6.

Lemma 7.11. *Let $\mathcal{H}$ be a Hilbert space with dimension n. Define a function μ_i which takes a self-adjoint operator T on $\mathcal{H}$ to its ith largest eigenvalue, counting multiplicity. Then $\mu_i(T - x \otimes x)$ varies continuously with x.*

Proof. Given the operator T on the Hilbert space $\mathcal{H}$ having dimension n, we can consider the matrix representation of T. We will identify T with its $n \times n$ matrix representation and proceed with the matrix proof. We know from Proposition 7.6 that the function $\mu_i : S_n \to \mathbb{C}$ which takes a self-adjoint matrix to its ith largest eigenvalue is continuous. Therefore, we only need show that the map from x to $T - x \otimes x$ is continuous.

Suppose $x, y \in \mathbb{C}^n$ such that $\|x - y\| < \delta < 1$. Then, for each $i = 1, 2, \ldots, n$, the vector entries are $|x_i - y_i| < \delta$. Notice that $\|(T - x \otimes x) - (T - y \otimes y)\| = \|x \otimes x - y \otimes y\|$. It was previously demonstrated that the matrix entries of the rank-one operator $(x \otimes x)$ are $x_i \overline{x}_j$ for $i, j = 1, 2, \ldots, n$. We can then compute the matrix entries of $x \otimes x - y \otimes y$.

$$\begin{aligned} |x_i\overline{x}_j - y_i\overline{y}_j| &= |x_i\overline{x}_j - x_i\overline{y}_j + x_i\overline{y}_j - y_i\overline{y}_j| \\ &\leq |x_i||\overline{x}_j - \overline{y}_j| + |\overline{y}_j||x_i - y_i| \\ &\leq \delta(\|x\| + \|y\|) \\ &\leq \delta(\|x\| + 1). \end{aligned}$$

In the last line, we use the Triangle Inequality and $\delta < 1$ to prove that $\|y\| \leq \|x\| + \delta < \|x\| + 1$.

This computation proves that $\|x \otimes x - y \otimes y\|_{\max} < \delta(\|x\| + 1)$ when $\|x - y\| < \delta < 1$. Therefore, in the maximum norm, $T - x \otimes x$ varies continuously with x. Given the equivalence of norms, we also know that this map is continuous with respect to the operator norm on $T - x \otimes x$. Composing this map with the continuous map μ_i which takes $T - x \otimes x$ to its ith largest eigenvalue, we have proved that the map from x to the ith largest eigenvalue is continuous. □

We now can fill in the details of the induction step to complete the proof of Proposition 7.10.

Case 1: $(k > n)$. We know that $a_1 + a_2 + \cdots + a_n = \mathrm{tr}(T) = k > n$, so $a_1 > 1$. Therefore, let $x_k = e_1$. Observe that the operator $T-(x_k \otimes x_k)$ is diagonal with entries $a_1 - 1, a_2, \ldots, a_n$, and is therefore still a positive invertible operator and, as we desired, has rank n and trace $k - 1 \geq n$.

Case 2: $(k = n)$. In this case, since $a_1 + \cdots + a_n = k = n$, we have $a_1 \geq 1$ and $a_n \leq 1$. We define the function μ_n as above to give us the nth largest eigenvalue (counting multiplicity) of any self-adjoint operator on $\mathcal{H}$. As an example, $\mu_n(T) = a_n$. We see that $\mu_n(T - (e_1 \otimes e_1)) \geq 0$ and $\mu_n(T - (e_n \otimes e_n)) \leq 0$. Using the fact from Lemma 7.11 that $\mu_n(T - (x \otimes x))$ is continuous with respect to the vector x, we see by the Intermediate Value Theorem that there is a unit vector y for which $\mu_n(T - (y \otimes y)) = 0$. Choose that y to be x_k. The remainder operator $T - (x_k \otimes x_k)$ then has rank $n - 1$ since it has 0 as its smallest eigenvalue. It also has trace of $k - 1 = n - 1$.

By induction, this completes the proof. □

We use this proposition to discover when an ellipsoid generated by a positive operator T contains an ellipsoidal tight frame. More particularly, if the dimension of the Hilbert space is n, we actually find out that every ellipsoid contains tight frames with k elements, where k can be any integer greater than or equal to n. This is pretty amazing! For example, given any ellipse you want to pick in $\mathbb{R}^2$ (centered at the origin), there will be some tight frame contained in that ellipse which has, say, 12 vectors, and there is one with 20 vectors, and one with 100 vectors.

Given a frame $\{x_i\}_{i=1}^k$ for $\mathcal{H}$, recall that the frame operator is defined to be the positive operator $S : \mathcal{H} \to \mathcal{H}$ taking $x \mapsto \sum_{i=1}^k \langle x, x_i \rangle x_i$. We can write S as in Equation (7.4):

$$S = \sum_{i=1}^{k} x_i \otimes x_i.$$

Also recall from Remark 3.23 that $\{x_i\}_{i=1}^k$ is a tight frame with frame bound A if and only if $S = AI$, where I is the identity operator on

$\mathcal{H}$. Therefore, finding a tight frame $\{x_i\}$ with frame bound A is equivalent to finding an expression of the operator AI as a sum of rank-one operators $x_i \otimes x_i$. The number of vectors k in the frame must be exactly equal to the number of rank-one operators in the sum.

Theorem 7.12 ([**28**]). *Let $\mathcal{H}$ be a Hilbert space with finite dimension n and T a positive operator on $\mathcal{H}$ with rank n. Then the ellipsoid $\mathcal{E}_T$ contains an ellipsoidal tight frame consisting of k vectors for any $k \geq n$.*

Proof. The ellipsoid $\mathcal{E}_T$ contains an ellipsoidal tight frame $\{x_i\}_{i=1}^k$ with k elements and frame bound A if and only if the frame operator AI can be written as a sum of the rank-one operators

$$AI = \sum_{i=1}^{k} x_i \otimes x_i.$$

Since each x_i is on the ellipsoid, we have for each i, $x_i = Ty_i$ for some unit vector y_i, so

$$AI = \sum_{i=1}^{k} Ty_i \otimes Ty_i.$$

This equation is equivalent to the operator AT^{-2} being written as a sum of rank-one projections:

$$\sum_{i=1}^{k} y_i \otimes y_i = T^{-1}\left(\sum_{i=1}^{k} Ty_i \otimes Ty_i\right)T^{-1} = AT^{-2}. \tag{7.5}$$

Given T and k, choose A such that the trace of AT^{-2} is equal to k. Then, by Proposition 7.10, there exist k unit vectors $y_1, y_2, \ldots, y_k$ such that

$$AT^{-2} = \sum_{i=1}^{k} y_i \otimes y_i.$$

This implies

$$AI = \sum_{i=1}^{k} Ty_i \otimes Ty_i,$$

which gives an ellipsoidal tight frame $\{Ty_i\}_{i=1}^k$ on $\mathcal{E}_T$ with k vectors. □

7.3. Frames with a Specified Frame Operator

In this section, we examine whether it is possible to find a frame for which we have prescribed the frame operator. Our previous problem, finding tight frames, is just the special case in which we demand that the frame operator be a scalar multiple of the identity operator. A frame $\{x_i\}_{i=1}^k$ with a known frame operator S, and thereby a known canonical dual frame $\{S^{-1}x_i\}_{i=1}^k$ (recall Chapter 6) may be just as useful in applications as a tight frame, but additionally may be able to take on a wider variety of properties. The first result we consider is whether we can find a frame with a given frame operator S in which the frame consists of only unit vectors. It turns out that this problem is equivalent to the result in Section 7.2, in which we showed that an ellipsoid always contains tight frames. The equivalence comes from the following computation.

Lemma 7.13. *Let S be a positive invertible operator on a Hilbert space $\mathcal{H}$ having dimension n. Given $k \geq n$, the following statements are equivalent:*

(i) *S is the frame operator for a frame $\{x_i\}_{i=1}^k$ in which $\|x_i\| = 1$ for each $i = 1, 2, \ldots, n$.*

(ii) *S can be written as a sum of rank-one projections.*

(iii) *The ellipsoid generated by $T = S^{-\frac{1}{2}}$ contains a Parseval frame having k vectors.*

(iv) $\operatorname{tr}(S) = k$.

Proof. The first and second statements are equivalent by the definition of the frame operator and the fact that the rank-one operator $x \otimes x$ is a projection if and only if $\|x\| = 1$. The third and fourth statements are equivalent by Theorem 7.12. The equivalence between the second and third statements can be seen in Equation (7.5), where S takes the place of AT^{-2} in the equation. The operator S can be written in the form $S = \sum_{i=1}^k x \otimes x_i$ if and only if

$$I = \sum_{i=1}^{k} \left[(S^{-\frac{1}{2}}x_i) \otimes (S^{-\frac{1}{2}}x_i) \right],$$

which implies that $\{S^{-\frac{1}{2}}x_i\}_{i=1}^k$ is an ellipsoidal tight frame (in fact, a Parseval frame) on the ellipsoid generated by $T = S^{-\frac{1}{2}}$. □

We have determined the condition on an operator S under which it is the frame operator for a uniform, or spherical, frame. We next consider when S could be the frame operator for a frame in which the norms of the vectors are specified by a sequence $\{a_1, a_2, \dots, a_k\}$ of positive real numbers.

The following lemma is a helpful tool in finding the conditions on the operator S and the sequence $\{a_i\}_{i=1}^k$ under which such a frame exists.

Lemma 7.14. *Let B be a positive operator with rank n and nonzero eigenvalues $b_1 \geq b_2 \geq \cdots \geq b_n > 0$ and with a corresponding orthonormal set of eigenvectors $\{e_i\}_{i=1}^n$. If c is a positive number with $b_j \geq c \geq b_{j+1}$ for some $1 \leq j \leq n-1$, then there is a unit vector x in $\operatorname{span}\{e_j, e_{j+1}\}$ such that $B - c(x \otimes x)$ is positive and has rank $n-1$.*

Proof. If A is a finite-rank self-adjoint operator and $c \geq \|A\|$ is a constant, then it can be shown that the least eigenvalue of A is given by $\|(A + cI)^{-1}\|^{-1} - c$ (see Exercise 5). Since the map from an operator to its norm is continuous, it follows that the function giving the least eigenvalue is continuous on the set of finite-rank self-adjoint operators. Define $A_x = B - c(x \otimes x)$ for x an arbitrary unit vector in $\operatorname{span}\{e_j, e_{j+1}\}$. The least eigenvalue of A_x is nonnegative for $x = e_j$ and nonpositive for $x = e_{j+1}$; hence $\operatorname{span}\{e_j, e_{j+1}\}$ contains a unit vector x for which the least eigenvalue of A_x is zero by the Intermediate Value Theorem. Therefore, A_x is a positive operator having rank $n-1$. □

Remark 7.15. Since the trace of A_x is $(\sum_1^n b_i) - c$, and eigenvalues other than b_j and b_{j+1} are unchanged, the remaining nonzero eigenvalue must be

$$\tilde{b} = b_j + b_{j+1} - c.$$

Moreover, observe that the new eigenvalue maintains the jth position in the ordering of all the eigenvalues:

$$b_1 \geq \cdots \geq b_{j-1} \geq \tilde{b} \geq b_{j+2} \geq \cdots \geq b_n.$$

We can use Lemma 7.14 to discover the conditions under which a frame exists (either tight or with specified frame operator S) whose elements have norms given by a finite positive sequence $\{a_1, a_2, \ldots, a_k\}$. Recall that we discussed a related problem in Section 3.6. We considered there the existence of a tight frame whose vectors have norms given by a sequence $\{a_i\}_{i=1}^k$. Proposition 3.40 gave the condition, called the fundamental inequality, under which such a tight frame exists. The following theorem solves the more general problem, in which the frame operator is specified, but is not necessarily a scalar multiple of the identity.

Theorem 7.16 ([**47**]). *Let B be a positive operator with rank n and nonzero eigenvalues $b_1 \geq b_2 \geq \cdots \geq b_n > 0$. Let $\{c_i\}_{i=1}^k$, with $k \geq n$ be a nonincreasing sequence of positive numbers such that $\sum_{i=1}^k c_i = \sum_{j=1}^n b_j$. There exist unit vectors $\{x_i\}_{i=1}^k$ such that*

$$B = \sum_{i=1}^{k} c_i (x_i \otimes x_i) \tag{7.6}$$

if and only if all of the following inequalities hold:

$$\begin{aligned} c_1 &\leq b_1, \\ c_1 + c_2 &\leq b_1 + b_2, \\ \vdots \quad &\vdots \quad \vdots \\ c_1 + c_2 + \cdots + c_{n-1} &\leq b_1 + b_2 + \cdots + b_{n-1}. \end{aligned} \tag{7.7}$$

If B can be written in the form of Equation (7.6), *we say B has a rank-one decomposition corresponding to $\{c_i\}_{i=1}^k$.*

Proof. Beginning with the *if* direction, we use induction on the rank n of the operator B, similar to the technique used in Proposition 7.10. The case $n = 1$ when B is already a rank-one operator is clear. We assume, inductively, that the assertion is true for positive operators of rank $n - 1$. To be precise, assume that, given $\widetilde{B}$ with positive eigenvalues $\tilde{b}_1, \tilde{b}_2, \ldots, \tilde{b}_{n-1}$ and given a sequence of positive numbers $\{\tilde{c}_i\}_{i=1}^{\tilde{k}}$ with any length $\tilde{k} \geq n - 1$ for which $\sum_{i=1}^{\tilde{k}} \tilde{c}_i = \sum_{j=1}^{n-1} \tilde{b}_j$, if property (7.7) holds for $\{\tilde{c}_i\}_{i=1}^{\tilde{k}}$ and $\{\tilde{b}_j\}_{j=1}^{n-1}$, then $\widetilde{B}$ has a rank-one decomposition corresponding to $\{\tilde{c}_i\}$.

From this assumption, we will show that, given the operator B and sequence $\{c_i\}_{i=1}^k$ from the statement of the theorem, if property (7.7) holds, then there exist unit vectors $\{x_i\}_{i=1}^k$ such that $B = \sum_{i=1}^k c_i(x_i \times x_i)$. We will accomplish this by showing that $B = \widetilde{B} + A$, where $\widetilde{B}$ has rank $n-1$ and $A = \sum_{i=1}^q c_i(x_i \otimes x_i)$, where $\{x_1, x_2, \ldots, x_q\}$ are unit vectors and A has been constructed to ensure that the inductive hypothesis can be applied to $\widetilde{B}$ and $\{c_i\}_{i=q+1}^k$. We will thereby attain the result.

We can now more explicitly give the details of the induction step. Given the positive rank-n operator B, let $\{e_i\}_1^n$ be an orthonormal set of eigenvectors for $b_1, b_2, \ldots, b_n$, respectively.

Case 1: If $b_1 \geq c_1 \geq b_n$, there exists an index l; $1 \leq l \leq n-1$ such that $b_l \geq c_1 \geq b_{l+1}$. By Lemma 7.14, there exists a unit vector x in the span of e_l and e_{l+1} such that $B - c_1(x \otimes x)$ has rank $n-1$ and eigenvalues in nonincreasing order $b_1, \ldots, b_{l-1}, \tilde{b}, b_{l+2}, \ldots, b_n$, where $\tilde{b} = b_l + b_{l+1} - c_1$. Let $x_1 = x$. It remains to check that the inequalities from Equation (7.7) hold for the operator $B - c_1(x_1 \otimes x_1)$ with its $n-1$ ordered nonzero eigenvalues and the sequence $\{c_2, \ldots, c_k\}$. Clearly, for $1 \leq r \leq l$, we have

$$c_2 + \cdots + c_r \leq c_1 + \cdots + c_{r-1} \leq b_1 + \cdots + b_{r-1}.$$

For the remaining inequalities $l+1 \leq r \leq n-1$,

$$\begin{aligned} c_1 + c_2 + \cdots + c_r &\leq b_1 + \cdots + b_l + b_{l+1} + \cdots + b_r, \\ c_2 + \cdots + c_r &\leq b_1 + \cdots + (b_l + b_{l+1} - c_1) + \cdots + b_r, \\ c_2 + \cdots + c_r &\leq b_1 + \cdots + \tilde{b} + \cdots + b_r. \end{aligned}$$

Notice that in the case where $r = n-1$, the above is an equality. Since we have shown that B can be reduced to a sum of a rank-one operator and an operator of rank $n-1$ which satisfies the hypotheses of the theorem, induction gives the remaining elements of the rank-one decomposition of B corresponding to the sequence $\{c_i\}_1^k$.

Case 2: If $c_1 < b_n$, then we are unable to use Lemma 7.14. We select rank-one operators to subtract from B which preserve the rank and decrease the smallest eigenvalue until the Case 1 property is attained. Let p be the largest integer such that $c_1 + c_2 + \cdots + c_p < b_n$. Note that Case 2 can only occur for $k > n$. Since the sums of each sequence are equal, $c_{p+1} + \cdots + c_k > b_1 + \cdots + b_{n-1}$, but because $c_{p+1} \le c_1 \le b_n \le b_{n-1}$, the sum on the left must have more terms. Therefore, $k - p > n - 1$, or alternatively, $1 \le p \le k - n$. Let $x_i = e_n$ for each $i = 1, 2, \ldots, p$. The operator $B - \sum_{i=1}^{p} c_i(x_i \otimes x_i)$ still has rank n and the eigenvalues in decreasing order are $b_1, b_2, \ldots, b_{n-1}, \tilde{b}$, where $\tilde{b} = b_n - \sum_{i=1}^{p} c_i$. By the selection of p, c_{p+1} exceeds or equals $\tilde{b}$, the smallest eigenvalue of $B - \sum_{i=1}^{p} c_i(x_i \otimes x_i)$. The method of Case 1 can now be applied to the operator $B - \sum_{i=1}^{p} c_i(x_i \otimes x_i)$ and the remaining sequence $c_{p+1}, \ldots, c_k$.

Next, to show the *only if* direction, assume B has a rank-one decomposition corresponding to $\{c_i\}$. Given a fixed j with $1 \le j \le k$, define P to be the orthogonal projection onto the span of $\{x_i\}_{i=1}^{j}$. Clearly, $\operatorname{rank}(P) \le j$. For each i, define $P_i = x_i \otimes x_i$. We then have:

$$PBP = P\Big(\sum_{i=1}^{k} c_i(x_i \otimes x_i)\Big)P = \sum_{i=1}^{k} c_i PP_iP \ge \sum_{i=1}^{j} c_i PP_iP = \sum_{i=1}^{j} c_i P_i$$

and therefore $\operatorname{tr}(PBP) \ge \operatorname{tr}\left(\sum_{i=1}^{j} c_i P_i\right) = c_1 + c_2 + \cdots + c_j$. (Verify this last step in Exercise 6.)

We next show that $\operatorname{tr}(PBP) \le b_1 + b_2 + \cdots + b_j$, which will complete the proof. Let $\{e_i\}_{i=1}^{n}$ be as above, and for notational purposes, set $b_{n+1} = 0$. For $1 \le i \le n$, define $Q_i = e_1 \otimes e_1 + \cdots + e_i \otimes e_i$. A calculation verifies that B can be written

$$B = \sum_{i=1}^{n} (b_i - b_{i+1})Q_i.$$

Then, $PBP = \sum_{i=1}^{n} (b_i - b_{i+1})PQ_iP$. Observe that $\operatorname{tr}(PQ_iP) = \operatorname{tr}(PQ_i) \le \min\{\operatorname{rank}(P), \operatorname{rank}(Q_i)\} \le \min\{j, i\}$. Therefore,

$$\begin{aligned}
\operatorname{tr}(PBP) &= \sum_{i=1}^{n} (b_i - b_{i+1}) \operatorname{tr}(PQ_iP) \\
&\le \sum_{i=1}^{j} (b_i - b_{i+1})i + j \sum_{i=j+1}^{n} (b_i - b_{i+1}) \\
&= (b_1 + b_2 + \cdots + b_j - jb_{j+1}) + j\,(b_{j+1} - b_{n+1}) \\
&= b_1 + b_2 + \cdots + b_j.
\end{aligned}$$

□

Remark 7.17. Theorem 7.16 is very closely related to the Schur Majorization Theorem and its converse, which can be found in [**45**]. The inequalities in Equation (7.7) describe a relationship known as majorization. (In our case, the sequence $\{c_i\}_{i=1}^k$ majorizes the sequence $\{b_i\}_{i=1}^n$.) Schur's Majorization Theorem states that, given an $n \times n$ self-adjoint matrix A, the sequence of diagonal entries of A majorizes its eigenvalues, where both are listed in nonincreasing order. The converse states that if a sequence c_i majorizes a sequence b_i, then there exists an $n \times n$ self-adjoint matrix G with diagonal entries c_i and eigenvalues b_i.

Remark 7.18. The hypotheses in Theorem 7.16 reduce to exactly the fundamental inequality from Equation (3.11) in Section 3.6 when $b_1 = b_2 = \cdots = b_n$. Thus, an immediate corollary of Theorem 7.16 is the result from Proposition 3.40 that the fundamental inequality is a necessary and sufficient condition for the existence of a tight frame for $\mathbb{R}^n$ consisting of vectors with norms $\sqrt{c_i}$; $i = 1, \ldots, k$.

The following example demonstrates the algorithm described in the proof of Theorem 7.16.

Example 7.19. Let $\mathcal{H} = \mathbb{R}^2$ and $B = \begin{bmatrix} 5 & 0 \\ 0 & 4 \end{bmatrix}$. Theorem 7.16 gives a procedure for constructing a rank-one decomposition of B corresponding to the sequence $\{c_i\}_{i=1}^4 = 3, 3, 2, 1$.

Since $c_1 < b_2$ (Case 2), we take $x_1 = \begin{bmatrix} 1 \\ 0 \end{bmatrix}$. This leaves $B - 3(x_1 \otimes x_1) = \begin{bmatrix} 5 & 0 \\ 0 & 1 \end{bmatrix}$ to decompose. We now have c_2 between the two eigenvalues 5 and 1 (Case 1). Let $x(t) = \sqrt{1-t}\begin{bmatrix} 1 \\ 0 \end{bmatrix} + \sqrt{t}\begin{bmatrix} 0 \\ 1 \end{bmatrix} = \begin{bmatrix} \sqrt{1-t} \\ \sqrt{t} \end{bmatrix}$. We wish to find t such that $\begin{bmatrix} 5 & 0 \\ 0 & 1 \end{bmatrix} - 3(x(t) \otimes x(t))$ has rank one; i.e., the determinant is zero. Straightforward calculation shows the solution $t = \frac{1}{6}$. Take $x_2 = x(\frac{1}{6}) = \begin{bmatrix} \sqrt{\frac{5}{6}} \\ \sqrt{\frac{1}{6}} \end{bmatrix}$. The remainder

$\begin{bmatrix} 5 & 0 \\ 0 & 1 \end{bmatrix} - 3(x_2 \otimes x_2) = \begin{bmatrix} \frac{5}{2} & -\frac{\sqrt{5}}{2} \\ -\frac{\sqrt{5}}{2} & \frac{1}{2} \end{bmatrix}$ has rank one and its range is spanned by the unit vector $z = \begin{bmatrix} \sqrt{\frac{5}{6}} \\ -\sqrt{\frac{1}{6}} \end{bmatrix}$. We then must have $x_3 = x_4 = z$, which completes the decomposition.

$$3\begin{bmatrix} 0 & 0 \\ 0 & 1 \end{bmatrix} + 3\begin{bmatrix} \frac{5}{6} & \frac{\sqrt{5}}{6} \\ \frac{\sqrt{5}}{6} & \frac{1}{6} \end{bmatrix} + (2+1)\begin{bmatrix} \frac{5}{6} & -\frac{\sqrt{5}}{6} \\ -\frac{\sqrt{5}}{6} & \frac{1}{6} \end{bmatrix} = \begin{bmatrix} 5 & 0 \\ 0 & 4 \end{bmatrix} = B.$$

The next example demonstrates that a rank-one decomposition is impossible when property (7.7) does not hold.

Example 7.20. The operator $B = \begin{bmatrix} 5 & 0 & 0 \\ 0 & 2 & 0 \\ 0 & 0 & 2 \end{bmatrix}$ does not have a rank-one decomposition corresponding to the sequence $\{c_i\}_{i=1}^{3} = \{4, 4, 1\}$. To see this, assume that we can find unit vectors x_1, x_2, x_3 such that $B = 4(x_1 \otimes x_1) + 4(x_2 \otimes x_2) + (x_3 \otimes x_3)$. Let P be the projection onto the span of $\{x_1, x_2\}$. Then $\operatorname{tr}(PBP) = \sum_{i=1}^{3} c_i \operatorname{tr}[P(x_i \otimes x_i)P] \geq 4 + 4 = 8$, because $P(x_i \otimes x_i)P = x_i \otimes x_i$, which has trace 1.

Given P any projection with rank two, using the argument from the last paragraph of Theorem 7.16, we have $\operatorname{tr}(PBP)$ less than or equal to 7, i.e., the sum of the largest two eigenvalues. The contradiction implies B does not have a rank-one decomposition corresponding to $\{4, 4, 1\}$.

As we have seen before, there is an immediate corollary of Theorem 7.16 which restates the results in terms of frame theory. Whenever the operator B can be written in the form of Equation (7.6), then there exists a frame $\{x_i\}_{i=1}^{k}$ with frame operator B such that the squares of the norms of the vectors are given by the sequence $\{c_1, c_2, \ldots, c_k\}$.

Corollary 7.21. *Let $\mathcal{H}$ be a Hilbert space with finite dimension n. Let B be a positive invertible operator on $\mathcal{H}$ with eigenvalues $b_1 \geq b_2 \geq \cdots \geq b_n > 0$, and for $k \geq n$ let $\{c_i\}_{i=1}^{k}$ be a sequence of positive numbers with $c_1 \geq c_2 \geq \cdots \geq c_k$ such that $\sum_{i=1}^{k} c_i = \sum_{j=1}^{n} b_j$. There exists a frame for $\mathcal{H}$ with k vectors $\{x_i\}_{i=1}^{k}$ having frame operator B*

and such that $\|x_i\| = \sqrt{c_i}, 1 \leq i \leq k$, *if and only if condition* (7.7) *from Theorem* 7.16 *is satisfied.*

Proof. B has a rank-one decomposition corresponding to $\{c_i\}_{i=1}^k$ if and only if there exist unit vectors $\{y_i\}_{i=1}^k$ such that

$$B = \sum_{i=1}^{k} c_i(y_i \otimes y_i) = \sum_{i=1}^{k} \sqrt{c_i}y_i \otimes \sqrt{c_i}y_i.$$

From the expression of the frame operator given in Equation (7.4), $\{x_i\}_{i=1}^k = \{\sqrt{c_i}y_i\}_{i=1}^k$ is a frame with frame operator B and $\|x_i\| = \sqrt{c_i}$. □

Example 7.22. Restating Example 7.19 in the language of Corollary 7.21 gives the frame for $\mathbb{R}^2$:

$$\left\{\sqrt{3}\begin{bmatrix}1\\0\end{bmatrix}, \sqrt{3}\begin{bmatrix}\sqrt{\frac{5}{6}}\\\sqrt{\frac{1}{6}}\end{bmatrix}, \sqrt{2}\begin{bmatrix}\sqrt{\frac{5}{6}}\\-\sqrt{\frac{1}{6}}\end{bmatrix}, \begin{bmatrix}\sqrt{\frac{5}{6}}\\-\sqrt{\frac{1}{6}}\end{bmatrix}\right\},$$

which has frame operator $B = \begin{bmatrix}5 & 0\\0 & 4\end{bmatrix}$ and the norms of the vectors are $\{\sqrt{3}, \sqrt{3}, \sqrt{2}, 1\}$.

7.4. Exercises

Exercise 1. Demonstrate that the equation $\sum_{i=1}^{n} \frac{(x_i)^2}{(a_i)^2} = 1$ for an ellipsoid in $\mathbb{R}^n$ corresponds to the set $T\mathcal{B}$, where $\mathcal{B} = \{x \in \mathbb{R}^n : \|x\| = 1\}$ and T is a diagonal invertible operator. If T is a general positive operator on $\mathbb{R}^n$, what are the possible equations for $T\mathcal{B}$?

Exercise 2. Prove that every operator on a finite-dimensional Hilbert space $\mathcal{H}$ which has rank of one can be written in the form $x \otimes y$, where $x, y \in \mathcal{H}$. *Hint*: This will involve the Riesz representation theorem.

Exercise 3. Prove that the definitions given in (7.1), (7.2), and (7.3) each satisfy the properties of a norm.

Exercise 4. Prove that the following two norms on $\mathbb{M}_n(\mathbb{C})$ are equivalent to the operator norm. Moreover, verify that norm equivalence is an equivalence relation, and thereby conclude that these norms are equivalent to each other as well.

(i) $\|A\|_1 = \sum_{j=1}^{n}\sum_{k=1}^{n} |a_{jk}|$.

(ii) $\|A\|_{\max} = \max\{|a_{jk}| \ : \ j,k = 1,2,\ldots,n\}$.

Exercise 5. Let A be a finite-rank self-adjoint operator and $c \geq \|A\|$. Prove that the least eigenvalue of A is given by $\|(A+cI)^{-1}\|^{-1} - c$.

Exercise 6. Prove that if $A \geq B$ for self-adjoint operators A and B, then $\operatorname{tr}(A) \geq \operatorname{tr}(B)$.

Exercise 7. Prove the following relationship between the sequence of the diagonal elements of a positive operator with respect to some orthonormal basis and the sequence of the norms in some rank-one decomposition of a positive operator. (You can take the underlying Hilbert space to be either real or complex.)

Suppose that $\mathcal{H}_n$ is an n-dimensional Hilbert space, and let A be a bounded operator on $\mathcal{H}_n$ with $A \geq 0$. Let A have a rank-one decomposition $A = \sum_{i=1}^{k} x_i \otimes x_i$, where $k \geq n$. Define the operator

$$\widetilde{A} = A \oplus 0 = \begin{bmatrix} A & 0 \\ 0 & 0 \end{bmatrix}$$

acting on the k-dimensional Hilbert space $\mathcal{H}_k$, where the zero direct summand has dimension $(k-n)$. Show that there is an orthonormal basis $\{f_i\}_{i=1}^{k}$ for $\mathcal{H}_k$ such that $\langle \widetilde{A} f_i, f_i \rangle = \|x_i\|^2$ for $i = 1,2,\ldots,k$.

Conversely, suppose that A is a given positive operator on $\mathcal{H}_n$ and suppose $\{f_i\}_{i=1}^{k}$ is an orthonormal basis for H_k. Let $d_i = \langle \widetilde{A} f_i, f_i \rangle$. Show that there is a sequence of vectors $\{x_1, x_2, \ldots, x_k\}$ in $\mathcal{H}_n$ such that $A = \sum_{i=1}^{k} x_i \otimes x_i$ and $d_i = \|x_i\|^2$ for all $i = 1,2,\ldots,k$.

Hint: First reduce to the case when $\operatorname{rank}(A) = n$. Then use frame theory to obtain a constructive proof of this result. That is, derive a formula for $\{f_i\}_{i=1}^{k}$ when $\{x_i\}_{i=1}^{k}$ is given, and a formula for $\{x_i\}_{i=1}^{k}$ when $\{f_i\}_{i=1}^{k}$ is given.

Chapter 8

Harmonic and Group Frames

In Chapter 7 we remarked that frames with special structures are important, both for applications to industrial problems and in their own right to enhance the theory of frames. In this chapter we will focus on *group frames*, which have a structure inherited from an underlying group. These frames are obtained by applying a unitary group representation to some fixed vector in a Hilbert space. Since unitary operators preserve the norm of any vector, every vector in a group frame must have the same norm. Therefore, group frames are special types of uniform frames. The first fundamental examples we introduce are the harmonic frames.

8.1. Harmonic Frames

There are several different ways to define harmonic frames. This section follows the argument of P. Casazza and J. Kovačević in [**21**]. Harmonic frames are subsets of the Euclidean Hilbert space $\mathbb{C}^m$. Let $w_1, w_2, \ldots, w_m$ be the distinct m^{th} roots of unity in $\mathbb{C}$. Define $\psi_k = \frac{1}{\sqrt{m}} \begin{bmatrix} w_1^k \\ w_2^k \\ \vdots \\ w_m^k \end{bmatrix}$ for $k = 0, 1, \ldots, m-1$, where one should note that we mean $w_i^k = (w_i)^k$. Our first observation is that these vectors form an orthonormal basis.

Lemma 8.1. *The sequence* $\{\psi_0, \psi_1, \ldots, \psi_{m-1}\}$ *is an orthonormal basis for* $\mathbb{C}^m$.

Observe that the columns of the matrix of the discrete Fourier transform introduced in Example 5.4 are an orthonormal basis of this form.

Proof. It suffices to show $\{\psi_0, \psi_1, \ldots, \psi_{m-1}\}$ is an orthonormal set since $\dim \mathbb{C}^m = m$. The computations that $\langle \psi_j, \psi_k \rangle = 0$ for $j \neq k$ and $\|\psi_k\| = 1$ follow from direct computation, recalling the fact that $1 + w + w^2 + \cdots + w^{m-1} = 0$ when w is an mth root of unity and $w \neq 1$. □

Proposition 8.2. *Let* $n \leq m$ *and* $w_1, w_2, \ldots, w_m$ *be as above. Let*
$\eta_k = \frac{1}{\sqrt{m}} \begin{bmatrix} w_1^k \\ w_2^k \\ \vdots \\ w_n^k \end{bmatrix}$. *Then* $\{\eta_0, \eta_1, \ldots, \eta_{m-1}\}$ *is a Parseval frame for* $\mathbb{C}^n$.

Proof. Let Θ be the matrix $\begin{bmatrix} \psi_0 & \psi_1 & \cdots & \psi_{m-1} \end{bmatrix}$. Then by the previous lemma, Θ is a unitary matrix on $\mathbb{C}^m$. Therefore if we consider the matrix T of only the first n rows of Θ, then the set of the column vectors $\{\eta_0, \eta_1, \ldots, \eta_{m-1}\}$ of T is a Parseval frame for $\mathbb{C}^n$. □

Definition 8.3. The Parseval frame $\{\eta_0, \eta_1, \ldots, \eta_{m-1}\}$ defined in Proposition 8.2 is called a *harmonic frame.*

Note that by rearranging the order of the roots of the unity, we could have many harmonic frames. Recall from Section 3.5 that two frames $\{\phi_0, \phi_1, \ldots, \phi_{m-1}\}$ and $\{\eta_0, \eta_1, \ldots, \eta_{m-1}\}$ for $\mathbb{C}^n$ are similar if there exists an invertible operator T on $\mathbb{C}^n$ such that $T\phi_j = \eta_j$ for each $j = 0, 1, \ldots, m-1$. Note that since harmonic frames are Parseval frames, we have from Lemma 3.32 that if harmonic frames are similar, they are also unitarily equivalent. In the rest of this chapter, we will use the term *equivalent* to discuss these unitarily equivalent harmonic or group frames.

There is a simple classification for all the harmonic frames.

Proposition 8.4. *Let $\{\eta_0, \eta_1, \ldots, \eta_{m-1}\}$ be the harmonic frame for $\mathbb{C}^n$ described in Proposition 8.2, where we require $n \leq m$. Also, let $\{\phi_0, \phi_1, \ldots, \phi_{m-1}\}$ be another harmonic frame for $\mathbb{C}^n$. Then the frames $\{\eta_0, \eta_1, \ldots, \eta_{m-1}\}$ and $\{\phi_0, \phi_1, \ldots, \phi_{m-1}\}$ are equivalent if and only if there exists a permutation σ of $\{1, 2, \ldots, n\}$ such that $\eta_{kj} = \phi_{k\sigma(j)}$ for all $0 \leq k \leq m-1$ and all $1 \leq j \leq n$, where $\eta_k = \begin{bmatrix} \eta_{k1} \\ \eta_{k2} \\ \vdots \\ \eta_{kn} \end{bmatrix}$ and $\phi_k = \begin{bmatrix} \phi_{k1} \\ \phi_{k2} \\ \vdots \\ \phi_{kn} \end{bmatrix}$.*

Proof. For the reverse direction, we assume that for the permutation σ, we have $\eta_{kj} = \phi_{k\sigma(j)}$ for $0 \leq k \leq m-1, 1 \leq j \leq n$. Define the linear operator T from $\mathbb{C}^n$ to $\mathbb{C}^n$ by

$$T\eta_k = \phi_k$$

for $0 \leq k \leq m-1$. Then it can be checked that T is a well-defined linear operator and T is invertible. We leave these computations to Exercise 1. Therefore, $\{\eta_0, \eta_1, \ldots, \eta_{m-1}\}$ and $\{\phi_0, \phi_1, \ldots, \phi_{m-1}\}$ are equivalent.

For the forward assertion, assume that $\{\eta_0, \eta_1, \ldots, \eta_{m-1}\}$ and $\{\phi_0, \phi_1, \ldots, \phi_{m-1}\}$ are equivalent. Then there exists an invertible operator T on $\mathbb{C}^n$ such that $\eta_k = T\phi_k$ for $0 \leq k \leq m-1$. Since we know $\{\phi\}_{i=0}^{m-1}$ is a harmonic frame, we can write $\phi_k = \frac{1}{\sqrt{m}} \begin{bmatrix} v_1^k \\ v_2^k \\ \vdots \\ v_n^k \end{bmatrix}$ where $v_1, v_2, \ldots, v_n$ are distinct m^{th} roots of unity; i.e., $\phi_{kj} = \frac{1}{\sqrt{m}} v_j$.

Given the set $\{w_1, w_2, \ldots, w_n\}$ of mth roots of unity determined by the vectors $\{\eta_j\}_{j=0}^{m-1}$, we claim that this set is equal to the set $\{v_1, v_2, \ldots, v_n\}$ due to the equivalence of the two harmonic frames. We prove this by contradiction. Assume that $\{w_1, w_2, \ldots, w_n\} \neq \{v_1, v_2, \ldots, v_n\}$. Without loss of the generality, we can assume that

$v_1 \neq w_j$ for any choice of j, $1 \leq j \leq n$. Let $\{e_1, e_2, \ldots, e_n\}$ be the standard orthonormal basis for $\mathbb{C}^n$. Then we have

$$\sum_{k=0}^{m-1} \overline{v}_1^k \eta_k = \frac{1}{\sqrt{m}} \sum_{j=1}^{n} \Big(\sum_{k=0}^{m-1} (\overline{v}_1 w_j)^k \Big) e_j = \sum_{j=1}^{n} 0 \cdot e_j = 0,$$

since $\bar{v}_1 w_j \neq 1$ for all $1 \leq j \leq n$, so the coefficient of e_j is always zero. Therefore, we also have

$$\sum_{k=0}^{m-1} \overline{v}_1^k \phi_k = \sum_{k=0}^{m-1} \overline{v}_1^k T^{-1} \eta_k = T^{-1} \sum_{k=0}^{m-1} \overline{v}_1^k \eta_k = T^{-1}(0) = 0.$$

However,

$$\left\langle \sum_{k=0}^{m-1} \overline{v}_1^k \phi_k, e_1 \right\rangle = \frac{1}{\sqrt{m}} \sum_{k=0}^{m-1} \overline{v}_1^k v_1^k = \sqrt{m},$$

which contradicts $\sum_{k=0}^{m-1} \overline{v}_1^k \phi_k$ being the zero vector. Therefore, the set $\{w_1, w_2, \ldots, w_n\}$ is equal to $\{v_1, v_2, \ldots, v_n\}$, as claimed. This proves the existence of the required permutation. □

Harmonic frames can be slightly generalized.

Lemma 8.5. *Fix $m \geq n$, $|c| = 1$, and $\{b_i\}_{i=1}^n$ with $|b_i| = \frac{1}{\sqrt{m}}$. Let $\{c_i\}_{i=1}^m$ be the mth roots of c in $\mathbb{C}$. For each $0 \leq k \leq m-1$, let*

$$\phi_k = \begin{bmatrix} c_1^k b_1 \\ c_2^k b_2 \\ \vdots \\ c_n^k b_n \end{bmatrix}.$$

The sequence $\{\phi_0, \phi_1, \ldots, \phi_{m-1}\}$ is a Parseval frame for $\mathbb{C}^n$.

Proof. This can be computed directly, so we leave it to Exercise 3. □

Definition 8.6. The frame defined in Lemma 8.5 is called a *generalized harmonic frame.*

The following proposition gives some properties which classify generalized harmonic frames.

Proposition 8.7. (i) *Every generalized harmonic frame is equivalent to a frame of the form* $\{d^k\eta_k\}_{k=0}^{m-1}$, *where* $|d| = 1$ *and* $\{\eta_k\}_{k=0}^{m-1}$ *is a harmonic frame.*

(ii) *Assume that* $m > n$. *Let* $\{\eta_k\}_{k=0}^{m-1}$ *and* $\{\phi_k\}_{k=0}^{m-1}$ *be harmonic frames for* $\mathbb{C}^n$ *and let* $|c| = 1$. *Then the generalized harmonic frame* $\{c^k\phi_k\}_{k=0}^{m-1}$ *is equivalent to the harmonic frame* $\{\eta_k\}_{k=0}^{m-1}$ *if and only if* c *is an* m^{th} *root of unity and there exists a permutation* σ *of* $\{1, 2, \ldots, n\}$ *such that* $\eta_{kj} = c^k\phi_{k\sigma(j)}$ *for all* $0 \le k \le m-1$ *and all* $1 \le j \le n$,

$$\textit{where } \eta_k = \begin{bmatrix} \eta_{k1} \\ \eta_{k2} \\ \vdots \\ \eta_{kn} \end{bmatrix} \textit{ and } \phi_k = \begin{bmatrix} \phi_{k1} \\ \phi_{k2} \\ \vdots \\ \phi_{kn} \end{bmatrix}.$$

(iii) *Let* $\{\eta_0, \eta_1, \ldots, \eta_{m-1}\}$ *and* $\{\phi_0, \phi_1, \ldots, \phi_{m-1}\}$ *be harmonic frames and let* $|c| = |d| = 1$. *Then the sequences* $\{c^k\eta_k\}_{k=0}^{m-1}$ *and* $\{d^k\phi_k\}_{k=0}^{m-1}$ *are equivalent generalized harmonic frames if and only if* $\frac{c}{d}$ *is an* m^{th} *root of unity and the two harmonic frames are equivalent.*

Proof. (i) Let $\{\phi_0, \phi_1, \ldots, \phi_{m-1}\}$ be a generalized harmonic frame for $\mathbb{C}^n$ with $\phi_k = \begin{bmatrix} c_1^k b_1 \\ c_2^k b_2 \\ \vdots \\ c_n^k b_n \end{bmatrix}$, where $|b_j| = \frac{1}{\sqrt{m}}$ for $1 \le j \le n$, and let $\{c_i\}_{j=1}^n$ be distinct m^{th} roots of c where $|c| = 1$.

Write $c = e^{i\theta}$ and $d = e^{\frac{i\theta}{m}}$. Since $\{c_1, c_2, \ldots, c_n\}$ are distinct m^{th} roots of c, there exist distinct m^{th} roots $\{w_1, w_2, \ldots, w_n\}$ of unity such that

$$c_j = dw_j, \qquad 1 \le j \le n.$$

Let $\eta_k = \frac{1}{\sqrt{m}} \begin{bmatrix} w_1^k \\ w_2^k \\ \vdots \\ w_n^k \end{bmatrix}$ for $0 \le k \le m-1$. We show that the linear map T given by $T\phi_k = d^k\eta_k$ defines a unitary operator on $\mathbb{C}^n$, and so $\{\phi_k\}_{k=0}^{m-1}$ will be equivalent to $\{d^k\eta_k\}_{k=0}^{m-1}$, as expected.

To see that T is unitary, let $a = \sum_{k=0}^{m-1} a_k\phi_k$ be any linear combination of the generalized harmonic frame vectors.

$$\begin{aligned}
\Big\|\sum_{k=0}^{m-1} a_k\phi_k\Big\|^2 &= \sum_{j=1}^{n}\Big|\sum_{k=0}^{m-1} a_k c_j^k b_j\Big|^2 \\
&= \frac{1}{m}\sum_{j=1}^{n}\Big|\sum_{k=0}^{m-1} a_k c_j^k\Big|^2 \\
&= \frac{1}{m}\sum_{j=1}^{n}\Big|\sum_{k=0}^{m-1} a_k d^k w_j^k\Big|^2 \\
&= \Big\|\sum_{k=0}^{m-1} a_k d^k \eta_k\Big\|^2 \\
&= \Big\|T\Big(\sum_{k=0}^{m-1} a_k\phi_k\Big)\Big\|^2.
\end{aligned}$$

Since $\|Ta\| = \|a\|$, we have proved that T is an isometry, and is therefore unitary, which completes the proof of (i).

(ii) By Proposition 8.4, it suffices to show that c is an mth root of unity if $\{\eta_k\}_{k=0}^{m-1}$ and $\{c^k\phi_k\}_{k=0}^{m-1}$ are equivalent. Let $\eta_{kj} = \frac{1}{\sqrt{m}}w_j^k$ with $\{w_1, w_2, \ldots, w_n\}$ being distinct m^{th} roots of unity.

Without loss of generality, we can assume $1 \notin \{w_1, w_2, \ldots, w_n\}$. (Otherwise, since $n < m$, we can choose an mth root of unity u such that $1 \notin \{uw_1, \ldots, uw_n\}$. Then replace η_k by $u^k\eta_k$, and ϕ_k by $u^k\phi_k$.) Thus we have $\sum_{k=0}^{m-1}\eta_k = 0$ since $\sum_{k=0}^{m-1} w_j^k = 0$ when $w_j \neq 1$.

Let $\phi_{kj} = \frac{1}{\sqrt{m}}v_j^k$ with $\{v_1, v_2, \ldots, v_n\}$ being distinct m^{th} roots of unity. If $c = v_j^{-1}$ for some $1 \le j \le n$, then we are done. Otherwise assume that $c \neq (v_j)^{-1}$ for all $1 \le j \le n$. Using the fact that $\{\eta_k\}_{k=0}^{m-1}$ and $\{c^k\phi_k\}_{k=0}^{m-1}$ are equivalent, and the fact that $\sum_{k=0}^{m-1}\eta_k = 0$, we have $\sum_{k=1}^{n} c^k\phi_k = 0$. So we have

$$0 = \sum_{k=1}^{m-1} c^k v_j^k = \sum_{k=0}^{m-1}(cv_j)^k = \frac{1-(cv_j)^m}{1-cv_j}.$$

Hence $1 = (cv_j)^m = c^m v_j^m = c^m$, as claimed.

(iii) follows from (ii) and the fact that $\{\eta_k\}_{k=0}^{m-1}$ and $\{(\frac{d}{c})^k\phi_k\}_{k=0}^{m-1}$ are equivalent when $\{c^k\eta_k\}_{k=0}^{m-1}$ and $\{d^k\phi_k\}_{k=0}^{m-1}$ are equivalent. □

The following theorem reveals the connection between harmonic or generalized harmonic frames and group frames. Group frames will be formally introduced in the next section.

Theorem 8.8. *Let $\{\phi_k\}_{k=0}^{m-1}$ be a generalized harmonic frame for $\mathbb{C}^n$. Then we have the following properties:*

(i) $\langle \phi_i, \phi_j \rangle = \langle \phi_{i+1}, \phi_{j+1} \rangle$ *for all* $0 \le i, j \le m-1$, *where* $\phi_m = \phi_0$.

(ii) *There exists a unitary operator U on $\mathbb{C}^n$ such that $U^m = I$, $U^k \ne I$ for $1 \le k \le m-1$, and $\phi_k = U^k\phi_0$ for $0 \le k \le m-1$.*

Moreover (i) *and* (ii) *are equivalent statements.*

Proof. Let $\phi_k = \begin{bmatrix} c_1^k b_1 \\ c_2^k b_2 \\ \vdots \\ c_n^k b_n \end{bmatrix}$ for $k = 0, 1, \ldots, m-1$ with $\{c_j\}_{j=1}^n$ being distinct m^{th} roots of c and $|c| = 1$, $|b_j| = \frac{1}{\sqrt{m}}$. Then we clearly have that $\phi_{k+m} = \phi_k$ for all $k \ge 0$.

(i) This is a direct calculation, so we leave it to Exercise 3.

(ii) Define U by $Ux = \sum_{k=0}^{m-1} \langle x, \phi_k \rangle \phi_{k+1}$. Then, by (i), for each j we have

$$\begin{aligned} U\phi_j &= \sum_{k=0}^{m-1} \langle \phi_j, \phi_k \rangle \phi_{k+1} \\ &= \sum_{k=0}^{m-1} \langle \phi_{j+1}, \phi_{k+1} \rangle \phi_{k+1} \\ &= \sum_{k=0}^{m-1} \langle \phi_{j+1}, \phi_k \rangle \phi_k \\ &= \phi_{j+1}. \end{aligned}$$

This gives the following for UU^*:

$$\begin{aligned} UU^*x &= \sum_{k=0}^{m-1} \langle U^*x, \phi_k \rangle \phi_{k+1} \\ &= \sum_{k=0}^{m-1} \langle x, U\phi_k \rangle \phi_{k+1} \\ &= \sum_{k=0}^{m-1} \langle x, \phi_{k+1} \rangle \phi_{k+1} = x, \end{aligned}$$

which implies that U is unitary. Clearly $U^m = I$ and $U^k \neq I$ for $1 \leq k \leq m-1$.

Next, we prove the equivalence of (i) and (ii).

(ii)$\rightarrow$(i) is immediate because U is unitary and therefore preserves inner products.

For (i)$\rightarrow$(ii), we have that

$$\begin{aligned} \left\| \sum_{k=0}^{m-1} \alpha_k \phi_{k+1} \right\|^2 &= \sum_{k,j=0}^{m-1} \alpha_k \bar{\alpha}_j \langle \phi_{k+1}, \phi_{j+1} \rangle \\ &= \sum_{k,j=0}^{m-1} \alpha_k \bar{\alpha}_j \langle \phi_k, \phi_j \rangle \\ &= \left\| \sum_{k=0}^{m-1} \alpha_k \phi_k \right\|^2 \end{aligned}$$

holds for any selection of scalars $\{\alpha_k\}_{k=0}^{m-1}$. Thus defining the linear operator U by $U\phi_k = \phi_{k+1}$ results in U being a unitary operator with $U^k\phi_0 = \phi_k$ for $0 \leq k \leq m-1$. □

From the previous theorem, we obtain the fact that every generalized harmonic frame has the form $\{U^k\phi : 0 \leq k \leq m-1\}$, where U is a unitary operator of order m; i.e., $U^m = I$ but $U^k \neq I$ for $1 \leq k < m$. We will generalize this in the next section.

8.2. Frame Representations and Group Frames

Let G and $\widetilde{G}$ be two groups. A mapping π from G to $\widetilde{G}$ is called a *group homomorphism* if $\pi(g_1g_2) = \pi(g_1)\pi(g_2)$ and $\pi(g^{-1}) = (\pi(g))^{-1}$ for all g, g_1, g_2 in G.

Definition 8.9. Let G be a group. A *unitary representation* π of G on a Hilbert space $\mathcal{H}$ is a group homomorphism from G into the group of all the unitary operators on $\mathcal{H}$. In other words, for every $g, h \in G$, $\pi(g), \pi(h)$ are unitary operators on $\mathcal{H}$ such that $\pi(g)\pi(h) = \pi(gh)$ and $\pi(g^{-1}) = (\pi(g))^{-1}$.

The set of all unitary operators on $\mathcal{H}$ is a group under the operation of composition. If U_1, U_2 are unitary operators, then U_1U_2 is also unitary, each unitary operator has an inverse $U^{-1} = U^*$, and the identity operator is the unitary operator which serves as the group identity. The Hilbert space $\mathcal{H}$ in the above definition is called the *representation space*. Two unitary representations π and Δ of a group G, respectively, on representation spaces $\mathcal{H}_\pi$ and $\mathcal{H}_\Delta$ are said to be *equivalent* if there is a unitary operator $U : \mathcal{H}_\pi \to \mathcal{H}_\Delta$ such that $U\pi(g)U^* = \Delta(g)$ holds for every $g \in G$.

An *invariant subspace* for a unitary representation π of G on $\mathcal{H}$ is a (closed) subspace M of $\mathcal{H}$ such that $\pi(g)M \subseteq M$ for all $g \in G$, or equivalently, the orthogonal projection P onto M commutes with every unitary operator $\pi(g)$ (see Lemma 8.10 below).

If M is an invariant subspace of π, then the restriction of π to M is also a unitary representation of G, and this representation is called a *subrepresentation* of π, and is denoted by π_P, where P is the orthogonal projection onto M.

Lemma 8.10. *Let π be a unitary representation of a group G on $\mathcal{H}$ and let M be a closed subspace of the representation space $\mathcal{H}$.*

(i) *M is an invariant subspace π if and only if $P\pi(g) = \pi(g)P$ holds for all $g \in G$, where P is the orthogonal projection from $\mathcal{H}$ onto M.*

(ii) *If M is an invariant subspace of π, then the restriction of π to M is also a unitary representation of G.*

Proof. We leave the proof of this lemma to Exercise 6. □

Definition 8.11. A unitary representation π of a group G on $\mathcal{H}$ is called a *frame representation* if there is a vector $\phi \in \mathcal{H}$ such that $\{\pi(g)\phi\}_{g\in G}$ is a frame for $\mathcal{H}$, and in this case we say that $\{\pi(g)\phi\}_{g\in G}$ is a *group frame or G-frame.*

Any G-frame is clearly a uniform frame since $\|\pi(g)\phi\| = \|\phi\|$. By Theorem 8.8, we know that general harmonic frames are special group frames with G being a cyclic group of order m. More generally, when G is an abelian group (i.e., $g_1g_2 = g_2g_1$ for all $g_1, g_2 \in G$), a G-frame is sometime also called a *geometrically uniform* frame in the literature (cf. [**11**]). For the rest of this section we always assume that G is a finite group and the representation space $\mathcal{H}$ is finite-dimensional.

The following proposition tells us that if a G-frame $\{\pi(g)\phi\}_{g\in G}$ is Parseval, then $\|\phi\|$ determines the frame redundancy.

Proposition 8.12. *Let $\{\pi(g)\phi\}_{g\in G}$ be a G-frame for $\mathcal{H}$ with frame bounds A and B. Then*

$$A \le \frac{m}{n}\|\phi\|^2 \le B,$$

where m is the order of G and $n = \dim \mathcal{H}$. In particular, $\|\phi\|^2 = \frac{n}{m}$ when the G-frame is Parseval.

Proof. Let S be the frame operator for the frame $\{\pi(g)\phi\}_{g\in G}$, and let $\lambda_1, \lambda_2, \ldots, \lambda_n$ be its eigenvalues. Then $A = \min_i\{\lambda_i\}$ and $B = \max_i\{\lambda_i\}$. Note that we can write S in its rank-one decomposition $S = \sum_{g\in G} \pi(g)\phi \otimes \pi(g)\phi$. Thus

$$\sum_{i=1}^{n} \lambda_i = \mathrm{tr}(S) = \sum_{g\in G} \mathrm{tr}[\pi(g)\phi \otimes \pi(g)\phi)] = \sum_{g\in G} \|\phi\|^2 = m\|\phi\|^2.$$

Thus the proposition follows. □

The next result tells us that the canonical dual of a group frame is also a group frame.

Proposition 8.13. *Let $\{\pi(g)\phi\}_{g\in G}$ be a G-frame for $\mathcal{H}$. Then the canonical dual has the form $\{\pi(g)\psi\}_{g\in G}$ for some $\psi \in \mathcal{H}$.*

Proof. Let S be the associated frame operator for $\{\pi(g)\phi\}_{g\in G}$. Then we have, for every $g \in G$, that

$$\begin{aligned} S\pi(g)x &= \sum_{g'\in G} \langle \pi(g)x, \pi(g')\phi \rangle \pi(g')\phi \\ &= \pi(g) \sum_{g'\in G} \left\langle x, \pi(g^{-1}g')\phi \right\rangle \pi(g^{-1}g')\phi \\ &= \pi(g) \sum_{h\in G} \langle x, \pi(h)\phi \rangle \pi(h)\phi \\ &= \pi(g)Sx \end{aligned}$$

for all $x \in \mathcal{H}$. Thus $S\pi(g) = \pi(g)S$ for all $g \in G$, which implies that $S^{-1}\pi(g) = \pi(g)S^{-1}$. Let $\psi = S^{-1}\phi$. Then for each $g \in G$, we have $S^{-1}\pi(g)\phi = \pi(g)\psi$. The canonical dual of $\{\pi(g)\phi\}_{g\in G}$ is $\{S^{-1}\pi(g)\phi\}_{g\in G} = \{\pi(g)\psi\}_{g\in G}$, and therefore is a G-frame. □

As a consequence of the proof of the above proposition, we immediately have:

Corollary 8.14. *Let $\{\pi(g)\phi\}_{g\in G}$ be a G-frame and let S be its frame operator. Then S commutes with $\pi(g)$ for every $g \in G$.*

Corollary 8.15. *Let π be a unitary representation of a group G on a finite-dimensional Hilbert space $\mathcal{H}$. Then the following are equivalent:*

(i) *There is a vector $\phi \in \mathcal{H}$ such that* $\text{span}\{\pi(g)\phi\}_{g\in G} = \mathcal{H}$.

(ii) *There exists ϕ in $\mathcal{H}$ such that $\{\pi(g)\phi\}_{g\in G}$ is a G-frame for $\mathcal{H}$.*

(iii) *There exists ψ in $\mathcal{H}$ such that $\{\pi(g)\psi\}_{g\in G}$ is a Parseval G-frame for $\mathcal{H}$.*

Proof. We know (i) and (ii) are equivalent from Section 3.3, where we showed that a sequence is a frame for a finite-dimensional Hilbert space $\mathcal{H}$ if and only if the sequence spans $\mathcal{H}$. We also know (iii) implies (ii) by the simple fact that a Parseval frame is a frame. We therefore only need to prove that (ii) implies (iii).

Let S be the analysis operator for the G-frame $\{\pi(g)\phi\}_{g\in G}$. By Corollary 8.14, S commutes with every $\pi(g)$ and by Corollary 2.78 we also know that $S^{\frac{1}{2}}$ commutes with each $\pi(g)$. Therefore, we also have

$S^{-\frac{1}{2}}$ commuting with each $\pi(g)$ in the case where S is invertible. This implies that $\{S^{-\frac{1}{2}}\pi(g)\phi\}_{g\in G} = \{\pi(g)S^{-\frac{1}{2}}\phi\}_{g\in G}$. Let $\psi = S^{-\frac{1}{2}}\phi$. Then $\{\pi(g)\psi\}_{g\in G}$ is a Parseval G-frame. □

Let π and Δ be two unitary representations of a group G on Hilbert spaces $\mathcal{H}$ and $\mathcal{K}$, respectively. The *direct sum* of π and Δ is the representation on $\mathcal{H} \oplus \mathcal{K}$ defined by:

$$(\pi \oplus \Delta)(g) = \pi(g) \oplus \Delta(g)$$

for every $g \in G$. This definition obviously can be generalized to the direct sum of several unitary representations.

Theorem 8.16. *Every unitary representation of a finite group G is a finite direct sum of frame representations.*

Proof. Let π be a unitary representation of a finite group G on a finite-dimensional Hilbert space $\mathcal{H}$. First pick any nonzero vector $\psi_1 \in \mathcal{H}$. If $M_1 = \text{span}\{\pi(g)\psi_1\}_{g\in G} \neq \mathcal{H}$, then $M_1^\perp \neq \{0\}$, and so we can pick another nonzero vector $\psi_2 \in M_1^\perp$. Repeating this procedure, we can find a finite number of vectors $\psi_1, \psi_2, \ldots, \psi_m$ such that $M_1, M_2, \ldots, M_m$ are mutually orthogonal and $M_1 \oplus M_2 \oplus \cdots \oplus M_m = \mathcal{H}$, where $M_j = \text{span}\{\pi(g)\psi_j\}_{g\in G}$ is invariant under π. Let π_j be the restriction of π to M_j. Then π_j is a unitary representation on M_j which has a spanning vector ψ_j and thus, by Corollary 8.15, it is a frame representation. Clearly, π is the direct sum of $\pi_1, \pi_2, \ldots, \pi_m$. □

In the rest of this section, we will discuss a variety of classifications of group frames and frame representations.

The most basic model for unitary representations is the so-called *left regular representation* λ of G on $\ell^2(G)$. Recall that we define the space $\ell^2(G)$ to be the set of all sequences $(a_g)_{g\in G}$ with each $a_g \in \mathbb{C}$ and $\sum_{g\in G} |a_g|^2 < \infty$. The standard orthonormal basis for $\ell^2(G)$ is $\{(e_h)\}_{h\in G}$ which is the sequence in which the entries $e_h(g) = 0$ for $g \neq h$ and $e_h(h) = 1$. Then the left regular representation on $\ell^2(G)$ is the unitary system $\{\lambda_g\}_{g\in G}$, where we describe the transformation of λ_g on each element of the standard orthonormal basis:

$$\lambda(g)e_h = e_{gh}, \quad h \in G.$$

Similarly, the *right regular representation* ρ is the unitary system $\{\rho_g\}_{g\in G}$ which is defined by:

$$\rho(g)e_h = e_{hg^{-1}}, \qquad h \in G.$$

Proposition 8.17. (i) *Both left and right regular representations are unitary representations on* $\ell^2(G)$.

(ii) *For every* $h \in G$, $\{\lambda(g)e_h\}_{g\in G}$ *is an orthonormal basis for* $\ell^2(G)$.

Proof. Exercise 7. □

The left regular representation plays a crucial role in classifying group frames. As we develop this classification, we will need the following lemma:

Lemma 8.18. *If* $\{\pi(g)\phi\}_{g\in G}$ *is a* G*-frame for* $\mathcal{H}$, *then the range space of its analysis operator is invariant under* $\lambda(G)$.

Proof. Let Θ be the analysis operator of $\{\pi(g)\phi\}_{g\in G}$ and let $M = \text{range}(\Theta)$. For any $x \in \mathcal{H}$ and every $h \in G$, we have

$$\begin{aligned}
\lambda(h)\Theta(x) &= \lambda(h)\sum_{g\in G}\langle x, \pi(g)\phi\rangle e_g \\
&= \sum_{g\in G}\langle \pi(h)x, \pi(h)\pi(g)\phi\rangle \lambda(h)e_g \\
&= \sum_{g\in G}\langle \pi(h)x, \pi(hg)\phi\rangle e_{hg} \\
&= \sum_{g\in G}\langle \pi(h)x, \pi(g)\phi\rangle e_g \\
&= \Theta(\pi(h)x).
\end{aligned}$$

Thus $\lambda(h)\Theta(x) \in \text{range}(\Theta)$, and so M is invariant under $\lambda(G)$. □

Theorem 8.19. *Every frame representation* π *is unitarily equivalent to a subrepresentation of the left regular representation* λ *of* G.

Proof. Let $\{\pi(g)\phi\}_{g\in G}$ be a Parseval frame for $\mathcal{H}$, which exists by Corollary 8.15, and let Θ be its analysis operator. Then by Lemma 8.18, the range space $M := \Theta(\mathcal{H})$ is invariant under the unitary operator $\lambda(g)$ for all $g \in G$. Let σ be the restriction of π to M.

We claim that σ and π are equivalent. In fact, clearly Θ is a unitary operator from $\mathcal{H}$ onto M. We need to check that $\Theta\pi(g) = \sigma(g)\Theta$ holds for every $g \in G$. The proof is almost identical to that of Lemma 8.18. Indeed, for every $x \in \mathcal{H}$ we have

$$\begin{aligned}
\sigma(g)\Theta(x) &= \lambda(g)\Theta(x) \\
&= \lambda(g) \sum_{h \in G} \langle x, \pi(h)\phi \rangle e_h \\
&= \sum_{h \in G} \langle x, \pi(h)\phi \rangle \lambda(g) e_h \\
&= \sum_{h \in G} \langle \pi(g)x, \pi(gh)\phi \rangle e_{gh} \\
&= \sum_{h \in G} \langle \pi(g)x, \ \pi(h)\phi \rangle e_h \\
&= \Theta(\pi(g)x).
\end{aligned}$$

Thus $\Theta\pi(g) = \sigma(g)\Theta$ as claimed. Therefore σ and π are equivalent. $\square$

As a consequence we have the following dilation result:

Corollary 8.20. *Let π be a frame representation of a group G on the Hilbert space $\mathcal{H}$. Assume that $\{\pi(g)\phi\}_{g \in G}$ is a Parseval frame for $\mathcal{H}$. Then there exists another frame representation Δ on $\mathcal{K}$ such that there exists a Parseval frame $\{\Delta(g)\eta\}_{g \in G}$ for $\mathcal{K}$ with the property that*

$$\{\pi(g)\phi \oplus \Delta(g)\eta\}_{g \in G}$$

is an orthonormal basis for $\mathcal{H} \oplus \mathcal{K}$.

Proof. Let M be the range of the analysis operator for $\{\pi(g)\phi\}_{g \in G}$, as in the proof of the previous theorem. Since M is invariant under the left regular representation λ, we find that $M^{\perp}$ is invariant under the left regular representation as well. Let P be the orthogonal projection onto M, let Δ be the restriction of the left regular to $M^{\perp}$, and let $\eta = P^{\perp} e_{\text{id}}$, where "id" is the group identity element of G. Then it can be checked (Exercise 8) that

$$\{\pi(g)\phi \oplus \Delta(g)\eta\}_{g \in G}$$

is an orthonormal basis for $\mathcal{H} \oplus \mathcal{K}$, where $\mathcal{K} = M^{\perp}$. $\square$

In order to describe a classification of frame representations, we need to introduce some definitions. Let $\mathcal{S}$ be a set of bounded linear operators on a Hilbert space $\mathcal{H}$, so $\mathcal{S} \subseteq \mathcal{B}(\mathcal{H})$. We use $\mathcal{S}'$ to denote the *commutant* of $\mathcal{S}$, which is the algebra consisting of all the bounded linear operators on $\mathcal{H}$ which commute with every element of $\mathcal{S}$. The algebra generated by a representation π is denoted by $\mathcal{A}_\pi$; i.e., $\mathcal{A}_\pi = \operatorname{span}\{\pi(g)\}_{g\in G}$.

Given an invariant subspace M of the left regular representation λ, we use λ_P to denote the subrepresentation of λ restricted to M, where P is the orthogonal projection onto M. We will denote the commutant of the group of unitary operators $\{\lambda_g\}_{g\in G}$ by $\lambda(G)'$.

Theorem 8.21. *Let λ_P and λ_Q be two subrepresentations of the left regular representation of G. Then they are equivalent if and only if there is an operator $V \in \lambda(G)'$ such that $V^*V = P$ and $VV^* = Q$, where V^* is the adjoint operator of V.*

The operator V is a partial isometry in $\lambda(G)'$ with support projection P and range projection Q. The two projections P and Q satisfying the condition in the above theorem are called *equivalent projections* in the algebra $\lambda(G)'$. We also say that the two corresponding subspaces range(P) and range(Q) are equivalent in $\lambda(G)'$.

Proof. For the sufficiency, if we also regard V as a unitary operator from the range space of P onto the range space of Q, then it induces the unitary equivalence between λ_P and λ_Q since

$$\begin{aligned} V\lambda_P(g) &= V\lambda(g)P = \lambda(g)VP \\ &= \lambda(g)V(V^*V) = \lambda(g)(VV^*)V \\ &= \lambda(g)QV = \lambda_Q(g)V. \end{aligned}$$

Conversely, assume that λ_P and λ_Q are equivalent, and let U be a unitary operator from the range of P onto the range of Q such that $U\lambda_P(g) = \lambda_Q(g)U$ holds for every $g \in G$. We define an operator V on $\ell^2(G)$ by letting it agree with U on the subspace $P\ell^2(G)$ and be zero on $P^\perp\ell^2(G)$. Then it can be checked (see Exercise 10) that V commutes with $\lambda(g)$ for all g, and thus $V \in \lambda(G)'$. Clearly, $VV^* = Q$ and $V^*V = P$. □

Combining Theorems 8.21 and 8.19 we immediately have the following result, which is our description of equivalent frame representations.

Corollary 8.22. *Let π and σ be two frame representations of a group G on $\mathcal{H}_\pi$ and $\mathcal{H}_\sigma$, respectively. Then the following are equivalent:*

(i) *π and σ are equivalent representations.*

(ii) *There exist group frames $\{\pi(g)\phi\}_{g\in G} \subset \mathcal{H}_\pi$ and $\{\sigma(g)\eta\}_{g\in G} \subset \mathcal{H}_\sigma$ which are (unitarily) equivalent frames.*

Proof. (i)→(ii): Let U be a unitary operator such that $U\pi(g) = \sigma(g)U$ for all $g \in G$. Let $\{\pi(g)\phi\}_{g\in G}$ be a frame for $\mathcal{H}_\pi$. Then $\{\sigma(g)U\phi\}_{g\in G} = \{U\pi(g)\phi\}_{g\in G}$ is a frame for $\mathcal{H}_\sigma$. Let $\eta = U\phi$. Then $\{\pi(g)\phi\}_{g\in G}$ and $\{\sigma(g)\eta\}_{g\in G}$ are (unitarily) equivalent frames.

(ii)→(i): Given the equivalent group frames $\{\pi(g)\phi\}_{g\in G}$ and $\{\sigma(g)\eta\}_{g\in G}$, let Θ_1 and Θ_2 be their respective analysis operators. Then they have the same range space, say M. By Theorem 8.19, both π and σ are equivalent to the subrepresentation of λ restricted to M. Hence π and σ are equivalent. □

8.3. Frame Vectors for Unitary Systems

In the rest of this chapter, we will discuss a more general setting: frames induced by a system (not necessarily a group) of unitary operators. This general setting was introduced by Dai, Han, and Larson in [**24, 42**] with the motivation from wavelets and functional analysis.

Definition 8.23. (i) A *unitary system* $\mathcal{U}$ on a Hilbert space $\mathcal{H}$ is a collection of unitary operators on $\mathcal{H}$ that contains the identity operator I.

(ii) A *wandering vector* for $\mathcal{U}$ is a vector $\psi \in \mathcal{H}$ such that

$$\mathcal{U}\psi := \{U\psi\}_{U\in\mathcal{U}}$$

is an orthonormal basis for $\mathcal{H}$.

(iii) A *frame vector* for $\mathcal{U}$ is a vector $\eta \in \mathcal{H}$ such that $\mathcal{U}\eta$ is a frame for $\mathcal{H}$. If $\mathcal{U}\eta$ is a Parseval frame for $\mathcal{H}$, we call η a *Parseval frame vector.*

We will use $\mathcal{W}(\mathcal{U})$ to denote the set of all the wandering vectors for a unitary system $\mathcal{U}$.

Proposition 8.24. *Assume that $\mathcal{U}$ is a unitary system on a finite-dimensional Hilbert space $\mathcal{H}$ such that $\mathcal{U}$ admits a wandering vector. Then both of the following are true:*

(i) *Every Parseval frame vector is also a wandering vector.*

(ii) *If $\mathcal{U}\eta$ is a frame for $\mathcal{H}$, then it is a linearly independent basis for $\mathcal{H}$.*

We remark that the above result is *not* true when $\mathcal{H}$ has infinite dimension.

Proof. Suppose that $\psi \in \mathcal{W}(\mathcal{U})$. Then we have that the number of elements in $\mathcal{U}$ is the same as the dimension of $\mathcal{H}$, say n. Let $\mathcal{U}\eta$ be a frame for $\mathcal{H}$. Then $\mathcal{U}\eta$ is a spanning set and hence contains at least n vectors. Since $\mathcal{U}$ contains n elements, it follows that $\mathcal{U}\eta$ must have exactly n elements, and hence must be a basis for $\mathcal{H}$. This proves (ii). If, in addition, $\mathcal{U}\eta$ is Parseval, then it is a Parseval basis and so it is an orthonormal basis. Thus η is a wandering vector and so (i) is proved. □

Let $\mathcal{S}$ be any subset of the bounded linear operators $\mathcal{B}(\mathcal{H})$ on $\mathcal{H}$ and let $x \in \mathcal{H}$ be a nonzero vector. The *local commutant* of $\mathcal{U}$ at x is the set of all linear operators T on $\mathcal{H}$ which commute with each $S \in \mathcal{S}$ at the point x:

$$\mathcal{C}_x(\mathcal{S}) := \{T \in \mathcal{B}(\mathcal{H}) : TSx = STx, \forall S \in \mathcal{S}\}.$$

It is straightforward to demonstrate that $\mathcal{C}_x(\mathcal{S})$ is a subspace of $\mathcal{B}(\mathcal{H})$, so we leave this to the exercises.

Lemma 8.25. *$\mathcal{C}_x(\mathcal{S})$ is always a subspace of $\mathcal{B}(\mathcal{H})$.*

Proof. Exercise 11. □

Moreover we also have the the following properties.

Lemma 8.26. *Let $\mathcal{S} \subset \mathcal{B}(\mathcal{H})$ and suppose there exists $x \in \mathcal{H}$ such that* $\operatorname{span}\{Sx\}_{S\in\mathcal{S}} = \mathcal{H}$. *Then both of the following statements hold:*

(i) *If $T \in \mathcal{C}_x(\mathcal{S})$ such that $Tx = 0$, then $T = 0$. That is, x is a separating vector for $\mathcal{C}_x(\mathcal{S})$.*

(ii) *If $\mathcal{S}$ is closed under multiplication (i.e., $S_1 S_2 \in \mathcal{S}$ whenever $S_1, S_2 \in \mathcal{S}$), then $\mathcal{C}_x(\mathcal{S}) = \mathcal{S}'$.*

Proof. (i) Assume that $T \in \mathcal{C}_x(\mathcal{S})$ such that $Tx = 0$. Then $T(Sx) = STx = 0$ for every $S \in \mathcal{S}$. Thus $Ty = 0$ for every $y \in \text{span}\{Sx\}_{S \in \mathcal{S}} = \mathcal{H}$. Hence $T = 0$.

(ii) Clearly, by the definition of the commutant, $\mathcal{C}_x(\mathcal{S}) \supseteq \mathcal{S}'$. To prove the equality, let $T \in \mathcal{C}_x(\mathcal{S})$. We need to show that for any $S \in \mathcal{S}$, we have $ST = TS$. In fact, let $S_1 \in \mathcal{S}$ be arbitrary. Then, since $SS_1 \in \mathcal{S}$, we have

$$TS(S_1 x) = T(SS_1)x = (SS_1)Tx.$$

Note that $S_1 Tx = TS_1 x$ since $T \in \mathcal{C}_x(\mathcal{S})$. Thus

$$TS(S_1 x) = ST(S_1 x),$$

which implies that $TSy = STy$ for all $y \in \text{span}\{S_1 x\}_{S_1 \in \mathcal{S}} = \mathcal{H}$. So $TS = ST$, as claimed. □

A useful fact is that the set of all wandering vectors for a unitary system $\mathcal{U}$ can be parameterized by the set of all unitary operators in the local commutant $\mathcal{C}_\psi(\mathcal{U})$ for any fixed wandering vector ψ.

Proposition 8.27. *Let $\mathcal{U}$ be a unitary system on a Hilbert space $\mathcal{H}$ and let $\psi \in \mathcal{W}(\mathcal{U})$. Then a vector ϕ is a wandering vector for $\mathcal{U}$ if and only if there exists a unitary operator V in $\mathcal{C}_\psi(\mathcal{U})$ such that $\phi = V\psi$.*

Proof. Let $V \in \mathcal{C}_\psi(\mathcal{U})$ be a unitary operator such that $\phi = V\psi$. Then we have $\mathcal{U}V\psi = V\mathcal{U}\psi$ since $UV\psi = VU\psi$ for every $U \in \mathcal{U}$. Since $\mathcal{U}\psi$ is an orthonormal basis for $\mathcal{H}$ and V is unitary, we have that $V\mathcal{U}\psi$ is also an orthonormal basis for $\mathcal{H}$. Thus $\mathcal{U}V\psi$ is an orthonormal basis for $\mathcal{H}$, which implies that ϕ is a wondering vector for $\mathcal{U}$.

For the converse assertion, assume that $\phi \in \mathcal{W}(\mathcal{U})$. We define a linear operator V by

$$VU\psi = U\phi, \quad \forall U \in \mathcal{U}.$$

Since V sends an orthonormal basis to an orthonormal basis, it follows that V is unitary. Moreover, since $I \in \mathcal{U}$, we have $V\psi = \phi$ which implies that $VU\psi = U\phi = UV\psi$ for all $U \in \mathcal{U}$. So $V \in \mathcal{C}_\psi(\mathcal{U})$. $\square$

However, for Parseval frame vectors only one direction of the above proposition is true:

Proposition 8.28. *Let $\mathcal{U}$ be a unitary system on a Hilbert space $\mathcal{H}$ and let η be a Parseval frame vector for $\mathcal{U}$.*

(i) *If there exists a unitary operator V in $\mathcal{C}_\eta(\mathcal{U})$ such that $\xi = V\eta$, then ξ is also a Parseval frame vector.*

(ii) *If $A \in \mathcal{C}_\eta(\mathcal{U})$ is an invertible operator, then $\mathcal{U}A\eta$ is a frame for $\mathcal{H}$.*

Proof. (i) For every $x \in \mathcal{H}$, we have

$$\begin{aligned}\sum_{U\in\mathcal{U}} |\langle x, U\xi\rangle|^2 &= \sum_{U\in\mathcal{U}} |\langle x, UV\eta\rangle|^2 \\ &= \sum_{U\in\mathcal{U}} |\langle x, VU\eta\rangle|^2 \\ &= \sum_{U\in\mathcal{U}} |\langle V^*x, U\eta\rangle|^2 \\ &= \|V^*x\|^2 = \|x\|^2.\end{aligned}$$

Thus we have proved (i).

(ii) For every $x \in \mathcal{H}$, we have

$$\begin{aligned}\sum_{U\in\mathcal{U}} |\langle x, UA\eta\rangle|^2 &= \sum_{U\in\mathcal{U}} |\langle x, AU\eta\rangle|^2 \\ &= \sum_{U\in\mathcal{U}} |\langle A^*x, U\eta\rangle|^2 \\ &= \|A^*x\|^2.\end{aligned}$$

Since A is invertible, we have that A^* is also invertible. Thus

$$\sum_{U\in\mathcal{U}} |\langle x, UA\eta\rangle|^2 = \|A^*x\|^2 \le \|A^*\|^2 \cdot \|x\|^2.$$

Note that

$$\|x\| = \|(A^*)^{-1}A^*x\| \le \|(A^*)^{-1}\| \cdot \|A^*x\|.$$

We have the other end of the frame inequality:

$$\sum_{U\in\mathcal{U}} |\langle x, UA\eta\rangle|^2 = \|A^*x\|^2 \geq \frac{1}{\|(A^*)^{-1}\|^2}\|x\|^2. \qquad \square$$

In the case where $\mathcal{U}$ is a group representation, we also have a parameterization result for the set of all Parseval frames. Since the proof is much more technical we only state the result without giving the proof. We encourage the interested reader to consult [**42**] for more details.

Theorem 8.29. [**42**] *Let $\mathcal{U}$ be a group unitary system (i.e., $\mathcal{U}$ is a group with respect to the operator multiplication) on a Hilbert space $\mathcal{H}$ and let $\mathcal{A} = \operatorname{span}\{U : U \in \mathcal{U}\}$. Assume that η is a fixed Parseval frame vector for $\mathcal{U}$. Then the following hold:*

(i) *A vector ξ is a Parseval frame vector for $\mathcal{U}$ if and only if there exists a unitary operator $V \in \mathcal{A}$ such that $\xi = V\eta$.*

(ii) *A vector ξ is a frame vector for $\mathcal{U}$ if and only if there exists an invertible operator $A \in \mathcal{A}$ such that $\xi = A\eta$.*

Finally, we discuss the conditions under which a linear combination of two frame vectors for a unitary system is still a frame vector.

Proposition 8.30. *Let $\mathcal{U}$ be a unitary system on a Hilbert space $\mathcal{H}$. If η and ξ are two Parseval frame vectors for $\mathcal{U}$ such that $\xi = V\eta$ for some unitary operator $V \in \mathcal{C}_\eta(\mathcal{U})$, then the nonzero vector $\alpha\eta + \beta\xi$ is a frame vector for $\mathcal{U}$, except possibly when $|\alpha| = |\beta|$.*

Proof. Let $A = \alpha I + \beta V$ with α, β not all zero. Then $A\eta = \alpha\eta + \beta\xi$ and $A \in \mathcal{C}_\eta(\mathcal{U})$ since $\mathcal{C}_\eta(\mathcal{U})$ is a linear subspace, and $I, V \in \mathcal{C}_\eta(\mathcal{U})$. Recall that the eigenvalues of any unitary operator are contained in $\mathbb{T} = \{z : |z| = 1\}$. Thus, by the Spectral Mapping Theorem, A is invertible when $|\alpha| \neq |\beta|$. And so, by Proposition 8.28(ii), $\alpha\eta + \beta\xi = A\eta$ is a frame vector for $\mathcal{U}$. $\square$

We have the following two special cases of Proposition 8.30:

Corollary 8.31. *Let $\mathcal{U}$ be a unitary system on a Hilbert space $\mathcal{H}$.*

(i) *For any two wandering vectors* $\psi, \phi \in \mathcal{W}(\mathcal{U})$, *we have that the nonzero vector* $\alpha\psi + \beta\phi$ *is a frame vector for* $\mathcal{U}$, *except possibly when* $|\alpha| = |\beta|$.

(ii) *If* $\mathcal{U}$ *is a group and* η *and* ξ *are two Parseval frame vectors, then the nonzero vector* $\alpha\eta + \beta\xi$ *is a frame vector for* $\mathcal{U}$, *except possibly when* $|\alpha| = |\beta|$.

Proof. (i) This follows from Proposition 8.30 and the parameterization result in Proposition 8.27.

(ii) From Theorem 8.29 we know that there exists a unitary operator $V \in \text{span}(\mathcal{U})$ such that $\xi = V\eta$. Let $A = \alpha I + \beta V$. Then $A\eta = \alpha\eta + \beta\xi$ and $A \in \text{span}(\mathcal{U})$. Thus, by Theorem 8.29(ii), $\alpha\eta + \beta\xi$ is a frame vector if A is invertible. The rest of the argument follows from the proof of Proposition 8.30. $\square$

Proposition 8.32. *Let* $\mathcal{U}$ *be a unitary system on a Hilbert space* $\mathcal{H}$, *and let* $\psi, \phi \in \mathcal{W}(\mathcal{U})$ *such that* $\phi = V\psi$ *for* V *a unitary operator in* $\mathcal{C}_\psi(\mathcal{U})$. *If* V *is self-adjoint, then*

$$\eta = \cos\theta \cdot \psi + i\sin\theta \cdot \phi$$

is also in $\mathcal{W}(\mathcal{U})$ *for every* $\theta \in [0, 2\pi)$.

Proof. Let $P = \frac{1}{2}(I + V)$. Then

$$P^* = \frac{1}{2}(I + V^*) = P$$

and

$$P^2 = \frac{1}{4}(I + 2V + V^2) = \frac{1}{4}(I + 2V + I) = P.$$

Thus P is an orthogonal projection and is contained in $\mathcal{C}_\psi(\mathcal{U})$.

Let

$$\omega_1 = \cos\theta + i\sin\theta \quad \text{and} \quad \omega_2 = \cos\theta - i\sin\theta.$$

Then $|\omega_1| = |\omega_2| = 1$. Let

$$W = \omega_1 P + \omega_2(I - P).$$

Then $W \in \mathcal{C}_\psi(\mathcal{U})$ and

$$W^*W = |\omega_1|^2 P + |\omega_2|^2(I - P) = I.$$

That is, W is a unitary operator in $\mathcal{C}_\psi(\mathcal{U})$, which implies by Proposition 8.27 that $W\psi$ is a wandering vector for $\mathcal{U}$. Note that

$$P\psi = \frac{1}{2}(\psi + V\psi) = \frac{1}{2}(\psi + \phi)$$

and

$$(I-P)\psi = \frac{1}{2}(I-V)\psi = \frac{1}{2}(\psi - \phi).$$

Thus

$$\begin{aligned} W\psi &= \omega_1 P\psi + \omega_2(I-P)\psi \\ &= \frac{1}{2}(\omega_1+\omega_2)\psi + \frac{1}{2}(\omega_1-\omega_2)\phi \\ &= \cos\theta\cdot\psi + i\sin\theta\cdot\phi \\ &= \eta. \end{aligned}$$

□

8.4. Exercises

Exercise 1. Let $\{\eta_0, \eta_1, \ldots, \eta_{m-1}\}$ and $\{\phi_0, \phi_1, \ldots, \phi_{m-1}\}$ be two harmonic frames for $\mathbb{C}^n$ such that there exists a permutation σ of $\{1, 2, \ldots, n\}$ with $\eta_{kj} = \phi_{k\sigma(j)}$ for all $0 \le k \le m-1$ and all $1 \le j \le n$. Define an operator T on $\mathbb{C}^n$ by

$$T\eta_k = \phi_k$$

for $0 \le k \le m-1$. Show that T is a well-defined linear operator and T is invertible.

Exercise 2. Construct all the harmonic frames with three vectors for $\mathbb{C}^2$.

Exercise 3. Complete the proof of Lemma 8.5.

Exercise 4. Let $\{\phi_0, \phi_1, \ldots, \phi_{m-1}\}$ be a generalized harmonic frame for $\mathbb{C}^n$. Define U by $Ux = \sum_{k=0}^{m-1} \langle x, \phi_k \rangle \phi_{k+1}$. Prove that $U\phi_k = \phi_{k+1}$, where $\phi_m = \phi_0$.

Exercise 5. Complete the proof of Theorem 8.8(i).

Exercise 6. Complete the proof Lemma 8.10.

Exercise 7. Let λ be the left regular representation of a group G on $\ell^2(G)$ defined by

$$\lambda(g)e_h = e_{gh}, \quad h \in G,$$

where $\{e_h : h \in G\}$ is the standard orthonormal basis for $\ell^2(G)$, and let ρ be the right regular representation of G defined by

$$\rho(g)e_h = e_{hg^{-1}}, \quad h \in G.$$

(i) Prove that $\lambda(g)\rho(h) = \rho(h)\lambda(g)$ holds for all $g, h \in G$.

(ii) Prove that both the left and right regular representations are unitary representations of G on $\ell^2(G)$.

(iii) Prove that for every $h \in G$, $\{\lambda(g)e_h\}_{g\in G}$ is an orthonormal basis for $\ell^2(G)$.

Exercise 8. Complete the last part of the proof of Corollary 8.20.

Exercise 9. Let π be a unitary representation of a group G on a Hilbert space $\mathcal{H}_\pi$. Prove that $\mathcal{A}_\pi = \mathrm{span}\{\pi(g)\}_{g\in G}$ is an algebra. In other words, show that it is a vector space which also has a distributive multiplication given by the composition of operators.

Exercise 10. Let λ_P and λ_Q be two equivalent subrepresentations of the left regular representation λ, and let U be a unitary operator from the range of P onto the range of Q such that $U\lambda_P(g) = \lambda_Q(g)U$ holds for every $g \in G$. We define an operator V on $\ell^2(G)$ such that $Vx = Ux$ when $x \in \mathrm{range}(P)$ and $Vx = 0$ when x is orthogonal to the range of P. Prove that V commutes with $\lambda(g)$ for all g, $VV^* = Q$ and $V^*V = P$.

Exercise 11. Prove that any local commutant $\mathcal{C}_x(\mathcal{S})$ is a subspace of the bounded operators $\mathcal{B}(\mathcal{H})$.

Exercise 12. Let $\mathcal{U}$ be a unitary system on a Hilbert space $\mathcal{H}$ and let η be a Parseval frame vector $\mathcal{U}$. Prove that if $A \in \mathcal{C}_\eta(\mathcal{U})$ is an invertible operator, then $\mathcal{U}A\eta$ is a frame for $\mathcal{H}$.

Chapter 9

Sampling Theory

Sampling theory is the study of the reconstruction of a function from its values (samples) on some subset of the domain of the function. Generally speaking, the setting for sampling theory is a vector space V of functions over some domain Ω for which pointwise evaluation is well defined.

Current applications of sampling theory include analog to digital (A/D), and subsequently digital to analog, conversion and magnetic resonance, and computerized tomography techniques in medical and geophysical imaging. Indeed, the sampling rate of compact disc (CD) players is determined precisely by the Shannon-Whitaker-Kotelnikov theorem (Theorem 9.20), which dictates the Nyquist rate, or the required frequency of samples, of an audio signal.

9.1. An Instructive Example

Sampling theory is the attempt to recover some unknown function from its known values at certain points. Suppose Ω is a set and f is a real- or complex-valued function on Ω. Suppose that $\Delta \subset \Omega$ (strict containment), and we know the values of f on Δ. Is there only one function g with domain Ω such that $g(x) = f(x)$ for all $x \in \Delta$? If so, how can we find g defined on Ω from the values of f on Δ?

If we don't have other information about the function f, the answer to the first question is no. We say that the question is *ill posed.* There are infinitely many functions on Ω whose values on Δ are the same as f's. To demonstrate this, select some $x_0 \in \Omega \setminus \Delta$ and for each real number α, define

$$g_\alpha(x) = \begin{cases} \alpha & x = x_0, \\ f(x) & x \neq x_0. \end{cases}$$

For every $\alpha \neq f(x)$, we have a different function $g(x) \neq f(x)$ with domain Ω whose values on Δ match those of f.

However, if we also have *a priori* some other information about f, then perhaps there might exist only one such function g whose values on Δ match those of f. Examples of such information might include the fact that f is a quadratic polynomial or f is an entire function.

Let us begin with a very simple yet completely descriptive example. Suppose we know the values of some unknown function f with domain $\mathbb{R}$ at the points $x = 0$ and $x = 1$. In particular, assume that we know $f(0) = 1$ and $f(1) = 2$. We don't know f, but suppose we also know *a priori* that f is a first-degree polynomial. Then, there is only one first-degree polynomial that fits the known values: $f(x) = x+1$. We know this because the graph of a first-degree polynomial is a line and a line is uniquely determined by two points.

To emphasize the idea, in this example we are given $\Omega = \mathbb{R}$ and $\Delta = \{0, 1\}$. The remarkable fact here is that the behavior of this unknown function f is *completely* determined by its behavior at only two points. Indeed, any first-degree polynomial is completely and uniquely determined by its values at 0 and 1; i.e., the vector space of functions

$$V = \{f : \mathbb{R} \to \mathbb{R} | f(x) = ax + b; a, b \in \mathbb{R}\}$$

contains only one function f such that $f(0) = 1$ and $f(1) = 2$.

On the other hand, if we know that the function f is a polynomial of degree 2 or less, but we only know its values at $x = 0, 1$, then we cannot uniquely determine the function f. There are many quadratic polynomials p which satisfy $p(0) = 1$ and $p(1) = 2$; $p(x) = x^2 + 1$ and $q(x) = 2x^2 - x + 1$ are two examples.

9.2. Sampling of Polynomials

Let us formalize our terminology. We begin with a vector space V of functions on some domain Ω. Suppose $\Delta \subset \Omega$. We will use the notation $f|_\Delta$ to mean the restriction of the function f to the set Δ. We say that Δ is a *set of uniqueness* for V if the following statement holds: for every $f, g \in V$,

$$f|_\Delta = g|_\Delta \Longrightarrow f = g.$$

Note that this says nothing about whether we can determine the function f even if we know $f|_\Delta$.

Clearly, $\Delta = \Omega$ is a set of uniqueness for V.

Now if, in addition, there exists a "reasonable" algorithm for computing f from $f|_\Delta$ (a process called reconstruction) we will say Δ is a *set of sampling.* In various applications, "reasonable" can mean various things; typically, reasonable means numerically stable – a condition which can be described via an inequality which resembles a frame condition. For now, let us simply say that a set of sampling possesses the uniqueness property as well as a reconstruction algorithm which we can set a computer to do for us.

We begin our exploration of sampling theory on the space of polynomials on the real line. We define the space $\mathbb{P}_N$ to be the set of all polynomials of degree N or less:

$$\mathbb{P}_N = \left\{ f : \mathbb{R} \to \mathbb{R} \ : \ f(x) = \sum_{n=0}^{N} a_n x^n, \ a_n \in \mathbb{R} \right\}.$$

A convenient construction in sampling theory is the *sampling transform*, which maps a function to a vector whose coordinates are the samples of the function. If $\mathbb{X} = \{x_1, x_2, \ldots, x_k\} \subset \mathbb{R}$, then the sampling transform associated to $\mathbb{X}$ on $\mathbb{P}_N$ is:

$$\Theta_{\mathbb{X}} : \mathbb{P}_N \to \mathbb{R}^k \quad \text{where} \quad f \mapsto \begin{bmatrix} f(x_1) \\ f(x_2) \\ \vdots \\ f(x_k) \end{bmatrix}. \tag{9.1}$$

It is straightforward to verify that this sampling transform is a linear map from the vector space $\mathbb{P}_N$ to the vector space $\mathbb{R}^k$ (Exercise 2). Moreover, the sampling transform encodes the sampling properties of the sampling set $\{x_1, x_2, \ldots, x_k\}$.

Proposition 9.1. *Suppose* $\mathbb{X} = \{x_1, x_2, \ldots, x_k\} \subset \mathbb{R}$. $\mathbb{X}$ *is a set of uniqueness for* $\mathbb{P}_N$ *if and only if the sampling transform* $\Theta_{\mathbb{X}}$ *is one-to-one.*

Proof. If we assume $\mathbb{X}$ is a set of uniqueness, then by definition, if $f, g \in \mathbb{P}_N$ and $f|_{\mathbb{X}} = g|_{\mathbb{X}}$, then $f = g$. Therefore, if $\Theta_{\mathbb{X}}(f) = \Theta_{\mathbb{X}}(g)$, then we have that $f(x_n) = g(x_n)$ for $n = 1, 2, \ldots, k$, so $f|_{\mathbb{X}} = g|_{\mathbb{X}}$ and thus $f = g$. This proves that $\Theta_{\mathbb{X}}$ is one-to-one.

Conversely, if we assume $\Theta_{\mathbb{X}}$ is one-to-one, then whenever $f, g \in \mathbb{P}_N$ and $\Theta_{\mathbb{X}}(f) = \Theta_{\mathbb{X}}(g)$, then we can conclude that $f = g$. So, if $f|_{\mathbb{X}} = g|_{\mathbb{X}}$, then $\Theta_{\mathbb{X}}(f) = \Theta_{\mathbb{X}}(g)$ and $f = g$, which shows that $\mathbb{X}$ is a set of uniqueness. □

Since the rank of a linear transformation is limited by the dimension of the range space, and for a set of uniqueness on $\mathbb{P}_N$ we need the sampling transform to be one-to-one, we have an immediate necessary condition on a set of uniqueness for $\mathbb{P}_N$.

Corollary 9.2. *If* $\{x_1, x_2, \ldots, x_k\} \subset \mathbb{R}$ *is a set of uniqueness for* $\mathbb{P}_N$, *then* $k \geq N + 1$.

The remarkable fact is that this necessary condition is also sufficient for $\mathbb{P}_N$.

Theorem 9.3. *Let* $\mathbb{X} = \{x_1, x_2, \ldots, x_{N+1}\} \subset \mathbb{R}$; *then* $\mathbb{X}$ *is a set of uniqueness for* $\mathbb{P}_N$.

Proof. By Proposition 9.1, it suffices to show that $\Theta_{\mathbb{X}}$ is one-to-one. Let's express $\Theta_{\mathbb{X}}$ in matrix form, denoted by $[\Theta_{\mathbb{X}}]$ using the basis $\{x^0, x^1, \ldots, x^N\}$ for $\mathbb{P}_N$ and the standard basis for $\mathbb{R}^{N+1}$. The nth column of the matrix $[\Theta_{\mathbb{X}}]$ corresponds to sampling the monomial

x^{n-1} at $\{x_1, x_2, \ldots, x_{N+1}\}$. Thus, we have

$$[\Theta_{\mathbb{X}}] = \begin{bmatrix} 1 & x_1 & x_1^2 & \cdots & x_1^N \\ 1 & x_2 & x_2^2 & \cdots & x_2^N \\ 1 & x_3 & x_3^2 & \cdots & x_3^N \\ \vdots & \vdots & \vdots & \ddots & \vdots \\ 1 & x_{N+1} & x_{N+1}^2 & \cdots & x_{N+1}^N \end{bmatrix}.$$

The sampling transform $\Theta_{\mathbb{X}}$ is one-to-one if and only if this $(N+1) \times (N+1)$ matrix is invertible, which is true if and only if the determinant of the matrix is nonzero. For reference, this matrix is called a Vandermonde matrix.

Claim: The determinant of the Vandermonde matrix is nonzero; in fact, it is:

$$\det([\Theta_{\mathbb{X}}]) = \prod_{1 \le i < j \le N+1} (x_j - x_i).$$

The idea of the proof of this determinant is elaborated in the Student Presentation in Section 10.5. □

If Δ is a set of uniqueness for V, and $\Delta \subset \Gamma \subset \Omega$, then by definition, Γ is also a set of uniqueness for V. Therefore, we have an immediate corollary.

Corollary 9.4. *Given any $\{x_1, x_2, \ldots, x_k\} \subset \mathbb{R}$, if $k \ge N+1$ then $\{x_1, x_2, \ldots, x_k\}$ is a set of uniqueness for $\mathbb{P}_N$.*

Theorem 9.5. *Let $\mathbb{X} = \{x_1, x_2, \ldots, x_{N+1}\} \subset \mathbb{R}$; then $\mathbb{X}$ is a set of sampling for $\mathbb{P}_N$.*

Proof. We know that $\mathbb{X}$ is a set of uniqueness from Theorem 9.3. Therefore, we need to show that if $f \in \mathbb{P}_N$ and we know the values $\{f(x_1), f(x_2), \ldots, f(x_{N+1})\}$, then we can actually reconstruct f. One way to do this would be to compute the inverse of the matrix $\Theta_{\mathbb{X}}$ from Theorem 9.3. We present now a reconstruction algorithm which carries out this computation explicitly.

Given $\{x_1, x_2, \ldots, x_{N+1}\} \subset \mathbb{R}$, we first construct for each $j = 1, 2, \ldots, N+1$ the following polynomials:

$$p_{x_j}(x) = \prod_{\substack{k=1 \\ k \neq j}}^{N+1} \frac{(x - x_k)}{(x_j - x_k)}.$$

Note that these polynomials all have degree N, and satisfy the conditions $p_{x_j}(x_j) = 1$ and $p_{x_j}(x_l) = 0$ for $l, j = 1, 2, \ldots, N$ where $l \neq j$.

If $f \in \mathbb{P}_N$, then the polynomial

$$g(x) = \sum_{j=1}^{N+1} f(x_j) p_{x_j}(x)$$

is an element of $\mathbb{P}_N$, and $f(x_j) = g(x_j)$ for $j = 1, 2, \ldots, N+1$. Since we already know that $\mathbb{X}$ is a set of uniqueness for $\mathbb{P}_N$, we must have that $f(x) = g(x)$, which gives

$$f(x) = \sum_{j=1}^{N+1} f(x_j) p_{x_j}(x). \tag{9.2}$$

□

We remark here that the polynomials $\{p_{x_j}(x)\}_{j=1}^{N+1}$ are called Lagrange polynomials, and the reconstruction algorithm in Theorem 9.5 is called Lagrange interpolation. This interpolation method provides an explicit reconstruction algorithm, hence we can conclude that $\{x_1, x_2, \ldots, x_k\}$ is a set of sampling.

Example 9.6. Suppose we sample an unknown quadratic polynomial $p(x)$ at the values $x = 0, 1, 2$ and obtain $p(0) = 2, p(1) = 1$, and $p(2) = 4$. What is $p(x)$? The Lagrange polynomials for this set of samples are:

$$\begin{aligned}
p_0(x) &= \frac{(x-1)}{(0-1)} \frac{(x-2)}{(0-2)} = \frac{1}{2}x^2 - \frac{3}{2}x + 1, \\
p_1(x) &= \frac{(x-0)}{(1-0)} \frac{(x-2)}{(1-2)} = -x^2 + 2x; \\
p_2(x) &= \frac{(x-0)}{(2-0)} \frac{(x-1)}{(2-1)} = \frac{1}{2}x^2 - \frac{1}{2}x.
\end{aligned}$$

Thus, using Equation (9.2) above, we can find $p(x)$:

$$\begin{aligned} p(x) &= p(0)p_0(x) + p(1)p_1(x) + p(2)p_2(x) \\ &= 2x^2 - 3x + 2. \end{aligned}$$

Typically, the existence of a reconstruction algorithm is expressed via two inequalities which yield numerical stability, and therefore a pseudo-inverse:

Definition 9.7. Suppose $\mathcal{H}$ is a Hilbert space of functions with domain Ω, and $\Delta \subset \Omega$ is countable (possibly even finite). We say that Δ is a *set of sampling* for $\mathcal{H}$ if there exist positive constants C_1, C_2 such that for all $f \in \mathcal{H}$,

$$C_1\|f\|^2 \leq \sum_{x\in\Delta} |f(x)|^2 \leq C_2\|f\|^2. \tag{9.3}$$

Because of the sampling inequalities in Equation (9.3), a function $f \in \mathcal{H}$ can be reconstructed from its samples on Δ by considering the *sampling transform*:

$$\Theta_\Delta : \mathcal{H} \to \ell^2(\Delta) \quad \text{where} \quad f \mapsto (f(x))_{x\in\Delta}.$$

Recall from Example 1.62 that the space $\ell^2(\Delta)$ is the set of square-summable sequences $(a_x)_{x\in\Delta}$. The sampling transform maps a function f from a Hilbert space of functions to a sequence containing the values of f at the points in the set Δ. The transform is bounded and has a bounded left inverse via the Moore-Penrose inverse, $\Theta_\Delta^\dagger$, which we recall from Section 2.5. Therefore,

$$\Theta_\Delta^\dagger (f(x))_{x\in\Delta} = f.$$

Note the resemblance of this definition to the frame inequalities in Definition 3.17. Since for each $x \in \Delta$ we have $|f(x)| \leq \sqrt{C_2}\|f\|$, we can define $\phi_x : \mathcal{H} \to \mathbb{C}$ by $\phi_x(f) = f(x)$, which is a bounded linear functional which we will call an *evaluation functional.* By the Riesz representation theorem, there must be a vector $v_x \in \mathcal{H}$ such that $\phi_x(f) = \langle f, v_x\rangle$. With this identification, the inequalities in Equation (9.3) are equivalent to the condition that the set of evaluation functionals $\{\phi_x : x \in \Delta\}$ is a frame for $\mathcal{H}$.

9.3. Sampling in Finite-Dimensional Spaces

We now consider a finite-dimensional Hilbert space $\mathcal{H}$ of functions on some domain Ω, where every evaluation functional is a bounded linear functional. Since $\mathcal{H}$ is finite-dimensional, a finite set of uniqueness Δ is necessarily a set of sampling. To see this, consider a finite set $\{x_1, x_2, \ldots, x_n\} \subset \Omega$ and the corresponding sampling transform:

$$\Theta_{\mathbb{X}} : \mathcal{H} \to \mathbb{C}^n \quad \text{where} \quad f \mapsto \begin{bmatrix} f(x_1) & f(x_2) & \cdots & f(x_n) \end{bmatrix}^T.$$

Since each evaluation functional $\phi_x : \mathcal{H} \to \mathbb{C}$ is bounded, say by M_x, we have the upper bound in the definition of a set of sampling:

$$\sum_{j=1}^{n} |f(x_j)|^2 \leq \sum_{j=1}^{n} M_{x_j} \|f\|^2 = C_2 \|f\|^2.$$

In order to establish the lower bound, consider the linear transformation $S = \Theta_{\mathbb{X}}^* \Theta_{\mathbb{X}} : \mathcal{H} \to \mathcal{H}$. Since $\Theta_{\mathbb{X}}$ is one-to-one, so is S, and therefore, since $\mathcal{H}$ is finite-dimensional, S is invertible. Therefore, we have:

$$\begin{aligned} \|f\|^2 &= \|S^{-1} S f\|^2 \\ &= \|S^{-1} \Theta_{\mathbb{X}}^* \Theta_{\mathbb{X}} f\|^2 \\ &\leq \|S^{-1} \Theta_{\mathbb{X}}^*\|^2 \|\Theta_{\mathbb{X}} f\|^2 \\ &= \|S^{-1} \Theta_{\mathbb{X}}^*\|^2 \left(\sum_{j=1}^{n} |f(x_j)|^2 \right). \end{aligned}$$

Therefore, we have a lower bound given by

$$\frac{1}{\|S^{-1} \Theta_{\mathbb{X}}^*\|^2} \|f\|^2 \leq \sum_{j=1}^{n} |f(x_j)|^2,$$

as required.

In this section, we will consider the Hilbert space $\ell^2(\mathbb{Z}_N)$, where $\mathbb{Z}_N = \{0, 1, \ldots, N-1\}$. We will denote the kth component of the sequence $v \in \ell^2(\mathbb{Z}_N)$ by $v[k]$. We can also equivalently think of $v \in \ell^2(\mathbb{Z}_N)$ as a function with domain $\mathbb{Z}_N$. Recall from Example 1.62

that the inner product on $\ell^2(\mathbb{Z}_N)$ is

$$\langle v, w\rangle = \sum_{k=0}^{N-1} v[k]\overline{w[k]}.$$

We will need two special orthonormal bases for $\ell^2(\mathbb{Z}_N)$. The first is the standard orthonormal basis $\{e_0, e_1, \dots, e_{N-1}\}$ where $e_n[k] = 0$ when $n \neq k$ and $e_n[n] = 1$. The second is the Fourier basis $\{f_0, f_1, \dots, f_{N-1}\}$ for $\ell^2(\mathbb{Z}_N)$, defined as follows:

$$f_n[k] = \frac{e^{2\pi ikn/N}}{\sqrt{N}}. \tag{9.4}$$

Recall the matrix for the discrete Fourier transform from Example 5.4. The columns of this matrix are the vectors of the Fourier basis.

Theorem 9.8. *The collection of vectors $\{f_0, f_1, \dots, f_{N-1}\} \subset \ell^2(\mathbb{Z}_N)$ defined by Equation (9.4) forms an orthonormal basis for $\ell^2(\mathbb{Z}_N)$.*

Proof. A straightforward computation shows that $\|f_n\|^2 = 1$ for $n = 0, 1, \dots, N-1$. Since there are N vectors, it suffices to show they are pairwise orthogonal. If $m, n \in \{0, 1, \dots, N-1\}$ and $m \neq n$, then

$$\begin{aligned}\langle f_m, f_n\rangle &= \sum_{k=0}^{N-1} \frac{e^{2\pi ikm/N}}{\sqrt{N}} \frac{e^{-2\pi ikn/N}}{\sqrt{N}}\\ &= \sum_{k=0}^{N-1} \frac{e^{2\pi ik(m-n)/N}}{N}\\ &= 0. \qquad (9.5)\end{aligned}$$

The proof of the last step, Equation (9.5) is left to Exercise 4. □

Since $\{f_0, f_1, \dots, f_{N-1}\}$ is an orthonormal basis, every vector $v \in \ell^2(\mathbb{Z}_N)$ can be written uniquely as

$$v = \sum_{n=0}^{N-1} \hat{v}_n f_n, \qquad \text{where} \qquad \hat{v}_n = \langle v, f_n\rangle.$$

We identify the coefficients $\hat{v}_n$ with a new vector $\hat{v} \in \ell^2(\mathbb{Z}_N)$ via $\hat{v}[n] = \hat{v}_n = \langle v, f_n\rangle$. This new vector $\hat{v}$ is called the Fourier transform of v, and the linear transformation

$$\mathcal{F}_N : \ell^2(\mathbb{Z}_N) \to \ell^2(\mathbb{Z}_N) \quad \text{where} \quad v \mapsto \hat{v}$$

that maps v to $\hat{v}$ is the discrete Fourier transform. When there is no ambiguity as to the dimension N, the subscript will be omitted.

Note that the matrix representation of the Fourier transform, with respect to the standard orthonormal basis, is

$$[\mathcal{F}_N]_{n,k} = \frac{e^{-2\pi i k n/N}}{\sqrt{N}},$$

where by an abuse of notation we index the rows and columns of the $N \times N$ matrix $[\mathcal{F}_N]$ by $\{0, 1, \ldots, N-1\}$.

A careful inspection of the Fourier basis vectors reveals the following characteristic: ignoring the normalization factor $\frac{1}{\sqrt{N}}$, the coordinates of the vectors consist of cycling through roots of unity. The first Fourier basis vector f_0 has coordinates (again ignoring the normalization factor): $(1, 1, \ldots, 1)$, so the coordinates are stationary on the unit circle. The next basis vector f_1 has coordinates which cycle through the Nth roots of unity, rotating counterclockwise around the unit circle exactly once. The third basis vector f_2 has coordinates which cycle through some of the Nth roots of unity, however, each root appears twice (provided that N is even), and the coordinates rotate around the unit circle twice. Finally, the last Fourier basis vector index f_{N-1} travels the unit circle $N-1$ times in the counterclockwise direction. However, we usually think of this as cycling through the roots of unity once in the clockwise direction.

Given this behavior of the Fourier basis vectors, we identify the basis vectors with frequencies – how frequently the coordinates of the vectors cycle through the unit circle. The first vector has frequency 0, the second has frequency 1, and so on. Thus, since $|\langle v, f_n \rangle|$ measures how closely aligned the vector f_n is with v, we naturally say that this inner product gives us a way to quantify how much of the frequency $n-1$ is in v. This identification of the Fourier basis with frequencies is one of the fundamental concepts of modern digital signal processing. We shall describe this more in our example of image reconstruction and compression below.

Definition 9.9. Suppose $F \subset \{f_0, f_1, \dots, f_{N-1}\}$; we define a subspace $S(F) \subset \ell^2(\mathbb{Z}_N)$ by

$$S(F) = \{v \in \ell^2(\mathbb{Z}_N) \ : \ v = \sum_{f_k \in F} c_k f_k\}.$$

Equivalently,

$$S(F) = \{v \in \ell^2(\mathbb{Z}_N) \ : \ \hat{v}[n] = 0 \text{ whenever } f_n \notin F\}.$$

The subspace $S(F)$ is called *bandlimited* in the sense that any $v \in S(F)$ has limited frequency content – if the frequency n corresponds to $f_n \notin F$, then that frequency does not contribute to vectors in $S(F)$.

If $F \subset \{f_0, f_1, \dots, f_{N-1}\}$, we will consider the analogous set, also called F by an abuse of notation, defined by $F = \{n \in \{0, 1, \dots, N-1\} : f_n \in F\}$. For $F \subset \{0, 1, \dots, N-1\}$, we analogously define the subspace $S(F) \subset \ell^2(\mathbb{Z}_N)$ by

$$S(F) = \{v \in \ell^2(\mathbb{Z}_N) \ : \ \hat{v}[n] = 0 \text{ whenever } n \notin F\}.$$

With this notation, we shall say that if $v \in S(F)$, then $\hat{v}$ is *supported* on F. Thus, $S(F)$ is all vectors of $\ell^2(\mathbb{Z}_N)$ whose Fourier transform is supported on F.

A remarkable and fundamental result concerning the standard orthonormal basis and the Fourier basis is the Fourier Uncertainty Principle [**26**]:

Theorem 9.10 (Fourier Uncertainty Principle). *Suppose $v \in \ell^2(\mathbb{Z}_N)$, $v \neq 0$ and write*

$$v = \sum_{n=0}^{N-1} t_n e_n = \sum_{m=0}^{N-1} s_m f_m.$$

If we let T_v denote the number of nonzero coefficients from among $\{t_0, t_1, \dots, t_{N-1}\}$, and let F_v denote the number of nonzero coefficients in $\{s_0, s_1, \dots, s_{N-1}\}$, then $T_v \cdot F_v \geq N$, so $T_v + F_v \geq 2\sqrt{N}$.

Proof. The proof of the Fourier Uncertainty Principle is simply several applications of the Cauchy-Schwarz inequality, albeit very clever ones. Without loss of generality, assume that $\|v\| = 1$. Consider:

$$\begin{aligned}
1 &= |\langle v, v\rangle| \\
&= \left|\left\langle \sum_{n=0}^{N-1} t_n e_n, \sum_{m=0}^{N-1} s_m f_m \right\rangle\right| \\
&\leq \sum_{n=0}^{N-1}\sum_{m=0}^{N-1} |t_n||s_m||\langle e_n, f_m\rangle| \\
&= \sum_{n=0}^{N-1} |t_n| \sum_{m=0}^{N-1} |s_m||\langle e_n, f_m\rangle| \\
&= \sum_{n=0}^{N-1} |t_n| \sum_{m=0}^{N-1} |s_m| \frac{1}{\sqrt{N}},
\end{aligned}$$

since $|\langle e_n, f_m\rangle| = \frac{1}{\sqrt{N}}$. Here is our first clever application of Cauchy-Schwarz: we view the above sum on the index n as an inner product (which we can do since everything is positive), but instead of applying the Cauchy-Schwarz inequality over the set $\{0, 1, \ldots, N-1\}$, we *only* consider those integers for which $|t_n| \neq 0$. What we get is:

$$\begin{aligned}
\sum_{n=0}^{N-1} |t_n| \left(\sum_{m=0}^{N-1} |s_m| \frac{1}{\sqrt{N}}\right) &\leq \sqrt{\sum_{n:|t_n|\neq 0} |t_n|^2} \sqrt{\sum_{n:|t_n|\neq 0} \left(\sum_{m=0}^{N-1} |s_m| \frac{1}{\sqrt{N}}\right)^2} \\
&= \sqrt{\sum_{n=0}^{N-1} |t_n|^2} \sqrt{\sum_{n:|t_n|\neq 0} \left(\sum_{m=0}^{N-1} |s_m| \frac{1}{\sqrt{N}}\right)^2}
\end{aligned}$$

where in the first square root we have added back in the $|t_n|$'s which are 0. However, that square root is the norm of v so it is, in fact, 1. Now, in the second square root, the sum on the index n is simply counting the number of $|t_n|$'s which are nonzero, which we called T_v. Thus,

$$\sqrt{\sum_{n:|t_n|\neq 0} \left(\sum_{m=0}^{N-1} |s_m| \frac{1}{\sqrt{N}}\right)^2} = \sqrt{T_v} \sum_{m=0}^{N-1} |s_m| \frac{1}{\sqrt{N}}.$$

We now apply Cauchy-Schwarz a second time on the index m, repeating the trick where we only consider those indices m for which

$|s_m| \neq 0$:

$$\begin{aligned}
\sqrt{T_v}\sum_{m=0}^{N-1}|s_m|\frac{1}{\sqrt{N}} &\leq \sqrt{T_v}\sqrt{\sum_{m:|s_m|\neq 0}|s_m|^2}\sqrt{\sum_{m:|s_m|\neq 0}\left(\frac{1}{\sqrt{N}}\right)^2} \\
&= \sqrt{T_v}\sqrt{\sum_{m=0}^{N-1}|s_m|^2}\sqrt{F_v\left(\frac{1}{\sqrt{N}}\right)^2} \\
&= \frac{1}{\sqrt{N}}\sqrt{T_v}\sqrt{F_v}.
\end{aligned}$$

Putting these inequalities together yields $1 \leq \frac{1}{\sqrt{N}}\sqrt{T_v}\sqrt{F_v}$; thus we have that $T_v \cdot F_v \geq N$.

The second inequality now follows from the fact that for any positive real numbers a and b, $\sqrt{ab} \leq \frac{a+b}{2}$ (see Exercise 3). □

Example 9.11. We illustrate the clever application of the Cauchy-Schwarz inequality with an example. Define vectors v and w by

$$v = \begin{bmatrix} \alpha_0 \\ 0 \\ \alpha_2 \\ 0 \\ 0 \\ \alpha_5 \\ 0 \\ 0 \end{bmatrix} \quad \text{and} \quad w = \begin{bmatrix} 1 \\ 1 \\ 1 \\ 1 \\ 1 \\ 1 \\ 1 \\ 1 \end{bmatrix},$$

where $\|v\| = 1$ and $\alpha_0, \alpha_2, \alpha_5 \geq 0$.

Then we note that

$$\sum_{k=0}^{7}|v[k]| = \alpha_0 + \alpha_2 + \alpha_5,$$

but this can also be written as

$$\langle v, w\rangle = \sum_{k=0}^{7}|v[k]|\overline{1}.$$

If we don't know $\alpha_0 + \alpha_2 + \alpha_5$ but we want to estimate it, we can apply Cauchy-Schwarz to the inner product:

$$\begin{aligned}\alpha_0 + \alpha_2 + \alpha_5 &= |\langle v, w\rangle| \\ &\leq \|v\|\|w\| \\ &= \sqrt{8}.\end{aligned}$$

This estimate is not much of an improvement over a more immediate estimate. Since we know that v is a unit vector, we know that α_0, α_2, α_5 are all no greater than 1, so we know $\alpha_0 + \alpha_2 + \alpha_5 \leq 3$.

However, since we know that v is 0 in five of its coordinates, we can get a much better estimate again using Cauchy-Schwarz, where this time we estimate the inner product of v with the vector

$$\tilde{w} = \begin{bmatrix} 1 \\ 0 \\ 1 \\ 0 \\ 0 \\ 1 \\ 0 \\ 0 \end{bmatrix}.$$

Now,

$$\begin{aligned}\alpha_0 + \alpha_2 + \alpha_5 &= |\langle v, \tilde{w}\rangle| \\ &\leq \|v\|\|w\| \\ &= \sqrt{3},\end{aligned}$$

which is a significant improvement over 3 and $\sqrt{8}$.

Notice that we are using the fact that we know that $v[k] \neq 0$ for $k = 0, 2, 5$. The same principle works if we only know that $v[k] \neq 0$ for three values of k, even if we don't know which indices k have nonzero entries.

The Fourier Uncertainty Principle has many important consequences. In particular, it gives us information about the linear independence and frame properties of subsets of the standard orthonormal basis and the Fourier basis. Before we specify some of these consequences, we need to discuss the connections between a bandlimited space $S(F)$ and the Hilbert space $\ell^2(F)$. Suppose $A \subset \{0, 1, \ldots, N-1\}$. As we did earlier in this chapter, we will define $\ell^2(A) = \{v : A \to \mathbb{C} : \sum_{k \in A} |v[k]|^2 < \infty\}$, and we identify $\ell^2(A)$ with the subspace $M \subset \ell^2(\mathbb{Z}_N)$ given by $M = \{v \in \ell^2(\mathbb{Z}_N) : v[k] = 0 \ \forall\ k \notin A\}$ via

$$\mathcal{I} : \ell^2(A) \to \ell^2(\mathbb{Z}_N) : v \mapsto \tilde{v}$$

where $\tilde{v}[k] = v[k]$ if $n \in A$, and $\tilde{v}[k] = 0$ otherwise. The transformation $\mathcal{I}$ is an isometry with range M. Therefore, we will make no distinction between $\ell^2(A)$ and M, and we will write $\ell^2(A) \subset \ell^2(\mathbb{Z}_N)$. To assist us in making this idea precise, we will define notation reminiscent of a characteristic function. Given $A \subset \{0, 1, \ldots, N-1\}$ and $v \in \ell^2(A)$, we define the vector $v\chi_A \in \mathbb{C}^N$ by

$$v\chi_A[k] = \begin{cases} v[k] & k \in A, \\ 0 & k \notin A. \end{cases}$$

Note that if $v \in \ell^2(\mathbb{Z}_N)$, then $v \in \ell^2(A)$ if and only if $v = v\chi_A$.

For $F \subset \{0, 1, \ldots, N-1\}$, there is a special connection between $S(F)$ and $\ell^2(F)$. Indeed, if $v \in S(F)$, then $\hat{v}[n] = 0$ if $n \notin F$, and so $\hat{v}\chi_F = \hat{v}$, whence $\hat{v} \in \ell^2(F)$. Conversely, if $v \notin S(F)$, then for some $k \notin F$, we have $\hat{v}[k] \neq 0$; hence $\hat{v} \notin \ell^2(F)$. Therefore, the Fourier transform $\mathcal{F}_N$ maps $S(F)$ (in the time domain) to $\ell^2(F)$ (in the Fourier domain).

Corollary 9.12. *If $T, F \subset \{0, 1, \ldots, N-1\}$ with $|T| + |F| < 2\sqrt{N}$, then the set $\{e_n : n \in T\} \cup \{f_m : m \in F\}$ is linearly independent in $\ell^2(\mathbb{Z}_N)$.*

Proof. Suppose $|T| + |F| < 2\sqrt{N}$ and

$$\sum_{n \in T} t_n e_n - \sum_{m \in F} s_m f_m = 0.$$

Then the vector $v = \sum_{n \in T} t_n e_n = \sum_{m \in F} s_m f_m$ would have the property that $T_v \leq |T|$ and $F_v \leq |F|$, and $T_v + F_v < 2\sqrt{N}$, so unless $t_n = 0$ and $s_m = 0$ for every $n \in T$ and $m \in F$, v would violate the Fourier Uncertaintly Principle. □

Theorem 9.13. *If $T, F \subset \{0, 1, \ldots, N-1\}$ with $|T| > N - 2\sqrt{N} + |F|$, then $\{f_n \chi_F | n \in T\}$ is a frame for $\ell^2(F)$.*

Proof. Since $\ell^2(F)$ is finite-dimensional, we need to show only that $\{f_n \chi_F | n \in T\}$ spans $\ell^2(F)$. Suppose that there is a $v \in \ell^2(F) \subset \ell^2(\mathbb{Z}_N)$ such that $\langle v, f_n \chi_F \rangle = 0$ for $n \in T$. Since $v[k] = 0$ if $k \notin F$, $\langle v, f_n \rangle = \langle v, f_n \chi_F \rangle = 0$ for $n \in T$, and so $F_v \leq N - |T|$. However, $v \in \ell^2(F)$, hence we have $T_v \leq |F|$. Whence, $T_v + F_v \leq N - |T| + |F| < 2\sqrt{N}$, and thus by the Fourier Uncertainty Principle, $v = 0$. □

Theorem 9.14. *Suppose $F \subset \{0, 1, \ldots, N-1\}$ and consider the vector space $S(F) \subset \ell^2(\mathbb{Z}_N)$. If $T \subset \{0, 1, \ldots, N-1\}$ is any subset such that $|T| > N - 2\sqrt{N} + |F|$, then T is a set of uniqueness (and hence a set of sampling) for $S(F)$.*

Proof. We present two proofs of the theorem, since they each provide important insight.

The first proof is similar to Theorem 9.13. Suppose $v, w \in S(F)$ and $v|_T = w|_T$. We wish to show that $v = w$ using the Fourier Uncertainty Principle. Let $y = v - w$. First, note that $y \in S(F)$, so $\hat{y}[m] = 0$ unless $m \in F$, whence $F_y \leq |F|$. Moreover, since $y[k] = 0$ if $k \in T$, we have that $T_y \leq N - |T|$. Combining these inequalities yields:

$$T_y + F_y \leq N - |T| + |F| < 2\sqrt{N},$$

which, by the Fourier Uncertainty Principle, implies that $y = 0$, and so T is a set of uniqueness for $S(F)$. Therefore, since we are sampling in a finite-dimensional space, T is also a set of sampling for $S(F)$.

The second proof shows the direct connection between $S(F)$ in the time domain and $\ell^2(F)$ in the Fourier domain. If $n \in T$, then $v[n] = \langle v, e_n \rangle$. Moreover, since the Fourier transform is a unitary operator, $v[n] = \langle \mathcal{F}v, \mathcal{F}e_n \rangle = \langle \hat{v}, f_n \rangle$. Since $v \in S(F)$, we know that $\hat{v}[m] = 0$ if $m \notin F$, and so $\hat{v} \in \ell^2(F)$. Moreover, Theorem 9.13 assures us that $\{f_n \chi_F : n \in T\}$ is a frame for $\ell^2(F)$, and so there exist positive constants C_1, C_2 such that $C_1 \|\hat{v}\|^2 \leq \sum_{n \in T} |\langle \hat{v}, f_n \rangle|^2 \leq C_2 \|\hat{v}\|^2$. Thus we have that

$$C_1 \|v\|^2 \leq \sum_{n \in T} |v[n]|^2 \leq C_2 \|v\|^2,$$

whence T is a set of sampling for $S(F)$. □

Example 9.15. We demonstrate the application of Theorems 9.13 and 9.14 with an example. Suppose $v \in \ell^2(\mathbb{Z}_8)$ and $v = \alpha_0 f_0 + \alpha_2 f_2 + \alpha_5 f_5$, so $\hat{v}[k] = 0$ if $k = 1, 3, 4, 6, 7$, and $v \in S(F)$, where $F = \{0, 2, 5\}$. Suppose we know the values $v[k]$, except for $v[1]$ and $v[5]$. Can we recover the missing values $v[1]$ and $v[5]$ from the known values $v[k]$, $k = 0, 2, 3, 4, 6, 7$? Yes, by Theorem 9.14, since we have that $|F| = 3$ (the size of the support of $\hat{v}$), $|T| = 6$ (the size of the set of known values of v), and thus $|T| > N - 2\sqrt{N} + |F|$ $(N = 8)$. Here is how we will reproduce our unknown entries: we know by Theorem 9.13 that $\{f_n \chi_F : n \in T\}$ is a frame for $\ell^2(F)$, where $T = \{0, 2, 3, 4, 6, 7\}$. Therefore,

$$\hat{v} = \begin{bmatrix} \alpha_0 \\ 0 \\ \alpha_2 \\ 0 \\ 0 \\ \alpha_5 \\ 0 \\ 0 \end{bmatrix} \in \ell^2(F)$$

can be recovered from the inner products $\langle \hat{v}, f_n \chi_F \rangle$ via the Moore-Penrose inverse. In particular, we have that

$$\langle \hat{v}, f_n \chi_F \rangle = \langle \hat{v}, f_n \rangle = v[n].$$

Therefore, if $\Theta : \ell^2(F) \to \ell^2(T)$ is the analysis operator of $\{f_n \chi_F : n \in T\} \subset \ell^2(F)$, then $\hat{v} \in \ell^2(F)$ can be recovered by

$$\hat{v} = \Theta^\dagger \begin{bmatrix} v[0] \\ v[2] \\ v[3] \\ v[4] \\ v[6] \\ v[7] \end{bmatrix} \tag{9.6}$$

and since $\hat{v} \in \ell^2(F)$ coincides with $\hat{v}\chi_F = \hat{v} \in \ell^2(\mathbb{Z}_8)$, we can use the inverse Fourier transform to obtain v from the right-hand side of Equation (9.6).

9.4. An Application: Image Reconstruction

A digital (or digitized) image consists of pixels with color intensity values for red, green, and blue. We shall restrict our attention to grayscale images, and thus each pixel has just one intensity value. Hence, a digital grayscale image is really just a matrix whose entries correspond to pixel intensity values. If an image has M rows and N columns of pixels, then we identify the image with a matrix V of dimensions $M \times N$.

To develop the necessary techniques, we will identify the image/matrix with a vector $V \in \ell^2(\mathbb{Z}_M \times \mathbb{Z}_N)$, where by $\ell^2(\mathbb{Z}_M \times \mathbb{Z}_N)$ we mean the set of all functions f on the Cartesian product $\mathbb{Z}_M \times \mathbb{Z}_N$ such that $\sum_{m=0}^{M-1} \sum_{n=0}^{N-1} |f[m,n]|^2 < \infty$. Just as we showed for $\ell^2(\mathbb{Z}_N)$, we also find that $\ell^2(\mathbb{Z}_M \times \mathbb{Z}_N)$ is a Hilbert space whose inner product is

$$\langle f, g \rangle_{\ell^2(\mathbb{Z}_M \times \mathbb{Z}_N)} = \sum_{m=0}^{M-1} \sum_{n=0}^{N-1} f[m,n]\overline{g[m,n]}.$$

We see that the corresponding norm is the Hilbert-Schmidt norm defined in Section 7.1.

One specific orthonormal basis, the standard orthonormal basis, for this Hilbert space is $\{e_{m,n} : m = 0, 1, \ldots, M-1;\ n = 0, 1, \ldots, N-1\}$, where

$$e_{m,n}[j,k] = \begin{cases} 1 & m = j \text{ and } n = k, \\ 0 & \text{otherwise.} \end{cases}$$

A careful inspection of the set $\{e_{m,n}\}$ will verify that $e_{m,n}[j,k] = e_m[j] \cdot \tilde{e}_n[k]$, where $\{e_m : m = 0, 1, \ldots, M-1\}$ and $\{\tilde{e}_n : n = 0, 1, \ldots, N-1\}$ are the standard orthonormal bases of $\ell^2(\mathbb{Z}_M)$ and $\ell^2(\mathbb{Z}_N)$, respectively. This procedure is called a tensor product of spaces.

Analogously, we have a (two-dimensional) Fourier basis for $\ell^2(\mathbb{Z}_M \times \mathbb{Z}_N)$ given by the tensor product of the two (one-dimensional) Fourier bases: for $m, j \in \{0, 1, \ldots, M-1\}$ and $n, k \in \{0, 1, \ldots, N-1\}$:

$$f_{m,n}[j,k] = \frac{e^{2\pi i m j/M}}{\sqrt{M}} \frac{e^{2\pi i n k/N}}{\sqrt{N}}.$$

We leave it to Exercise 6 to verify that this is, in fact, an orthonormal basis of $\ell^2(\mathbb{Z}_M \times \mathbb{Z}_N)$.

In digital image processing, and in particular, digital image *compression*, the Fourier basis is used (or a variant, called the cosine basis). We shall describe compression in more detail, but for now, let us describe generally the Fourier transform of images. Images typically are composed more of low frequencies than high frequencies – it is the high frequencies which give an image its detail, with sharp edges and fine textures. But the shapes of objects in an image are typically described quite well using only low frequencies. For example, in the following images, the original image shown in Figure 9.1

Figure 9.1. Original image.

Figure 9.2. Image reconstruction using only 320 Fourier coefficients.

is approximated by the image shown in Figure 9.2 using only 320

Fourier coefficients. The second image is not an excellent approximation of the original image, but we can make use of this bandlimited image to produce a better approximation.

Remark 9.16. Both of the images in these figures contain 256×256 pixels, thus, the raw image data consists of 2^{16} values. However, the second image can be reconstructed using only 320 Fourier coefficients; thus, in essence, instead of storing 2^{16} numbers, we only need to store 320 numbers in order to completely reconstruct the image in Figure 9.2. The original image, which would require 65 megabytes of storage, can be reduced to an image which would require less than .5 megabytes – a compression ratio of 200 : 1. This is a simple (in fact crude) description of image compression – the attempt to store an image using the least number of bits on a computer. The JPEG image compression algorithm is based on this idea, although much more sophisticated.

Suppose that the initial image transmitted from the Viking explorer is the bandlimited image in Figure 9.2. However, for some unknown reason, after the Viking explorer transmitted the image data, we received the image shown in Figure 9.3.

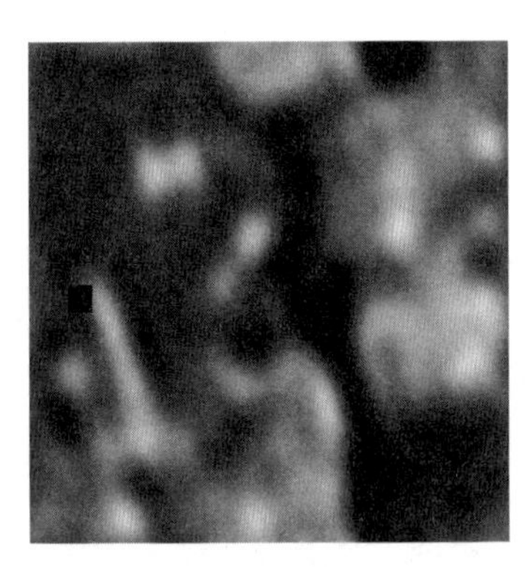

Figure 9.3. Bandlimited image with some missing pixels.

Will it be possible to reproduce the pixel values which were lost in transmission? Here the Fourier Uncertainty Principle comes to our rescue. If we suppose that the number of missing pixels is small, and we also suppose that the image is bandlimited to an *a priori* known band, then the Fourier Uncertainty Principle gives a sampling theorem, and tells us that there are unique values for the missing pixels, which we can reconstruct using frame theory. Let us be more specific.

Theorem 9.17 (Fourier Uncertainty Principle/Sampling Theorem for Bandlimited Images). *Suppose that V is an image of size $M \times N$ which is bandlimited to a set $F \subset \mathbb{Z}_M \times \mathbb{Z}_N$ with cardinality $|F|$. If the pixel values of the image V are known on pixels in the set $T \subset \mathbb{Z}_M \times \mathbb{Z}_N$, with $|T| - |F| > MN - 2\sqrt{MN}$, then the remaining $MN - |T|$ unknown pixel values can be uniquely reconstructed.*

Remark 9.18. We make the following fundamental remark, which is that the precise locations of the known pixels T or the specific frequencies F are irrelevant, only the *size* of those sets. Thus, for any specified set F, any pixels can be lost as long as the total is sufficiently small. Conversely, as long as we know sufficiently many pixel values, and the original image was bandlimited to a sufficiently small frequency band, then the actual frequencies do not matter. However, and this is crucial, for us to reconstruct the unknown pixels, we must *already know* the specific frequency band in which the image is contained. We will describe later what possibilities exist if the original image was not bandlimited or the frequency band was unknown.

Proof. The Fourier basis for $\ell^2(\mathbb{Z}_M \times \mathbb{Z}_N)$, which is the tensor product of the Fourier bases for $\ell^2(\mathbb{Z}_M)$ and $\ell^2(\mathbb{Z}_N)$ satisfies the analogous Fourier Uncertainty Principle. Namely, if $v \in \ell^2(\mathbb{Z}_M \times \mathbb{Z}_N)$ is nonzero and we have

$$v = \sum_{m=0}^{M-1} \sum_{n=0}^{N-1} t_{m,n} e_{m,n} = \sum_{m=0}^{M-1} \sum_{n=0}^{N-1} s_{m,n} f_{m,n},$$

and if we let T_v be the number of nonzero coefficients $t_{m,n}$ and F_v be the number of nonzero coefficients $s_{m,n}$, then $T_v \cdot F_v \geq MN$, so $T_v + F_v \geq 2\sqrt{MN}$. (The proof is Exercise 7.)

Therefore, the analogous statement to Theorem 9.14 is valid: If $T, F \subset \{0, 1, \ldots, M-1\} \times \{0, 1, \ldots, N-1\}$ is such that $|T| > MN - 2\sqrt{MN} + |F|$, then T is a set of sampling for $S(F)$. It follows that if an image is a vector in $S(F)$, and the pixel values of the image are known on T, then the image is uniquely determined by the known pixel values, and thus any missing pixel values can be reconstructed. □

The theorem tells us there is a unique solution to the reconstruction of the missing pixels under the constraint that the original image is bandlimited to a preset band. Thus, the missing pixels in Figure 9.3 can be reconstructed as in Figure 9.2. The question that remains is: How are those pixels reconstructed? Below we will describe a more general image reconstruction algorithm, which also works for the setting just described above.

Suppose now, that our original image before transmission is the *nonbandlimited* image from Figure 9.1 and after transmission, we receive the following:

Figure 9.4. Nonbandlimited image with missing pixels.

Will it be possible to reconstruct the missing pixel values in this case? The Fourier Uncertainty Principle won't help us this time, since the original image is not bandlimited, or at least the size of the set of frequencies in the image is too large. The reconstruction problem now becomes ill posed, for there is not a unique solution to the missing pixels. In fact, it is possible that the missing pixels were all black in the original image, so the image shown might be completely correct! However, experience tells us that this is not likely, that there must be "better" values for the missing pixels. How might we find them?

The solution we will pose shortly rests on two important facts – the first we've mentioned explicitly; the second is much more subtle.

(1) Images can be well approximated using relatively few Fourier coefficients.

(2) The inequality in the Fourier Uncertainty Principle does not cover the worst possible case; that is, there are specific examples of sets T and F with $|T| - |F| = MN - 2\sqrt{MN}$ for which the missing pixels cannot be *uniquely* reconstructed. However, this situation is quite rare, and so it is possible that for some combinations of sets T and F, as long as they are compatible in some sense, it may be that $|T| - |F| \leq MN - 2\sqrt{MN}$, but the missing pixels can be reconstructed, at least fairly well.

First, we need to describe the interaction between individual pixel values and the Fourier basis. Recall that $\{e_{m,n} : m = 0, 1, \ldots, M - 1;\ n = 0, 1, \ldots, N-1\}$ denotes the standard orthonormal basis, whose vectors contain the value 1 in the $(m,n)^{\text{th}}$ pixel position, and the value 0 everywhere else. Suppose $V \in \ell^2(\mathbb{Z}_M \times \mathbb{Z}_N)$ is an image, whose pixel values are $V[m,n]$; then

$$V = \sum_{m=0}^{M-1} \sum_{n=0}^{N-1} V[m,n] e_{m,n} = \sum_{m=0}^{M-1} \sum_{n=0}^{N-1} \langle V, e_{m,n} \rangle e_{m,n}.$$

Now, the discrete Fourier transform $\mathcal{F}$ is linear, and maps the standard orthonormal basis to the Fourier basis. So, if $\{f_{m,n} : m = 0, 1, \ldots, M - 1;\ n = 0, 1, \ldots, N - 1\}$ denotes the Fourier basis for $\ell^2(\mathbb{Z}_M \times \mathbb{Z}_N)$, we have that

$$\mathcal{F}(V) = \sum_{m=0}^{M-1} \sum_{n=0}^{N-1} V[m,n] f_{m,n} = \sum_{m=0}^{M-1} \sum_{n=0}^{N-1} \langle V, e_{m,n} \rangle f_{m,n}.$$

On the other hand, since the Fourier basis is an orthonormal basis, we have that

$$\mathcal{F}(V) = \sum_{m=0}^{M-1} \sum_{n=0}^{N-1} \langle \mathcal{F}(V), f_{m,n} \rangle f_{m,n}$$

and therefore $V[m,n] = \langle \mathcal{F}(V), f_{m,n} \rangle$.

At this point, let us suppose that we can find a set $F \subset \mathbb{Z}_M \times \mathbb{Z}_N$ with the following two properties:

(1) The original image V (i.e., the image without any missing pixels) can be well approximated by some vector W in the bandlimited space $\mathcal{S}(F)$.

(2) The collection $\{f_{m,n}\chi_F : (m,n) \in T\}$ is a frame for $\ell^2(F)$, where $T \subset \mathbb{Z}_M \times \mathbb{Z}_N$ is the set of pixel locations where the pixel values of the image are known.

Since $\{f_{m,n}\chi_F\}$ is a frame for $\ell^2(F)$, we can reconstruct any $W \in \mathcal{S}(F)$ by inner products of $\widehat{W}$ with $\{f_{m,n}\chi_F\}$ using the Moore-Penrose inverse. Those inner products are the pixel values of W on T. Now, we are trying to recover missing pixels of V, and we do not know W, so we cannot use the pixel values of W as the inner products. So instead we will use the pixel values of V, the known pixel values, as an approximation for the pixel values of W. Indeed, if W is a good approximation of V, then the pixel values should be very close as well.

We now endeavor to reconstruct the missing pixels under our assumption that $F \subset \{0, 1, \ldots, M-1\} \times \{0, 1, \ldots, N-1\}$ is chosen such that Properties (1) and (2) above hold. Here is the algorithm for this reconstruction.

Step 1: Define the analysis operator of the frame $\{f_{m,n}\chi_F : (m,n) \in T\}$:

$$\Theta : \ell^2(F) \to \ell^2(T) : v \mapsto (\langle v, f_{m,n}\chi_F \rangle)_{(m,n)\in T}.$$

Step 2: Compute the Moore-Penrose inverse $\Theta^\dagger : \ell^2(T) \to \ell^2(F)$ of Θ.

Step 3: Form the vector $A \in \ell^2(T)$ by $A[m,n] = V[m,n]$ for $(m,n) \in T$.

Step 4: Compute $B \in \ell^2(F)$ defined by $B = \Theta^\dagger A$.

Step 5: Form the vector $B \in \ell^2(\mathbb{Z}_M \times \mathbb{Z}_N)$ by $B = B\chi_F$.

Step 6: Compute the vector $W \in \ell^2(\mathbb{Z}_M \times \mathbb{Z}_N)$ by $W = \mathcal{F}^{-1}B$.

This will give us a bandlimited image W which is a good approximation to V. Now, we extract from W the pixels which are missing from V and replace them in V. Thus, we have an image which is V where the pixels were unaffected, and which is W where the pixels were missing.

Figure 9.5. Reconstructed image. The pixels missing from the image in Figure 9.4 have been replaced with pixel values from a bandlimited approximation image.

9.5. Sampling in Infinite-Dimensional Spaces

In this section, we will describe sampling theory in infinite-dimensional spaces, focusing in particular on a space called the Paley-Weiner space. For some of the results, we will need to use the Lebesgue integral. If you are not familiar with Lebesgue integration, you may use the Riemann integral some of the time to help your intuition; however, to understand the following material properly, Lebesgue measure and integration are essential. Excellent texts on that material include those by Royden [**50**] and Folland [**31**]. All integrals below are of the Lebesgue type, although all of the following integrals can be considered improper Riemann integrals until we reach the integral in Equation (9.10).

Let us begin with a description of the Paley-Weiner space, which is often called a bandlimited space. We start with the collection of all continuous functions $f \in C(\mathbb{R})$ such that

$$\int_{-\infty}^{\infty} |f(x)|^2 \, dx < \infty$$

(here, since $|f(x)|^2$ is continuous and nonnegative, this integral may be regarded as an improper Riemann integral). We next add the condition that

$$\int_{-\infty}^{\infty} |f(x)| \, dx < \infty$$

as well. Now, we add the following third condition: for every $\xi \in \mathbb{R}$ such that $|\xi| > \frac{1}{2}$,

$$\int_{-\infty}^{\infty} f(x) e^{-2\pi i x \xi} \, dx = 0.$$

Let us denote this collection of functions by $A_{\frac{1}{2}}$. It is readily verified that this collection of functions is a vector space. We define an inner product on this space; given $f, g \in A_{\frac{1}{2}}$,

$$\langle f, g \rangle_{A_{\frac{1}{2}}} = \int_{-\infty}^{\infty} f(x)\overline{g(x)} dx.$$

The resulting norm is given by

$$\|f\|_{A_{\frac{1}{2}}} = \left(\int_{-\infty}^{\infty} |f(x)|^2 \, dx \right)^{\frac{1}{2}}.$$

We now have that $A_{\frac{1}{2}}$ is a normed inner product space. The final step in the construction of the Paley-Weiner space is to complete this linear space with respect to the norm. The result is a Hilbert space which we shall denote by $B_{\frac{1}{2}}$.

It turns out that this Hilbert space can be concretely represented as a space of continuous functions on $\mathbb{R}$ (a fact which also requires Lebesgue measure and integration), but for our purposes, we can describe the space as follows: if $g \in C(\mathbb{R})$, then $g \in B_{\frac{1}{2}}$ provided for any $\epsilon > 0$, there exists a function $f \in A_{\frac{1}{2}}$ such that

$$\int_{-\infty}^{\infty} |g(x) - f(x)|^2 \, dx < \epsilon. \tag{9.7}$$

Next, we describe the Fourier transform of a function. Given any function $f \in A_{\frac{1}{2}}$, we can define a new function on $\mathbb{R}$, denoted by $\hat{f}$, given by

$$\hat{f}(\xi) = \int_{-\infty}^{\infty} f(x) e^{-2\pi i x \xi} \, dx. \tag{9.8}$$

Note that, since $f \in A_{\frac{1}{2}}$, for $|\xi| > \frac{1}{2}$, $\hat{f}(\xi) = 0$, so we will only concern ourselves with $\xi \in [-\frac{1}{2}, \frac{1}{2}]$. It can be shown (nontrivially) that $\hat{f} \in C(\mathbb{R})$, and more importantly (and highly nontrivially), that

$$\int_{-\frac{1}{2}}^{\frac{1}{2}} |\hat{f}(\xi)|^2 \, d\xi = \int_{-\infty}^{\infty} |f(x)|^2 \, dx. \tag{9.9}$$

Let $\widehat{A}_{\frac{1}{2}}$ be the set of all functions $\hat{f} \in C(\mathbb{R})$ which corresponds to an $f \in A_{\frac{1}{2}}$ by the definition in Equation (9.8); then $\widehat{A}_{\frac{1}{2}}$ is also a normed linear space, with norm

$$\|\hat{f}(\xi)\|_{\widehat{A}_{\frac{1}{2}}} = \left(\int_{-\frac{1}{2}}^{\frac{1}{2}} |\hat{f}(\xi)|^2 d\xi \right)^{\frac{1}{2}}.$$

Moreover, we have the transformation $f \mapsto \hat{f}$ denoted:

$$\mathcal{F} : A_{\frac{1}{2}} \to \widehat{A}_{\frac{1}{2}}$$

which is linear (easy to check), onto (by definition), one-to-one (by Equation (9.9)), and is an isometry:

$$\|\mathcal{F} f\|_{\widehat{A}_{\frac{1}{2}}} = \|f\|_{A_{\frac{1}{2}}}.$$

Since $\mathcal{F}$ is an isometry, it can be *uniquely* extended to all of $B_{\frac{1}{2}}$, since it is defined on $A_{\frac{1}{2}}$, which is dense in $B_{\frac{1}{2}}$. We will call the extension of $\mathcal{F}$ to $B_{\frac{1}{2}}$ the *Fourier transform* $\mathcal{F}$ on $B_{\frac{1}{2}}$. The range of the Fourier transform consists of all functions $h(\xi)$ on $\mathbb{R}$ which are Lebesgue measurable and satisfy

$$\int_{-\infty}^{\infty} |h(\xi)|^2 d\xi < \infty. \tag{9.10}$$

(Here we can no longer avoid the Lebesgue integral; this must be regarded as such.) Moreover, the set

$$\left\{ \xi \in \mathbb{R} : |\xi| > \frac{1}{2} \text{ and } h(\xi) \neq 0 \right\}$$

has Lebesgue measure 0. In other words,

$$\int_{-\infty}^{-\frac{1}{2}} |h(\xi)|^2 d\xi = \int_{\frac{1}{2}}^{\infty} |h(\xi)|^2 d\xi = 0.$$

Therefore, for all intents and purposes, the function h "lives" only on the interval $[-\frac{1}{2}, \frac{1}{2}]$.

In summary, the Fourier transform on $B_{\frac{1}{2}}$ maps functions g from $B_{\frac{1}{2}}$ to functions $\hat{g}$ in the space $L^2[-\frac{1}{2}, \frac{1}{2}]$, where we define this space to be all Lebesgue measurable functions f with domain $[-\frac{1}{2}, \frac{1}{2}]$ and taking values in the extended complex numbers such that

$$\int_{-\frac{1}{2}}^{\frac{1}{2}} |f(x)|^2 \, \mathrm{d}x < \infty.$$

The Fourier transform is an isometry and hence is one-to-one. It is also surjective, and therefore is a unitary operator between the two Hilbert spaces.

Since the Fourier transform is a unitary operator, it is invertible, and in fact the inverse is its adjoint. We will denote the inverse Fourier transform with $\mathcal{F}^{-1} : L^2[-\frac{1}{2}, \frac{1}{2}] \to B_{\frac{1}{2}}$. There is an integral formula for the inverse Fourier transform, called the Fourier inversion formula, given by

$$[\mathcal{F}^{-1}h](x) = \int_{-\frac{1}{2}}^{\frac{1}{2}} h(\xi)e^{2\pi i \xi x} \, \mathrm{d}\xi,$$

which is valid for every $h \in L^2[-\frac{1}{2}, \frac{1}{2}]$. Recall that the integral formula for the Fourier transform was only applicable when we chose $f \in A_{\frac{1}{2}}$. The integral formula for the inverse Fourier transform is valid on the entire domain $L^2[-\frac{1}{2}, \frac{1}{2}]$.

In particular, if $f \in B_{\frac{1}{2}}$, then for every $x \in \mathbb{R}$,

$$f(x) = \int_{-\frac{1}{2}}^{\frac{1}{2}} \hat{f}(\xi)e^{2\pi i \xi x} \, \mathrm{d}\xi. \tag{9.11}$$

If we inspect this integral formula a little more closely, we see that it is actually an inner product in $L^2([-\frac{1}{2}, \frac{1}{2}])$. We give the space $L^2[-\frac{1}{2}, \frac{1}{2}]$ the inner product

$$\langle f, g \rangle_2 = \int_{-\frac{1}{2}}^{\frac{1}{2}} f(x)\overline{g(x)} \, \mathrm{d}x.$$

We also define the characteristic function of a set $E \subset \mathbb{R}$ by

$$\chi_E(x) = \begin{cases} 1 & x \in E, \\ 0 & x \notin E. \end{cases}$$

We can therefore see that the integral form of the Fourier inversion formula is the inner product of the functions $\hat{f}(\xi)$ and $e^{-2\pi i\xi x}\chi_{[-\frac{1}{2},\frac{1}{2}]}(\xi)$:

$$f(x) = \langle \hat{f}(\xi), e^{-2\pi i\xi x}\chi_{[-\frac{1}{2},\frac{1}{2}]}(\xi)\rangle. \tag{9.12}$$

Since the Fourier transform is a unitary operator, and therefore its inverse is unitary as well, we can write an expression for the evaluation of f at x as an inner product of f with another function:

$$f(x) = \left\langle f(y), [\mathcal{F}^{-1}(e^{-2\pi i\xi x}\chi_{[-\frac{1}{2},\frac{1}{2}]}(\xi))](y) \right\rangle. \tag{9.13}$$

We only need to compute the inverse Fourier transform in the second argument. Note that in Equation (9.13), the variable x is fixed. Now, provided $y \neq x$:

$$\begin{aligned}
[\mathcal{F}^{-1}(e^{-2\pi i\xi x}\chi_{[-\frac{1}{2},\frac{1}{2}]}(\xi))](y) &= \int_{-\frac{1}{2}}^{\frac{1}{2}} (e^{-2\pi i\xi x}\chi_{[-\frac{1}{2},\frac{1}{2}]}(\xi))e^{2\pi i\xi y}\,\mathrm{d}\xi \\
&= \int_{-\frac{1}{2}}^{\frac{1}{2}} \chi_{[-\frac{1}{2},\frac{1}{2}]}(\xi)e^{2\pi i\xi(y-x)}\,\mathrm{d}\xi \\
&= \frac{1}{2\pi i(y-x)} e^{2\pi i\xi(y-x)}\Big|_{-\frac{1}{2}}^{\frac{1}{2}} \\
&= \frac{e^{\pi i(y-x)} - e^{-\pi i(y-x)}}{2\pi i(y-x)} \\
&= \frac{\sin(\pi(y-x))}{\pi(y-x)}. \qquad (9.14)
\end{aligned}$$

In the case that $y = x$, the value of the integral is 1; moreover,

$$\lim_{x\to y} \frac{\sin(\pi(y-x))}{\pi(y-x)} = 1.$$

The function

$$\phi(y) = \begin{cases} \dfrac{\sin(\pi y)}{\pi y} & y \neq 0, \\ 1 & y = 0, \end{cases}$$

is called the sinc function, and is the inverse Fourier transform of $\chi_{[-\frac{1}{2},\frac{1}{2}]}(\xi)$. In summary, for every $f \in B_{\frac{1}{2}}$ and for every $x \in \mathbb{R}$, Equation (9.13) becomes

$$f(x) = \langle f(y), \operatorname{sinc}(y-x)\rangle = \int_{-\infty}^{\infty} f(y)\operatorname{sinc}(y-x)\,\mathrm{d}y. \tag{9.15}$$

Going back to $\hat{f} \in L^2([-\frac{1}{2}, \frac{1}{2}])$, note that Equation (9.13) tells us that the value of $f(x)$ depends on the exponential $e^{-2\pi i \xi x}$; it turns out that we only need to worry about integer values of x. Indeed, we consider the set $\{e^{-2\pi i \xi n} : n \in \mathbb{Z}\}$ as a subset of $L^2([-\frac{1}{2}, \frac{1}{2}])$. We drop the $\chi_{[-\frac{1}{2}, \frac{1}{2}]}(\xi)$, with the understanding that the exponentials are restricted to $[-\frac{1}{2}, \frac{1}{2}]$.

For two integers $n \neq m$,

$$\begin{aligned}\langle e^{-2\pi i \xi n}, e^{-2\pi i \xi m}\rangle &= \int_{-\frac{1}{2}}^{\frac{1}{2}} e^{-2\pi i \xi n} e^{2\pi i \xi m}\, d\xi \\ &= \int_{-\frac{1}{2}}^{\frac{1}{2}} e^{2\pi i \xi (m-n)}\, d\xi \\ &= \operatorname{sinc}(m-n) \\ &= 0.\end{aligned}$$

This computation shows that the set of exponentials $\{e^{-2\pi i \xi n} : n \in \mathbb{Z}\}$ is an orthonormal set in $L^2([-\frac{1}{2}, \frac{1}{2}])$. It can be shown, using measure theory, that the set is also complete. In other words,

Theorem 9.19. *The set* $\{e^{-2\pi i \xi n} : n \in \mathbb{Z}\}$ *is an orthonormal basis for* $L^2([-\frac{1}{2}, \frac{1}{2}])$.

Therefore, for every $g \in L^2([-\frac{1}{2}, \frac{1}{2}])$,

$$g(\xi) = \sum_{n\in\mathbb{Z}} \langle g(\xi), e^{-2\pi i \xi n}\rangle e^{-2\pi i \xi n}.$$

In particular, if $f \in B_{\frac{1}{2}}$,

$$\hat{f}(\xi) = \sum_{n\in\mathbb{Z}} \langle \hat{f}(\xi), e^{-2\pi i \xi n}\rangle e^{-2\pi i \xi n}.$$

But we've just seen that the inner products in the sum are actually the values of f at the integers, so

$$\hat{f}(\xi) = \sum_{n\in\mathbb{Z}} f(n) e^{-2\pi i \xi n}.$$

Now taking the inverse Fourier transform of this equation, and using the computation from Equation (9.14) above, we have

$$f(y) = \sum_{n\in\mathbb{Z}} f(n) \operatorname{sinc}(y-n).$$

Thus, we have just proved the first and most important sampling theorem [**8**]:

Theorem 9.20 (Shannon-Whitaker-Kotelnikov). *Suppose* $f \in B_{\frac{1}{2}}$*; then for every* $x \in \mathbb{R}$*,*

$$f(x) = \sum_{n \in \mathbb{Z}} f(n) \operatorname{sinc}(x - n);$$

the sum converges both in norm in $B_{\frac{1}{2}}$ *and also uniformly in* x*.*

More generally, the set of integers is a set of sampling for the space $B_{\frac{1}{2}}$*, and the reconstruction of any function* $f \in B_{\frac{1}{2}}$ *from its samples on the integers is obtained from the integer translates of the* sinc *function.*

9.5.1. Irregular Sampling. The Shannon-Whitaker-Kotelnikov theorem is the fundamental theorem in sampling theory. In it, however, the locations of the samples of the function are very specific; namely the integers. Moreover, the space between any two consecutive samples is the same. This is called regular sampling, where the samples are obtained on a set which is geometrically uniform.

However, this is not always possible, or even desirable. If we allow the possibility that consecutive samples need not be regularly spaced, then we have the idea of irregular sampling. Here, we still consider the space of functions $B_{\frac{1}{2}}$, but now we know the values of the function $f \in B_{\frac{1}{2}}$ at some set $\{\lambda_n\}_{n \in \mathbb{Z}} \subset \mathbb{R}$; i.e., we know the values $\{f(\lambda_n)\}$. For example, suppose for each interval $[n, n+1)$, $\lambda_n \in [n, n+1)$ was chosen at random, and we sample the unknown function f at those points.

The questions are the same as before:

(1) Is there a function $g \in B_{\frac{1}{2}}$, with $g \neq f$, such that $g(\lambda_n) = f(\lambda_n)$ for every $n \in \mathbb{Z}$? (In other words, is $\{\lambda_n\}_{n \in \mathbb{Z}}$ a set of uniqueness for $B_{\frac{1}{2}}$?)

(2) Can we reconstruct f on all of $\mathbb{R}$ from only its samples $\{f(\lambda_n)\}$ in a stable manner? (In other words, is $\{\lambda_n\}$ a set of sampling for $B_{\frac{1}{2}}$?)

As a nearly trivial example, let $\{\lambda_n\}$ be as follows:

$$\lambda_{2n} = n; \qquad \lambda_{2n+1} = n + 2^{-(|n|+1)}.$$

If we know $\{f(\lambda_n)\}_{n\in\mathbb{Z}}$, can we find $f(x)$, uniquely and stably? The answer is yes: first, if f and g are both elements of $B_{\frac{1}{2}}$, and $f(\lambda_n) = g(\lambda_n)$ for all $n \in \mathbb{Z}$, then certainly $f(m) = g(m)$ for every $m \in \mathbb{Z}$, since $\lambda_{2m} = m$. The Shannon-Whitaker-Kotelnikov theorem says that we must have $g = f$; moreover, the reconstruction formula given in the theorem will give us the function $f(x)$ from its samples at $\{\lambda_{2n}\}_{n\in\mathbb{Z}}$:

$$\begin{aligned} f(x) &= \sum_{n\in\mathbb{Z}} f(\lambda_n)\frac{(1+(-1)^n)}{2}\operatorname{sinc}(x-\lambda_n) \\ &= \sum_{m\in\mathbb{Z}} f(m)\operatorname{sinc}(x-m). \end{aligned}$$

Note that we don't care about the odd-index values $\{f(\lambda_{2n+1})\}_{n\in\mathbb{Z}}$. These are not needed in order to reconstruct f so we can simply ignore them. However, there is a reconstruction formula that does utilize all of the samples:

$$f(x) = \sum_{n\in\mathbb{Z}} f(\lambda_n)\phi_{\lambda_n}(x),$$

though in general, $\phi_{\lambda_n}(x)$ is *not* of the form $\operatorname{sinc}(x-\lambda_n)$. Sampling on $\{\lambda_n\}_{n\in\mathbb{Z}}$ is an example of *oversampling*, or collecting more samples than needed for reconstruction.

Which subsets $\{\lambda_n\} \subset \mathbb{R}$ are sets of sampling for $B_{\frac{1}{2}}$? Let us first describe precisely what we mean by a set of sampling.

Definition 9.21. A set $\{\lambda_n\}_{n\in\mathbb{Z}} \subset \mathbb{R}$ is a set of sampling for $B_{\frac{1}{2}}$ if there are constants $C_1, C_2 > 0$ such that for every $f \in B_{\frac{1}{2}}$, the following inequality holds:

$$C_1 \int_{-\infty}^{\infty} |f(x)|^2\,\mathrm{d}x \le \sum_{n\in\mathbb{Z}} |f(\lambda_n)|^2 \le C_2 \int_{-\infty}^{\infty} |f(x)|^2\,\mathrm{d}x. \tag{9.16}$$

The left inequality says that if $\{\lambda_n\}_{n\in\mathbb{Z}}$ is a set of sampling, then it is at least a set of uniqueness. To see this, let $f, g \in B_{\frac{1}{2}}$ and $f(\lambda_n) = g(\lambda_n)$ for all $n \in \mathbb{Z}$. Then the function $h = f - g \in B_{\frac{1}{2}}$ has the property that $\sum_{n\in\mathbb{Z}} |h(\lambda_n)|^2 = 0$; therefore $\int_{-\infty}^{\infty} |h(x)|^2\,\mathrm{d}x = 0$ whence $f = g$. Note that here we are using the fact that C_1 is strictly greater than zero.

Second, both inequalities assure that f can be reconstructed in a stable way from its samples via a Moore-Penrose inverse. Here is how it works: we define the *sampling transform*

$$\Theta : B_{\frac{1}{2}} \to \ell^2(\mathbb{Z}) \quad \text{given by} \quad f \mapsto (f(\lambda_n))_n;$$

that is, $\Theta(f)$ is the infinite sequence consisting of the samples of f at λ_n. This transformation is well defined; i.e., $(f(\lambda_n))_n \in \ell^2(\mathbb{Z})$ since

$$\sum_{n\in\mathbb{Z}} |f(\lambda_n)|^2 \leq C_2 \int_{-\infty}^{\infty} |f(x)|^2 \, \mathrm{d}x < \infty.$$

Note that we are using the fact that C_2 is a positive, finite constant.

Moreover, this transformation is linear by definition, and the lower bound from Equation (9.16) assures that there is a Moore-Penrose inverse $\Theta^\dagger : \ell^2(\mathbb{Z}) \to B_{\frac{1}{2}}$. Therefore, if we know the samples of f on $\{\lambda_n\}$, we can reconstruct $f(x)$ by computing

$$f = \Theta^\dagger((f(\lambda_n))_n).$$

The trick is computing the Moore-Penrose inverse $\Theta^\dagger$.

Remark 9.22. In actual sampling applications, there are of course only finitely many samples, in which case the sampling transform is a finite-dimensional matrix. However, the Moore-Penrose inverse still involves the inversion of a matrix, and if the matrix is large, say of size on the order of $100,000 \times 100,000$, then having a computer calculate the inverse is very expensive and time consuming. Thus, other more sophisticated techniques are used. For details, see [**38**].

Next, we want to examine which subsets $\{\lambda_n\}_{n\in\mathbb{Z}} \subset \mathbb{R}$ are sets of sampling for $B_{\frac{1}{2}}$. We can rephrase the question in terms of frame theory as follows. If $f \in B_{\frac{1}{2}}$, then by Equation (9.12), for every $\lambda_n \in \mathbb{R}$,

$$f(\lambda_n) = \langle \hat{f}(\xi), e^{-2\pi i \xi \lambda_n} \chi_{[-\frac{1}{2},\frac{1}{2}]}(\xi) \rangle.$$

Thus, the set of sampling criterion in Equation (9.16) of Definition 9.21 becomes

$$C_1 \|f(x)\|^2 \leq \sum_{n\in\mathbb{Z}} |\langle \hat{f}(\xi), e^{-2\pi i \xi \lambda_n} \chi_{[-\frac{1}{2},\frac{1}{2}]}(\xi) \rangle|^2 \leq C_2 \|f(x)\|^2,$$

and by virtue of the fact that the Fourier transform is a unitary operator,

$$C_1\|\hat{f}(\xi)\|^2 \leq \sum_{n\in\mathbb{Z}} |\langle \hat{f}(\xi), e^{-2\pi i\xi\lambda_n}\chi_{[-\frac{1}{2},\frac{1}{2}]}(\xi)\rangle|^2 \leq C_2\|\hat{f}(\xi)\|^2.$$

This is precisely the frame condition of the collection $\{e^{-2\pi i\xi\lambda_n}\}_{n\in\mathbb{Z}} \subset L^2[-\frac{1}{2},\frac{1}{2}]$.

Thus, the question "Which subsets $\{\lambda_n\}_{n\in\mathbb{Z}} \subset \mathbb{R}$ are sets of sampling for $B_{\frac{1}{2}}$?" is equivalent to the question, "Which subsets $\{\lambda_n\}_{n\in\mathbb{Z}} \subset \mathbb{R}$ have the property that $\{e^{-2\pi i\xi\lambda_n} : n \in \mathbb{Z}\}$ forms a frame for $L^2[-\frac{1}{2},\frac{1}{2}]$?" This second question was initially asked by Duffin and Schaeffer in 1952 [**27**], and the problem was not completely solved until 50 years later by Ortega-Cerdà and Seip [**49**]. The final solution given there is quite complicated involving sophisticated measure theory, complex analysis, and functions of bounded mean oscillation.

We can describe, however, an almost complete solution. The description is in terms of what is called Beurling density. Let $\Lambda = \{\lambda_n\}_{n\in\mathbb{Z}} \subset \mathbb{R}$; we define the *upper Beurling density* of Λ by

$$D^+(\Lambda) = \limsup_{r\to\infty} \sup\left\{\frac{\#(\{\lambda_n\}\cap[x-r,x+r])}{2r} : x\in\mathbb{R}\right\},$$

and the *lower Beurling density* by

$$D^-(\Lambda) = \liminf_{r\to\infty} \inf\left\{\frac{\#(\{\lambda_n\}\cap[x-r,x+r])}{2r} : x\in\mathbb{R}\right\}.$$

The upper density is large if there are arbitrarily large intervals with many of the λ_n's in it, whereas the lower density is small if there are arbitrarily large intervals with few of the λ_n's in it. Both, in some sense, measure the typical number of λ_n's in intervals of large size.

Theorem 9.23 (Beurling).

(i) *The set* $\Lambda = \{\lambda_n\}_{n\in\mathbb{Z}} \subset \mathbb{R}$ *gives rise to a bounded sampling transform on* $B_{\frac{1}{2}}$ *if and only if* $D^+(\Lambda) < \infty$*; i.e., there exists an upper bound* C_2 *that satisfies Equation* (9.16).

(ii) *The set* Λ *is a set of uniqueness for* $B_{\frac{1}{2}}$ *if and only if* $D^-(\Lambda) \geq 1$.

(iii) *If* $D^+(\Lambda) < \infty$ and $D^-(\Lambda) > 1$, *then the set* $\Lambda = \{\lambda_n\}_{n\in\mathbb{Z}} \subset \mathbb{R}$ *is a set of sampling for* $B_{\frac{1}{2}}$; *i.e., there exist* C_1 *and* C_2 *that satisfy Equation* (9.16).

Note in the last statement, the lower Beurling density is strictly greater than 1. This is a sufficient but not necessary condition, however. Therefore, Theorem 9.23 is not a complete description of the sets of sampling for $B_{\frac{1}{2}}$ because there exist some sets $\{\lambda_n\}_{n\in\mathbb{Z}}$ having lower Beurling density equal to 1 which are sets of sampling, but other sets have lower Beurling density of 1 and are not sets of sampling.

In summary, Theorem 9.23 says that if we sample a function in $B_{\frac{1}{2}}$ frequently enough, but not too frequently, then we can, in principle, stably recover the function from its samples.

9.6. Exercises

Exercise 1. Find all polynomials f of degree at most 2 which satisfy $f(0) = 1$ and $f(1) = 2$.

Exercise 2. Show that the sampling transform defined in Equation (9.1) is a linear transformation.

Exercise 3. Prove that the arithmetic mean of two positive numbers is greater than the geometric mean; i.e., $\sqrt{ab} \leq \frac{a+b}{2}$.

Exercise 4. Prove that for any integer $m \neq 0$, $\sum_{k=0}^{N-1} e^{\frac{2\pi i k m}{N}} = 0$.

Exercise 5. If $F \subset \{f_0, f_1, \ldots, f_{N-1}\}$ show that $S(F) \subset \ell^2(\mathbb{Z}_N)$ is a subspace with dimension equal to the number of elements in F. Indeed, every $v \in S(F)$ can be written uniquely as $\sum_{n\in F} a_n f_n$.

Exercise 6. Prove that the tensor product of two Fourier bases is again an orthonormal basis. (This is in fact true for any pair of orthonormal bases.)

Exercise 7. Prove the analogous Fourier Uncertainty Principle for the tensor product of two Fourier bases.

Chapter 10

Student Presentations

Each section in this chapter gives a detailed proof of one of the important concepts from this book. The intention is that a student or group of students can independently work through these proofs, and then give a seminar-style presentation on this topic.

10.1. Eigenspace Decomposition

We begin with the proof of Proposition 2.45, which characterizes the diagonalizable matrices. After this, we will discuss the diagonalization properties of self-adjoint matrices.

Proposition (**2.45**). *Let A be an $n \times n$ matrix with entries in $\mathbb{F}$, where we recall $\mathbb{F}$ is either the real numbers $\mathbb{R}$ or the complex numbers $\mathbb{C}$. Suppose that $\{\lambda_1, \lambda_2, \ldots, \lambda_k\}$ are all the distinct eigenvalues of A. Then the following are equivalent:*

(i) *A is similar to a diagonal matrix.*

(ii) *$\mathbb{F}^n$ has a basis consisting of eigenvectors of A.*

(iii) $\dim \mathbb{F}^n = \dim E_{\lambda_1} + \dim E_{\lambda_2} + \cdots + \dim E_{\lambda_k}$.

(iv) $\mathbb{F}^n = E_{\lambda_1} \dot{+} E_{\lambda_2} \dot{+} \cdots \dot{+} E_{\lambda_k}$, *where $\dot{+}$ denotes the (not necessarily orthogonal) direct sum. (See Section 1.7.)*

(v) *There exist one-dimensional subspaces $V_1, V_2, \dots, V_n$ of $\mathbb{F}^n$ which are A-invariant and such that $\mathbb{F}^n = V_1 \dot{+} V_2 \dot{+} \cdots \dot{+} V_n$, where a subspace V is called A-invariant if $AV \subseteq V$.*

Proof. (i)→(ii): Suppose that A is similar to a diagonal matrix. Then there exists an invertible matrix B such that $B^{-1}AB = D$, where D is a diagonal matrix with diagonal entries $\{\lambda_1, \lambda_2, \dots, \lambda_k\}$, with perhaps some of the values are repeated. Let $\{u_i\}_{i=1}^n$ be the standard basis for $\mathbb{F}^n$ (or, more generally, any basis such that each u_i is an eigenvector of D). Then it is straightforward to check that $B^{-1}AB = D$ implies that $\{Bu_i\}_{i=1}^n$ will be a basis consisting of eigenvectors of A. (See the proof of Proposition 2.42.)

(ii)→(iii): We already know that $\dim \mathbb{F}^n \geq \dim E_{\lambda_1} + \dim E_{\lambda_2} + \cdots + \dim E_{\lambda_k}$ since we proved in Exercise 12 in Chapter 2 that eigenvectors from different eigenspaces are linearly independent. Thus we have the equality immediately if $\mathbb{F}^n$ has a basis consisting of eigenvectors of A.

(iii)→(iv): Let $\{u_{ij}\}_{j=1}^{m_i}$ be a basis for E_{λ_i} for each $i = 1, 2, \dots, k$. Then $m_1 + m_2 + \cdots + m_k = \sum_{i=1}^k \dim E_{\lambda_i} = n$. Since $\{u_{ij} : i = 1, 2, \dots, k;\ j = 1, 2, \dots, m_i\}$ is linearly independent, it is a basis for $\mathbb{F}^n$. Therefore $\mathbb{F}^n = E_{\lambda_1} \dot{+} E_{\lambda_2} \dot{+} \cdots \dot{+} E_{\lambda_k}$.

(iv)→(v): Let $\{u_{ij}\}_{j=1}^{m_i}$ be a basis for E_{λ_i} for $i = 1, 2, \dots, k$. Since $\mathbb{F}^n = E_{\lambda_1} \dot{+} E_{\lambda_2} \dot{+} \cdots \dot{+} E_{\lambda_k}$, we have from Exercise 36 in Chapter 1 that $\{u_{ij} : i = 1, 2, \dots, k;\ j = 1, 2, \dots, m_i\}$ is a basis for $\mathbb{F}^n$. For each i, j, let $V_{ij} = \operatorname{span}\{u_{ij}\}$. We have

$$AV_{ij} = \operatorname{span}\{Au_{ij}\} = \operatorname{span}\{\lambda_i u_{ij}\} = \operatorname{span}\{u_{ij}\} \subseteq V_{ij}.$$

Therefore, V_{ij} is a one-dimensional A-invariant subspace and $\mathbb{F}^n$ is the direct sum of all the V_{ij}'s.

(v)→(i): Suppose that there exist one-dimensional A-invariant subspaces $V_1, V_2, \dots, V_n$ such that $\mathbb{F}^n = V_1 \dot{+} V_2 \dot{+} \cdots \dot{+} V_n$. Let u_i be a nonzero vector in V_i, for each $i = 1, 2, \dots, n$, so we have $V_i = \operatorname{span}\{u_i\}$. Then $Au_i = \lambda_i u_i$ for some scalar λ_i. Notice that $\{u_i\}_{i=1}^n$ is a basis for $\mathbb{F}^n$. Let B be the unique matrix such that $Be_i = u_i$ for all $1 \leq i \leq n$, where $\{e_i\}_{i=1}^n$ is the standard orthonormal basis for $\mathbb{F}^n$. Then B is invertible, and in fact, B is the matrix with columns $\{u_i\}_{i=1}^n$. We have $ABe_i = Au_i = \lambda_i u_i = \lambda_i Be_i = B(\lambda_i e_i)$ for each $i = 1, 2, \ldots, n$. Hence $B^{-1}ABe_i = \lambda_i e_i$, which implies that $B^{-1}AB = D$ with $D = \operatorname{diag}(\lambda_1, \lambda_2, \ldots, \lambda_n)$. □

Next we present a property of self-adjoint matrices which leads us to the conclusion that all self-adjoint matrices are similar to a diagonal matrix.

Proposition 10.1 (Schur). *Let T be a linear operator on $\mathcal{H}$. Then there exists an orthonormal basis $\{u_i\}_{i=1}^n$ for $\mathcal{H}$ such that the matrix form of T corresponding to $\{u_i\}_{i=1}^n$ is upper triangular.*

Proof. We prove this by induction on n. Clearly the result is true for $n = 1$. Now assume that it is true for $n - 1$.

Let z be a unit eigenvector of T^*, so we have $T^*z = \lambda z$ for some $\lambda \in \mathbb{C}$ and $\|z\| = 1$. Let $W = \operatorname{span}\{z\}$. Then we observe that $W^\perp$ is invariant under T since if $\langle x, z \rangle = 0$, then

$$\langle Tx, z \rangle = \langle x, T^*z \rangle = \overline{\lambda} \langle x, z \rangle = 0.$$

By the inductive hypothesis, there exists an orthonormal basis, say $\{u_1, u_2, \ldots, u_{n-1}\}$, for the $(n-1)$-dimensional space $W^\perp$ such that the matrix form of the restriction of T to $W^\perp$ corresponding to $\{u_1, u_2, \ldots, u_{n-1}\}$ is upper triangular. It is clear that the set $\{u_1, u_2, \ldots, u_{n-1}, z\}$ is an orthonormal basis for $\mathcal{H}$. Because of the invariance of $W^\perp$ under T, we also can conclude that the matrix form of T with respect to this basis is a partitioned matrix

$$\begin{bmatrix} A & B \\ C & D \end{bmatrix},$$

where A is the $(n-1) \times (n-1)$ upper triangular matrix representation of the restriction of T to $W^\perp$ and C must be a zero matrix of size $1 \times (n-1)$. Therefore, the matrix form of T with respect to this orthonormal basis is upper triangular. □

Corollary 10.2. *Let A be an $n \times n$ matrix. Then A is self-adjoint if and only if there exists a unitary matrix U such that U^*AU is diagonal with real entries.*

Proof. Suppose U is a unitary matrix such that $U^*AU = D$ is diagonal and the entries of D are real. Then $A = UDU^*$ and $A^* = (UDU^*)^* = UD^*U^* = UDU^* = A$. We are using the fact here that the entries of D are real, so $\overline{d_i} = d_i$ for each entry. Therefore, A is self-adjoint.

Now assume that A is self-adjoint. By Schur's theorem, there exists a unitary matrix U such that $U^*AU = B$ is upper triangular. Since $A^* = A$, we have that $B^* = B$. Therefore B must be diagonal and all the entries must be real. □

10.2. Square Roots of Positive Operators

Recall that an $n \times n$ matrix A is positive if $A^* = A$ and $\langle Ax, x \rangle \geq 0$ for all $x \in \mathbb{F}^n$. Now suppose that A is a positive matrix. Then, from Corollary 10.2, U is a unitary matrix such that $A = U^*DU$, where $D = \operatorname{diag}(\lambda_1, \lambda_2, \ldots, \lambda_n)$ with each $\lambda_i \geq 0$.

For each $\alpha > 0$, we define the matrix $A^\alpha = U^*D_\alpha U$, where

$$D_\alpha = \operatorname{diag}(\lambda_1^\alpha, \lambda_2^\alpha, \ldots, \lambda_n^\alpha).$$

In particular, we call $A^{\frac{1}{2}}$ a *square root* of A.

We will use the result from Corollary 2.78, which makes use of the Spectral Theorem, that given a positive operator A, if B is an $n \times n$ matrix such that $BA = AB$, then $BA^\alpha = A^\alpha B$ for any positive real number α.

We next extend the notion of a square root of any positive operator. Let T be a positive operator on a Hilbert space $\mathcal{H}$ having dimension n. Pick any orthonormal basis $\{e_i\}_{i=1}^n$ for $\mathcal{H}$. Let $A = [a_{ij}]$ be the $n \times n$ matrix such that

$$Te_j = \sum_{i=1}^{n} a_{ij} e_i, \quad j = 1, 2, \ldots, n.$$

Let $B := [b_{ij}] = A^{-\frac{1}{2}}$ be the square root of the matrix A. Define the linear operator S on $\mathcal{H}$ by

$$Se_j = \sum_{i=1}^{n} b_{ij} e_i, \quad j = 1, 2, \ldots, n.$$

We will define the operator S to be the *square root* of the positive operator T, and will denote it $S = T^{\frac{1}{2}}$. Again as a result of Corollary 2.78, we have if T is a positive operator and if C is a linear operator on $\mathcal{H}$ such that $CT = TC$, then $CT^{\frac{1}{2}} = T^{\frac{1}{2}}C$.

The next proposition gives the proof of the properties of the square root given in Proposition 2.52.

Proposition (2.52). *Let T be a positive operator on a Hilbert space $\mathcal{H}$ having dimension n. Then there exists a unique positive linear operator S such that $S^2 = T$.*

Proof. Existence: Let A be the matrix representation of T with respect to the orthonormal basis $\{e_i\}_{i=1}^n$. Let S and B be the corresponding operator and the matrix defined to be the square roots of T and A respectively. It is clear by the definition that B is exactly the matrix form of S corresponding to the given orthonormal basis. Let $x = \sum_{i=1}^n c_i e_i \in \mathcal{H}$ and write $c = \begin{bmatrix} c_1 & c_2 & \cdots & c_n \end{bmatrix}^T \in \mathbb{C}^n$. Then we have

$$\begin{aligned} \langle Sx, x \rangle &= \langle Bc, c \rangle \\ &= \left\langle U^* D_{\frac{1}{2}} Uc, c \right\rangle \\ &= \left\langle D_{\frac{1}{2}} Uc, Uc \right\rangle \\ &= \sum_{i=1}^n \lambda_i^{\frac{1}{2}} |z_i|^2 \geq 0, \end{aligned}$$

where $Uc = \begin{bmatrix} z_1 & z_2 & \cdots & z_n \end{bmatrix}^T$. We see that S is positive. Clearly, we have that $B^2 = (U^* D_{\frac{1}{2}} U) U^* D_{\frac{1}{2}} U = U^* D U = A$, and therefore the operator forms also satisfy $S^2 = T$.

Uniqueness: Assume that S' is a positive operator such that $(S')^2 = T$. We need to show that $S' = S$. For any $x \in \mathcal{H}$, let $y = (S' - S)x$. Since S' commutes with T, it follows from Corollary 2.78 that $S'S = SS'$. Thus we have $(S' + S)(S' - S) = (S')^2 - S^2 =$

$T - T = 0$. Therefore, we have

$$\begin{aligned}\langle S'y, y \rangle + \langle Sy, y \rangle &= \langle (S' + S)y, y \rangle \\ &= \langle (S' + S)(S' - S)x, y \rangle \\ &= \left\langle ((S')^2 - S^2)x, y \right\rangle = 0.\end{aligned}$$

Since S' and S are positive, this implies that $\langle S_1 y, y \rangle = \langle Sy, y \rangle = 0$. By the existence part of the proposition, there exists a positive operator, say E, such that $E^2 = S$. Then we have

$$\|Ey\|^2 = \left\langle E^2 y, y \right\rangle = \langle Sy, y \rangle = 0.$$

Hence $Ey = 0$ and also $Sy = E^2 y = 0$. Similarly, we also have $S'y = 0$. Consequently,

$$\|S'x - Sx\|^2 = \left\langle (S' - S)^2 x, x \right\rangle = \langle (S' - S)y, x \rangle = 0$$

for every $x \in \mathcal{H}$. Thus $S' = S$ as claimed. Notice that the uniqueness also verifies that the square root operator $S = T^{\frac{1}{2}}$ is independent of the choice of orthonormal basis used to represent the matrix A for T. □

10.3. Polar Decomposition

In this section, we give a detailed proof of Theorem 2.64, which describes the expression of any operator on a Hilbert space $\mathcal{H}$ as a product of a partial isometry and a positive operator. This is known as the polar decomposition of the operator.

Theorem (2.64). *Let T be an operator from a Hilbert space $\mathcal{H}$ to a Hilbert space $\mathcal{K}$. Then there is a partial isometry U from $\mathcal{H}$ to $\mathcal{K}$ such that*

$$T = U|T|.$$

Moreover, if T is injective, then U is an isometry and is unique.

We note that the proof we provide is for finite-dimensional Hilbert spaces. However, the polar decomposition property holds in infinite dimensions as well. The standard proof for infinite dimensions is nearly identical to the proof we give, except that in the general setting some limit arguments and continuity considerations need to be employed.

Recall from Definition 2.60 that a *partial isometry* is a linear operator $U : \mathcal{H} \to \mathcal{K}$ such that the restriction of U to the orthogonal complement $[\ker(U)]^\perp$ of its kernel is an isometry.

Proof. Let $\mathcal{R} = T\mathcal{H}$ be the range of T. Recall that we define $|T| = (T^*T)^{\frac{1}{2}}$, and let $\mathcal{D} = |T|\mathcal{H}$ be the range of $|T|$. Then $\mathcal{R}$ is a subspace of $\mathcal{K}$, and $\mathcal{D}$ is a subspace of $\mathcal{H}$. (Indeed, note that $T : \mathcal{H} \to \mathcal{K}$ and $T^* : \mathcal{K} \to \mathcal{H}$, so $T^*T : \mathcal{H} \to \mathcal{H}$, and hence $|T| : \mathcal{H} \to \mathcal{H}$.)

We will first define U as an operator from $\mathcal{D}$ to $\mathcal{R}$, and then extend to an operator from $\mathcal{H}$ to $\mathcal{K}$.

If $v \in \mathcal{D}$ is arbitrary, choose $x \in \mathcal{H}$ such that $v = |T|x$, and let $w = Tx$. The vector x might not be unique. But if x' is any other vector in $\mathcal{H}$ such that $v = |T|x'$, then

$$|T|(x - x') = 0.$$

So, since T and $|T|$ have the same kernels (as a result of Lemma 2.57), we have that

$$T(x - x') = 0.$$

Thus $Tx = Tx'$. This shows that for a given $v \in \mathcal{D}$, the vector w we constructed did not depend on the choice we made of the vector x as long as we required that x satisfies the equation $v = |T|x$.

For each $x \in \mathcal{D}$, the corresponding vector w in the above construction is therefore completely determined with no ambiguity. Define a map

$$L : \mathcal{D} \to \mathcal{R}$$

by this procedure. That is, for each $v \in \mathcal{D}$, choose $x \in \mathcal{H}$ such that $|T|x = v$, and define $Lv = Tx$. This mapping L is well defined.

From the definition, L is an isometry. In fact we have: $\|Lv\| = \|Tx\| = \||T|x\| = \|v\|$, where the second equation holds by Lemma 2.57. The mapping L is also linear, but that fact is not so obvious and requires a proof.

We first prove that L is "additive" (i.e., preserves addition). Suppose that $v_1, v_2 \in \mathcal{D}$, and let $w_1 = Lv_1$ and $w_2 = Lv_2$. Let $v_3 = v_1 + v_2$ and $w_3 = w_1 + w_2$. We must show that $Lu_3 = w_3$.

By the construction of L we can choose x_1 and x_2 in $\mathcal{H}$ such that $|T|x_1 = v_1$ and $|T|x_2 = v_2$. Then $w_1 = Tx_1$ and $w_2 = Tx_2$, also by the construction of L. Since T and $|T|$ are linear, we have that

$$T(x_1 + x_2) = Tx_1 + Tx_2 = w_1 + w_2 = w_3,$$

and

$$|T|(x_1 + x_2) = |T|x_1 + |T|x_2 = v_1 + v_2 = v_3.$$

Let $x_3 = x_1 + x_2$. Since x_3 is a vector in $\mathcal{H}$ satisfying $|T|x_3 = v_3$, we must have

$$Lv_3 = Tx_3 = w_3,$$

as we were required to show.

We also need to show that L "preserves scalar multiplication". Let $\lambda \in \mathbb{F}$ and $v \in \mathcal{D}$ be arbitrary. We must show that $L(\lambda v) = \lambda L(v)$. Choose $x \in \mathcal{H}$ such that $|T|x = v$. Then $Lv = Tx$ by the construction of L. Since $|T|$ is linear we have $|T|(\lambda x) = \lambda|T|x = \lambda v$, so again by the construction of L we have

$$L(\lambda v) = T(\lambda x) = \lambda Tx = \lambda Lv,$$

where the middle equality uses the linearity of T.

We have proven that L is additive and preserves scalar multiplication; hence L is linear. Therefore L is a linear isometry from $\mathcal{D}$ to $\mathcal{R}$. To extend L to an operator U on the larger domain $\mathcal{H}$, let $\mathcal{E}$ be the orthogonal complement of $\mathcal{D}$ in $\mathcal{H}$. Then every vector x in $\mathcal{H}$ can be written uniquely as a sum $x = x' + v$, where $x' \in \mathcal{E}$ and $v \in \mathcal{D}$. So we may, without ambiguity, define

$$Ux = Lv,$$

where v is the unique vector in $\mathcal{D}$ with the property that there exists a vector $x' \in \mathcal{E}$ with $x = x' + v$. Note that from the definition we have $Ux = 0$ whenever $x \in \mathcal{E}$.

Since L is linear, this newly defined map U is linear. And since $Lv \neq 0$ whenever $x \in \mathcal{D}$, the kernel of U must be $\mathcal{E}$. The *support* of U is the orthogonal complement of the kernel of U, which is $\mathcal{D}$. Moreover, the restriction of U to $\mathcal{D}$ is L, which is an isometry. Therefore, U is a partial isometry.

Now we verify that $Tx = U|T|x$ for all $x \in \mathcal{H}$. Indeed, if we let $v = |T|x$, then $v \in \mathcal{D}$, and by the construction of L we have

$$Lv = Tx.$$

That is, $L|T|x = Tx$ for all $x \in \mathcal{H}$. Since $|T|x \in \mathcal{D}$, by the construction of U, we have $L|T|x = U|T|x$. Thus, $U|T|x = Tx$ for all $x \in \mathcal{H}$, and therefore $T = U|T|$, as required in the statement of the proposition.

If, in addition, T is invertible, then so is $|T|$ since they have the same kernel. Therefore $\mathcal{D} = \mathcal{H}$, which implies that $U = L$ is an isometry.

In order to prove the uniqueness of U, let U' be another isometry from $\mathcal{H}$ to $\mathcal{K}$ such that $T = U'|T|$. Then we have $U|T| = U'|T|$. Therefore

$$U = U|T|\ |T|^{-1} = U'|T|\ |T|^{-1} = U',$$

as claimed. □

Lemma 10.3. *Let T be a bounded linear operator from $\mathcal{H}$ to $\mathcal{K}$. Then* $\mathrm{range}(T^*) = \mathrm{range}(|T|)$.

Proof. By the polar decomposition $T = V|T|$, we have that $T^* = |T|V^*$. So $\mathrm{range}(T^*) \subseteq \mathrm{range}(|T|)$. On the other hand, $y \in \ker(T) = \mathrm{range}(T^*)^\perp$ if and only if $y \in \ker(T^*T)$, which is in turn equivalent to $y \in \ker(|T|)$ because

$$\||T|y\|^2 = \langle\, |T|y, |T|x \,\rangle = \langle\, T^*Ty, y \,\rangle\,.$$

Thus $\mathrm{range}(T^*) = \ker(T)^\perp = \ker(|T|)^\perp = \mathrm{range}(|T|)$, as claimed. □

The following result shows that if T is an operator from a Hilbert space to itself, the polar decomposition gives T as a product of a unitary operator and a positive operator.

Corollary 10.4. *Let T be a bounded linear operator from $\mathcal{H}$ to $\mathcal{H}$. Then there exists a unitary operator U on $\mathcal{H}$ such that $T = U|T|$.*

Proof. Recall from Proposition 2.34 that for any operator T on $\mathcal{H}$, we can write $\mathcal{H} = \ker(T) \oplus \mathrm{range}(T^*)$. By Theorem 10.3, we can write T in its polar decomposition $T = V|T|$, where V is a partial isometry with initial space $\mathrm{range}(|T|)$ and final space $\mathrm{range}(T)$. By Lemma 10.3, we also know that $\mathrm{range}(|T|) = \mathrm{range}(T^*)$ and by Corollary 2.58 we have $\ker(|T|) = \ker(T)$. Combining these results, we see that $\mathrm{range}(T) = \mathrm{range}(|T|)$, and therefore V is a bijection from $\mathrm{range}(|T|)$ to $\mathrm{range}(T)$.

Let W be any unitary operator on $\ker(T) = \ker(|T|)$. Then we can define an operator U on $\mathcal{H}$ by

$$Ux = \begin{cases} Vx & x \in \text{range}(|T|) = \text{range}(T^*), \\ Wx & x \in \ker(T). \end{cases}$$

We see that U is surjective on $\mathcal{H}$, and is an isometry by the Pythagorean Theorem. Therefore, U is a unitary operator on $\mathcal{H}$ and for any $x \in \mathcal{H}$, we have

$$U|T|x = V|T|x = Tx$$

since $|T|x \in \text{range}(|T|)$. □

10.4. Oblique Projections and Frames

We present a proof of Theorem 5.13 in this section. We first need three lemmas. The first two were given as exercises in Chapter 5.

Lemma 10.5. *Suppose $\mathcal{H} = M \dot{+} N$ and let P be a linear operator on $\mathcal{H}$, where "$\dot{+}$" is the vector space (not necessarily orthogonal) direct sum (see Definition* 1.27*). Then the following are equivalent:*

(i) *P is an oblique projection on $\mathcal{H}$ such that $P\mathcal{H} = M$.*

(ii) *P has the following matrix form with respect to the decomposition $\mathcal{H} = M \dot{+} N$.*

$$P = \begin{bmatrix} I_M & A \\ 0 & 0 \end{bmatrix},$$

for some bounded linear operator A from M to N.

Lemma 10.6. *If P is an oblique projection on $\mathcal{H}$, then* $\text{range}(P) \cap \ker(P) = \{0\}$ *and so* $\mathcal{H} = \text{range}(P) \dot{+} \ker(P)$, *where* $\ker(P) = \{x \in \mathcal{H} : Px = 0\}$.

Lemma 10.7. *Let Θ be the analysis operator for a frame $\{x_i\}_{i=1}^k$ of $\mathcal{H}$. Assume that $\mathcal{K}$ is another Hilbert space and $\{u_i\}_{i=1}^k$ is an orthonormal basis for $\mathcal{K}$. Define $T : \mathcal{H} \to \mathcal{K}$ by*

$$Tx = \sum_{i=1}^{k} \langle x, , x_i \rangle \, u_i, \quad x \in \mathcal{H}.$$

Then $\Theta^*\Theta = T^*T$. Moreover, $\dim \ker(\Theta^*) = \dim \ker(T^*)$.

Proof. Let $\{e_i\}_{i=1}^k$ be the standard orthonormal basis for $\mathbb{C}^k$, and define $U : \mathbb{C}^k \to \mathcal{K}$ by $Ue_i = u_i$. Then U is unitary and

$$\begin{aligned} Tx &= \sum_{i=1}^k \langle x, x_i \rangle u_i \\ &= \sum_{i=1}^k \langle x, x_i \rangle Ue_i \\ &= U\sum_{i=1}^k \langle x, x_i \rangle e_i \\ &= U\Theta(x), \qquad x \in \mathcal{H}. \end{aligned}$$

So $T = U\Theta$, which implies that $T^*T = \Theta^*U^*U\Theta = \Theta^*\Theta$, and $\dim\ker(\Theta^*) = \dim\ker(T^*)$. □

Now we are ready to prove Theorem 5.13:

Theorem (5.13). *Let $\{x_i\}_{i=1}^k$ be a frame for $\mathcal{H}$ with lower frame bound ≥ 1, and let Θ be its analysis operator. Then the following are equivalent:*

(i) *There exist a Hilbert space $\mathcal{K} \supseteq \mathcal{H}$, an orthonormal basis $\{u_i\}_{i=1}^k$ for $\mathcal{K}$, and an oblique projection P on $\mathcal{K}$ such that $x_i = Pu_i$ for all i and $P\mathcal{K} = \mathcal{H}$.*

(ii) $\dim \operatorname{range}(\Theta^*\Theta - I_{\mathcal{H}}) \leq \dim \Theta(\mathcal{H})^{\perp}$.

Proof. (i)→(ii): Assume that $\mathcal{K} \supseteq \mathcal{H}$ and $x_i = Pu_i$ for all i, where $\{u_i\}_{i=1}^k$ is an orthonormal basis for $\mathcal{K}$ and P is an oblique projection such that $P\mathcal{K} = \mathcal{H}$. Then

$$\begin{aligned} P^*x &= \sum_{i=1}^k \langle P^*x, u_i \rangle u_i \\ &= \sum_{i=1}^k \langle x, Pu_i \rangle u_i \\ &= \sum_{i=1}^k \langle x, x_i \rangle u_i \end{aligned}$$

for all $x \in \mathcal{K}$. Let T be the restriction of P^* to $\mathcal{H}$; i.e., $Tx = P^*x$ when $x \in \mathcal{H}$. Then, by Lemma 10.6, $T^*T = \Theta^*\Theta$ and $\dim\ker(\Theta^*) =$

$\dim\ker(T^*) = \dim\ker(P)$. Note that $\mathcal{H} = \operatorname{range}(P)$. Thus, by Lemma 10.6, $\mathcal{K} = \mathcal{H} \oplus \ker(P)$. From Lemma 10.5, P has the form

$$P = \begin{bmatrix} I_{\mathcal{H}} & A \\ 0 & 0 \end{bmatrix}$$

for some $A \in \mathcal{B}(\ker(P), \mathcal{H})$ (Recall that the notation $\mathcal{B}(\mathcal{H}_1, \mathcal{H}_2)$ is used to denote the set of all bounded linear operators from $\mathcal{H}_1$ to $\mathcal{H}_2$.) Thus $PP^*x = (I_{\mathcal{H}} + AA^*)x$ for all $x \in \mathcal{H}$. Note that $T^*Tx = PP^*x$ for all $x \in \mathcal{H}$. Hence $T^*T = I_{\mathcal{H}} + AA^*$, and so

$$\Theta^*\Theta - I_{\mathcal{H}} = T^*T - I_{\mathcal{H}} = AA^*,$$

which implies that

$$\begin{aligned} \dim\operatorname{range}(\Theta^*\Theta - I_{\mathcal{H}}) &= \dim\operatorname{range}(AA^*) \\ &\leq \dim\ker(P) \\ &= \dim\ker(\Theta^*) \\ &= \dim\Theta(\mathcal{H})^{\perp}. \end{aligned}$$

(ii)$\rightarrow$(i): Assume that $\dim\operatorname{range}(\Theta^*\Theta - I) \leq \dim\ker(\Theta^*)$. By the lower frame bound condition, we have $\Theta^*\Theta - I \geq 0$. Let $A = \sqrt{\Theta^*\Theta - I}$. By Lemma 10.3, we have $\operatorname{range}(A) = \operatorname{range}(\Theta^*\Theta - I)$, and thus $\dim\operatorname{range}(A) \leq \dim\ker(\Theta^*)$. This allows us to define a partial isometry $V : \ker(\Theta^*) \to \mathcal{H}$ such that $\operatorname{range}(V) = \operatorname{range}(A)$ In fact, let $\{f_i\}_{i=1}^k$ and $\{g_j\}_{j=1}^{\ell}$ be orthonormal bases for $\ker(\Theta^*)$ and $\operatorname{range}(A)$, respectively. Then $k \geq \ell$. Define V by $Vf_i = g_i$ for $1 \leq i \leq \ell$, and $Vx = 0$ when $x \perp f_i$ for all $1 \leq i \leq \ell$. Then V will be a partial isometry satisfying the requirement.

Let $\mathcal{K} = \mathcal{H} \oplus \ker(\Theta^*)$ (where we identify $\mathcal{H}$ with $\mathcal{H} \oplus 0$ and identify $\ker(\Theta^*)$ with $0 \oplus \ker(\Theta^*)$). Define $T \in \mathcal{B}(\mathbb{C}^k, \mathcal{K})$ by $Tx = \Theta^*(x) \oplus 0$. Let $Y = AV \in B(\ker(\Theta^*), \mathcal{H})$, and let

$$P = \begin{bmatrix} I_{\mathcal{H}} & Y \\ 0 & 0 \end{bmatrix}$$

with respect to the decomposition $\mathcal{K} = \mathcal{H} \oplus \ker(\Theta^*)$. Then P is an oblique projection with $\operatorname{range}(P) = \mathcal{H}$. Moreover, since $YY^* = AVV^*A = A^2$, we have that

$$PP^* = \begin{bmatrix} I_{\mathcal{H}} + YY^* & 0 \\ 0 & 0 \end{bmatrix} = \begin{bmatrix} I_{\mathcal{H}} + A^2 & 0 \\ 0 & 0 \end{bmatrix} = \begin{bmatrix} \Theta^*\Theta & 0 \\ 0 & 0 \end{bmatrix} = TT^*.$$

By the uniqueness of the square root of a positive operator, we have $|P^*| = |T^*|$.

Let $\Theta = V_1|T|$ be the polar decomposition of Θ such that $V_1 : \mathcal{H} \to \mathbb{C}^k$ is the partial isometry with initial space $\ker(\Theta)^\perp$ and final space range(Θ). Since Θ is one-to-one, we have that $\ker(\Theta)^\perp = \mathcal{H}$. Thus V_1 is an isometry. So we have $\Theta^* = |\Theta|V_1^*$ with V_1^* is a partial isometry with initial space range(Θ) and final space $\mathcal{H}$. Define $U : \mathbb{C}^k \to \mathcal{K} = \mathcal{H} \oplus \ker(\Theta^*)$ by

$$Ux = V_1^* Qx \oplus Q^\perp x,$$

where Q is the orthogonal projection from $\mathbb{C}^k$ onto range(Θ). Thus U is an isometry since V_1^* is. This implies that U is unitary because $\dim \mathbb{C}^k = \dim \mathcal{K} = k < \infty$. Moreover, $T = |T^*|U$.

We now consider the polar decomposition of P. By Corollary 10.4, $P^* = W|P^*|$ for some unitary W on $\mathcal{K}$, so $P = |P^*|W^*$. We then have

$$T = |T^*|U = |P^*|U = PWU.$$

Let $u_i = WUe_i$, where $\{e_i\}_{i=1}^k$ is the standard orthonormal basis of $\mathbb{C}^k$. Then $\{u_i\}_{i=1}^k$ is an orthonormal basis of $\mathcal{K}$ since both U and W are unitary. Finally,

$$Pu_i = PWUe_i = Te_i = \Theta^*(e_i) \oplus 0 = x_i \oplus 0 = x_i. \qquad \square$$

10.5. Vandermonde Determinant

In this section, we carefully show that a Vandermonde matrix is invertible by explicitly computing its determinant. Recall that a Vandermonde matrix is of the form:

$$V = \begin{bmatrix} 1 & x_1 & x_1^2 & \cdots & x_1^N \\ 1 & x_2 & x_2^2 & \cdots & x_2^N \\ \vdots & \vdots & \vdots & \ddots & \vdots \\ 1 & x_{N+1} & x_{N+1}^2 & \cdots & x_{N+1}^N \end{bmatrix},$$

where $x_1, x_2, \ldots, x_{N+1}$ are distinct real numbers.

Proposition 10.8. *The determinant of the* $(N+1) \times (N+1)$ *Vandermonde matrix* V *defined above is*

$$|V| = \prod_{\substack{i,j=1,\dots,N+1 \\ i>j}} (x_i - x_j) \tag{10.1}$$

where all of the terms are nonzero. Therefore, the determinant of V *is nonzero and* V *is invertible.*

Proof. The proof is accomplished by induction on N. It is easily verified that the determinant formula (10.1) holds in the case where $N = 1$. We present a specific inductive step of $N = 2$ to $N = 3$, and leave the remaining details to the reader. Consider the 4×4 case: in the first step we multiply the third column by x_1 and then subtract it from the fourth column:

$$\begin{vmatrix} 1 & x_1 & x_1^2 & x_1^3 \\ 1 & x_2 & x_2^2 & x_2^3 \\ 1 & x_3 & x_3^2 & x_3^3 \\ 1 & x_4 & x_4^2 & x_4^3 \end{vmatrix} = \begin{vmatrix} 1 & x_1 & x_1^2 & 0 \\ 1 & x_2 & x_2^2 & x_2^3 - x_2^2 x_1 \\ 1 & x_3 & x_3^2 & x_3^3 - x_3^2 x_1 \\ 1 & x_4 & x_4^2 & x_4^3 - x_4^2 x_1 \end{vmatrix}$$

$$= \begin{vmatrix} 1 & x_1 & x_1^2 & 0 \\ 1 & x_2 & x_2^2 & x_2^2(x_2 - x_1) \\ 1 & x_3 & x_3^2 & x_3^2(x_3 - x_1) \\ 1 & x_4 & x_4^2 & x_4^2(x_4 - x_1) \end{vmatrix}.$$

We next multiply the second column by x_1 and subtract it from the third:

$$\begin{vmatrix} 1 & x_1 & x_1^2 & 0 \\ 1 & x_2 & x_2^2 & x_2^2(x_2 - x_1) \\ 1 & x_3 & x_3^2 & x_3^2(x_3 - x_1) \\ 1 & x_4 & x_4^2 & x_4^2(x_4 - x_1) \end{vmatrix} = \begin{vmatrix} 1 & x_1 & 0 & 0 \\ 1 & x_2 & x_2^2 - x_2 x_1 & x_2^2(x_2 - x_1) \\ 1 & x_3 & x_3^2 - x_3 x_1 & x_3^2(x_3 - x_1) \\ 1 & x_4 & x_4^2 - x_4 x_1 & x_4^2(x_4 - x_1) \end{vmatrix}$$

$$= \begin{vmatrix} 1 & x_1 & 0 & 0 \\ 1 & x_2 & x_2(x_2 - x_1) & x_2^2(x_2 - x_1) \\ 1 & x_3 & x_3(x_3 - x_1) & x_3^2(x_3 - x_1) \\ 1 & x_4 & x_4(x_4 - x_1) & x_4^2(x_4 - x_1) \end{vmatrix}.$$

Analogously, we multiply the first column by x_1 and subtract it from the second, yielding:

$$\begin{aligned}
&\begin{vmatrix} 1 & 0 & 0 & 0 \\ 1 & x_2 - x_1 & x_2(x_2 - x_1) & x_2^2(x_2 - x_1) \\ 1 & x_3 - x_1 & x_3(x_3 - x_1) & x_3^2(x_3 - x_1) \\ 1 & x_4 - x_1 & x_4(x_4 - x_1) & x_4^2(x_4 - x_1) \end{vmatrix} \\
&= \begin{vmatrix} x_2 - x_1 & x_2(x_2 - x_1) & x_2^2(x_2 - x_1) \\ x_3 - x_1 & x_3(x_3 - x_1) & x_3^2(x_3 - x_1) \\ x_4 - x_1 & x_4(x_4 - x_1) & x_4^2(x_4 - x_1) \end{vmatrix} \\
&= (x_2 - x_1)(x_3 - x_1)(x_4 - x_1) \begin{vmatrix} 1 & x_2 & x_2^2 \\ 1 & x_3 & x_3^2 \\ 1 & x_4 & x_4^2 \end{vmatrix} \\
&= (x_2 - x_1)(x_3 - x_1)(x_4 - x_1) \prod_{\substack{i,j=2,\ldots,4 \\ i>j}} (x_i - x_j) \\
&= \prod_{\substack{i,j=1,\ldots,4 \\ i>j}} (x_i - x_j).
\end{aligned}$$

Therefore, if the formula from (10.1) holds for $N = 2$, it also holds for $N = 3$. This can be generalized to an inductive argument. □

Chapter 11

Anecdotes: Frame Theory Projects by Undergraduates

These anecdotes portray just a few of the many experiences students have had while studying this material. As with any research project, every student will take away something different, depending on their own background, interest, and work habits. These are just a few of the students who we've observed undergo a meaningful transformation while studying frames. We wanted to share these snapshots with the readers of this book.

In the spring of 2002, the authors attended an sectional meeting of the American Mathematical Society in Atlanta. We heard a talk by Matt Fickus discussing the work he had done in his Ph.D. thesis and in a subsequent paper with John Benedetto [**9**]. He was examining existence and structure of finite uniform frames. Dave Larson asked a question about whether tight frames lying within an ellipsoid had been studied, and since the answer was negative, this became one of our topics of conversation in the REU that summer.

Students that summer were particularly drawn to the frame theory, since many questions could be asked and answered using standard techniques from linear algebra. We introduced the ellipsoid question at a fundamental level, starting in low dimensions and with orthonormal bases rather than frames. The first question was this: Given any ellipse in $\mathbb{R}^2$ with center at the origin, does this ellipse contain a scalar multiple of an orthonormal basis? (In other words, the vectors must be orthogonal and equal length, but that length need not be 1.) By the next day, several students could present a proof that such a basis did in fact always exist. One nice approach involved finding the intersections of circles with the ellipse and using the Intermediate Value Theorem to prove there must be a circle at which the intersection points correspond to orthogonal vectors.

The follow-up question proved a bit more difficult: Is the same result true in $\mathbb{R}^3$? Does there always exist a scaled orthonormal basis in every ellipsoid centered at the origin? I turns out that there is, in fact, always such a basis, and this took students a week or so to work out. This time it was a group of about three students who arrived at the solution. Again, they looked at the intersection of a sphere and an ellipsoid, and found an algorithm to rotate the standard orthonormal basis and prove that there exists an orientation and a scaling in which all three vectors scaled by the same factor lie on the ellipse.

One student continued to think about how to extend this algorithm to arbitrary finite dimensions, and after another week of hard work and little sleep, he was successful. With help from a mentor, he formulated his proof into an inductive argument that proved that every ellipsoid in $\mathbb{R}^n$ contains a scaled orthonormal basis for $\mathbb{R}^n$. Never content, though, he continued to work on the problem, and to everyone's amazement, during the last week of the REU, he found a way to extend the result to tight frames. His idea was clever: Create a degenerate ellipsoid in which you have extra dimensions with infinite semimajor axes, and follow the algorithm to find a scaled orthonormal basis. The projection of this basis to the original space will be a tight frame lying on the ellipsoid, and the dimension of the larger space gives the number of vectors in the tight frame. Therefore, for any $k \geq n$ and any ellipsoid in $\mathbb{R}^n$, there is a tight frame of k vectors contained in the ellipsoid.

We have since found several equivalent results, some already in the literature and having nothing to do with frames, but this shouldn't detract from this clever student's result. It was a real breakthrough, and within the context of frames, definitely original research. At the time of this writing, he is presently attending graduate school at Texas A&M University and has participated as a graduate student and resident frames expert in the summer REU.

A student taking part in the Texas A&M REU in 2006 had a different experience with the topic of frames. He realized for the first time that summer that it is essential to work out proofs and exercises on your own to truly understand a mathematical subject. Instead of selecting a research topic, he chose to work his way through Chapter 2 of this book. He attempted to prove each theorem on his own, as well as each of the exercises. His feedback at the end of the REU was that this experience gave him both a heightened appreciation for the linear algebra he'd learned before and an increased motivation to study the analytical aspects of frames and wavelets. We, the authors, found it gratifying that a student found our book to be helpful and inspirational as a textbook for advanced linear algebra.

An earlier draft of this book was used by Keri Kornelson to teach a seminar course at Grinnell College in 2006. Near the end of the term, the class was working carefully through Chapter 7. The argument that eigenvalues and operators in a finite-dimensional Hilbert space vary continuously with each other was not present in this earlier draft, and so the class was taking some time to fully understand this detail. Not long afterward, as an inspirational last-day-of-class lecture, Kornelson introduced the Kadison-Singer conjecture. This is a long-standing open problem in operator theory for which there are several equivalent formulations that use the language of frames. (See [**18**] for details.) The idea was to show the class how relevant and deep frame theoretical questions can be. In particular, the class discussed a version called the Paving Conjecture, which deals with finite-dimensional matrices and their operator norms.

One of the students decided to play around with this conjecture a little bit, since we had been studying norms of matrices quite recently. He had the ingenious idea to convert the problem to an equivalent norm, perhaps the Hilbert-Schmidt norm. It turns out that the paving conjecture is true in this norm, but the equivalence of the norms does not force the conjecture to hold in the operator norm. Nevertheless, the student was *very* excited for a little bit thinking he'd solved a big open problem. This is a great example of how our students combine facts from different sources in new ways to build insights and intuitions.

The idea of orthogonality of frames and multiplexing was used in a new and interesting way during REU projects directed by Eric Weber in the summers of 2003 (at the University of Wyoming) and 2004 (at Iowa State University). The projects had the students investigate whether frames could be used for cryptographic purposes. The students discovered that frames cannot be used for cryptography, since they proved that the algorithm can be broken by standard attacks. Together, we discovered that another group of researchers had proposed a very similar cryptographic algorithm to which our argument was transferable. Both projects resulted in published journal articles [**43, 10**] and motivated several of the participants into further study in cryptography. In fact, one student claimed that our project was "the most exciting thing I've been a part of", and was the deciding factor in her continuing on to graduate school at Iowa State University.

Below is a list of graduate and undergraduate students who have participated in a course, research program, or seminar on frames with one or more of the authors. Their discussions, questions, presentations, and research projects played a vital role in the evolution of this book, and their careful reading helped us in the editorial process. We could write an anecdote about each of them, and the way in which their enthusiasm fueled our own interest in writing this book.

Kevin Abbott, Gaik Ambartsoumian, Ben Aurispa, Scott Armstrong, Doug Babcock, Ben Backup, Eric Bahuaud, Aaron Bailey, Erik Baumgarten, Chris Barot, Nate Berglund, Ghanshyam Bhatt, A. Bhutta, Dakota Blair, John Boncek, Will Boney, John Bowers, Devlyn Brown, Jacqui Burchfield, Jan Cameron, Walker Carlisle, Tony Castaldo, Zach Catlin, Mehmet Celik, Xianjin Chen, Ivan Christov, Ila Cobbs, Kristen Creech, Adam Cross, Ralph Culver, James Davis, Rachel Derber, Alejandro Dominguez, Detelin Dosev, Jennifer Derringer, Scott Evans, Andrew Felker, Bill Finkenkeller,

H. Foroosh, Dan Freeman, John Fulk, Michael Fulkerson, Brandon George, Alex Gittens, Stephanie Green, Paul Gustafson, Jacqueline Haines, Ryan Harkins, Andrew Harrell, Micah Hawkins, Troy Henderson, A.J. Hergenroeder, Maria Hernandez, David Herzog, James Hichcock, Matt Hirn, Larry Holifield, Rolf Hoyer, Crystal Hoyt, Jessica Hubbs, James Hughes, Ali-Amir Husain, Robert Jacobson, Michael Jennings, Wu Jing, Ryan Johnson, Chelsea Kaihoi, Seungil Kim, Taejong Kim, Emily King, Marta Kobiela, Lori Kraus, Trent Lalonde, Chris LeBailly, Quoc Le Gia, Vince Lemoine, Emily Levenberg, Jerry Lopez, Brad Lutes, Avram Lyon, Martin Machalak, Drew Matteson, Brady McCary, Amy Neff, Jennifer Novak, Nga Nguyen, Chris O'brien, Sayaka Olsen, Gary Olson, Beng Ong, Ryan Pedersen, Norman Perlmutter, Jason Pfister, Lova Randrianarivony, Daniel Redelmeierm, Darren Rhea, Lance Ridpath, Krista Rister, Stuart Rogers, David Rose, Patience Sanders, Nathan Savir, Rachel Saul, R. Semmoum, Qiling Shi, Kristi Shryock, Lydia Smith, Cole Sodja, Ely Spears, Nate Strawn, James Tener, Ryan Thomas, Fancisco Torres-Ayala, Dimitar Trenev, Justin Turner, Kyle Vigil, Laura Walters, Phillip Watkins, Ryan Westbrook, Andrew Westmeyer, Theresa Wolf, Jeffery Wong, Brian Worthen, Ryoji Yamamoto, Xiaofei Zhang, Zhigang Zhang, Bentuo Zheng, Siwei Zhu, Erica Zrubek.

Bibliography

[1] A. Aldroubi, *Portraits of frames,* Proc. Amer. Math. Soc. **123** (1995), no. 6, 1661–1668.

[2] A. Aldroubi, D. Larson, W. Tang, and E. Weber, *Geometric aspects of frame representations of abelian groups*, Trans. Amer. Math. Soc. **356** (2004), no. 12, 4767–4786.

[3] J. Antezana, G. Corach, M. Ruiz, and D. Stojanofff, *Oblique projections and frames,* Proc. Amer. Math. Soc. **134** (2006), 1031–1037.

[4] S. Axler, *Linear algebra done right*, second ed., Undergraduate Texts in Mathematics, Springer-Verlag, New York, NY, 1997.

[5] R. Balan, *A study of Weyl-Heisenberg and wavelet frames*, Ph.D. thesis, Princeton University, Princeton, NJ, 1998.

[6] R. Balan, *Equivalence relations and distances between Hilbert frames,* Proc. Amer. Math. Soc., **127** (1999), 2353–2366.

[7] R. Balan, *Density and redundancy of the noncoherent Weyl-Heisenberg superframes*, The functional and harmonic analysis of wavelets and frames, Contemp. Math, vol. 247, Amer. Math. Soc. 1999, pp. 29–41.

[8] J. Benedetto and P.J.S.G. Ferriera (eds.), *Modern sampling theory,* Birkhauser, Boston, MA, 2001.

[9] J. J. Benedetto and M. Fickus, *Finite normalized tight frames*, Adv. Comp. Math. **18** (2003), 357–385.

[10] G. Bhatt, L. Kraus, L. Walters, and E. Weber, *On hiding messages in the oversampled Fourier coefficients*, J. Math. Anal. Appl. **320** (2006), no. 1, 492–498.

[11] H. Bolcskei and Y. Eldar, *Geometrically uniform frames,* IEEE Trans. Inform. Theory **49** (2003), 993–1006.

[12] B. Bodmann and V. Paulsen, *Frames, graphs and erasures,* Linear Algebra Appl. **404** (2005), 118–146.

[13] J. Boncek, *Studies in tight frames and polar derivatives*, Ph.D. thesis, University of Central Florida, Orlando, FL, 2003.

[14] P. Casazza, *The art of frame theory*, Taiwanese J. Math. **4**(2000), 129–201.

[15] P. Casazza, *Modern tools for Weyl-Heisenberg (Gabor) frame theory,* Adv. Imag. Elect. Phys. **115** (2001), 1–127.

[16] P. Casazza, *Custom building finite frames,* Wavelets, frames and operator theory, Contemp. Math. 345, Amer. Math. Soc., Providence, RI, 2004, pp. 61–86.

[17] P. Casazza, M. Fickus, J. Kovačević, M. Leon, and J. Tremain, *A physical interpretation of finite frames.* Harmonic Analysis and Applications in Appl. Numer. Harmon. Anal., Birkhäser, Boston, MA, 2006, pp. 51–76.

[18] P. Casazza, M. Fickus, J. Tremain, and E. Weber, *The Kadison-Singer Problem in Mathematics and Engineering*, Operator Theory, Operator Algebras and Applications, Contemp. Math. **414**, Amer. Math. Soc., Providence, RI, 2006, pp. 299–356.

[19] P. Casazza, D. Han, and D. Larson, *Frames in Banach spaces,* Analysis of Wavelets and Frames, Contemp. Math. **247**, Amer. Math. Soc., Providence, RI, 1999, pp. 149–182.

[20] P. Casazza and J. Kovačević, *Uniform Tight Frames for signal processing and communication,* Proc. SPIE, 2001.

[21] P. Casazza and J. Kovačević, *Uniform tight frames with erasures,* Adv. in Computational Mathematics **18** (2003), 387–430.

[22] O. Christensen, *An introduction to frames and Riesz bases*, Applied and Numerical Harmonic Analysis, Birkhäser, Boston, MA, 2003.

[23] B. Ćurgus and V. Mascioni, *Roots and polynomials as homeomorphic spaces*, arXiv:math.GM/0502037 v.1, 2005.

[24] X. Dai and D. Larson, *Wandering vectors for unitary systems and orthogonal wavelets,* Mem. Amer. Math. Soc. **134** (1998), no. 640.

[25] I. Daubechies, *Ten lectures on wavelets*, SIAM Press, Philadelphia, PA, 1992.

[26] D. Donoho and P. Stark, *Uncertainty principles and signal recovery,* SIAM J. Appl. Math. **49** (1989), no. 3, 906–931.

[27] R. Duffin and A. Schaeffer, *A class of nonharmonic Fourier series,* Trans. Amer. Math. Soc. **72** (1952), 341–366.

[28] K. Dykema, D. Freeman, K. Kornelson, D. Larson, M. Ordower, and E. Weber, *Ellipsoidal tight frames and projection decompositions of operators*, Illinois J. Math. **48** (2004), no. 2, 477–489.

[29] D. Feng, L. Wang, and Y. Wang, *Generation of finite tight frames by Householder transformations,* Adv. Comput. Math. **24** (2006), 297–309.

[30] M. Fickus, B. Johnson, K. Kornelson, and K. Okoudjou, *Convolutional frames and the frame potential*, Appl. Comput. Harmon. Anal. **19** (2005), no. 1, 77–91.

[31] G. B. Folland, *Real analysis*, second ed., Pure and Applied Mathematics (New York), John Wiley & Sons Inc., New York, 1999, Modern techniques and their applications, A Wiley-Interscience Publication.

[32] S. Friedberg, A. Insel, and L. Spence, *Linear Algebras,* fourth edition, Prentice Hall, Upper Saddle River, NJ, 2003.

[33] J.P. Gabardo and D. Han, *Subspace Weyl-Heisenberg frames*, J. Fourier Anal. Appl. **7** (2001), no. 4, 419–433.

[34] J.P. Gabardo and D. Han, *Frame representations for group-like unitary operator systems*, J. Operator Theory **49** (2003), no. 2, 223–244.

[35] J.P. Gabardo and D. Han, *The uniqueness of the dual of Weyl-Heisenberg subspace frames*, Appl. Comput. Harmon. Anal. **17** (2004), no. 2, 226–240.

[36] J.P. Gabardo, D. Han, and D. Larson, *Gabor frames and operator algebras*, Wavelet Applications in Signal and Image Processing, Proc. SPIE, vol. 4119, 2000, pp. 337–345.

[37] D. Gabor, *Theory of Communication,* J. Inst. Elec. Eng. (London) **93** (1946), 429–457.

[38] K. Gröchenig, *Acceleration of the frame algorithm*, IEEE Transactions on Signal Processing **41** (1993), no. 12, 3331–3340.

[39] K. Gröchenig, *Foundations of Time-Frequency Analysis*, Applied and Numerical Harmonic Analysis, Birkhäuser Boston, Boston, MA, 2001.

[40] D. Han, *Classification of finite group frames and super-frames,* Can. Math. Bull **50** (2007), 85–96.

[41] D. Han, *Frame representations and Parseval duals with applications to Gabor frames,* Trans. Amer. Math. Soc. (to appear).

[42] D. Han and D. R. Larson, *Frames, bases, and group representations*, Mem. Amer. Math. Soc. **147** (2000), no. 697, 1–94.

[43] R. Harkins, E. Weber, and A. Westmeyer, *Encryption schemes using finite frames and Hadamard arrays,* Experiment. Math. **14** (2005), no. 4, 423–433.

[44] R. Holmes and V. Paulsen, *Optimal frames for erasures*, Linear Algebra Appl. **377** (2004), 31–51.

[45] R. Horn and C. Johnson, *Matrix analysis*, Cambridge University Press, Cambridge, UK, 1985.

[46] R. Kadison, *The Pythagorean theorem: I. The finite case*, Proc. Natl. Acad. Sci. USA **99** (2002), no. 7, 4178–4184.

[47] K. Kornelson and D. Larson, *Rank-one decomposition of operators and construction of frames*, Wavelets, Frames, and Operator Theory, Contemp. Math, vol. 345, Amer. Math. Soc., 2004, pp. 203–214.

[48] M. Marden, *Geometry of Polynomials*, second edition, Mathematical Surveys and Monographs, vol. 3, Amer. Math. Soc., Providence, RI, 1966.

[49] J. Ortega-Cerdà and K. Seip, *Fourier frames*, Ann. of Math. (2) **155** (2002), no. 3, 789–806.

[50] H. L. Royden, *Real analysis*, third ed., Macmillan Publishing Company, New York, NY, 1988.

[51] W. Rudin, *Functional Analysis*, McGraw-Hill, New York, NY, 1973.

[52] D. Uherka and A. Sergott, *On the continuous dependence of the roots of a polynomial on its coefficients*, Amer. Math. Monthly **84** (1977), no. 5, 368–370.

[53] G. Weiss and E. Hernandez, *A first course on wavelets,* CRC Press, Boca Raton, FL, 1996.

[54] R. Young, *An introduction to nonharmonic Fourier series*, Academic Press, New York, NY, 1980.

[55] A.I. Zayed, *Advances in Shannon's sampling theory,* CRC Press, Boca Raton, FL, 1993.

Index of Symbols

Index

Titles in This Series

40 **Deguang Han, Keri Kornelson, David Larson, and Eric Weber,** Frames for undergraduates, 2007

39 **Alex Iosevich,** A view from the top: Analysis, combinatorics and number theory, 2007

38 **B. Fristedt, N. Jain, and N. Krylov,** Filtering and prediction: A primer, 2007

37 **Svetlana Katok,** p-adic analysis compared with real, 2007

36 **Mara D. Neusel,** Invariant theory, 2007

35 **Jörg Bewersdorff,** Galois theory for beginners: A historical perspective, 2006

34 **Bruce C. Berndt,** Number theory in the spirit of Ramanujan, 2006

33 **Rekha R. Thomas,** Lectures in geometric combinatorics, 2006

32 **Sheldon Katz,** Enumerative geometry and string theory, 2006

31 **John McCleary,** A first course in topology: Continuity and dimension, 2006

30 **Serge Tabachnikov,** Geometry and billiards, 2005

29 **Kristopher Tapp,** Matrix groups for undergraduates, 2005

28 **Emmanuel Lesigne,** Heads or tails: An introduction to limit theorems in probability, 2005

27 **Reinhard Illner, C. Sean Bohun, Samantha McCollum, and Thea van Roode,** Mathematical modelling: A case studies approach, 2005

26 **Robert Hardt, Editor,** Six themes on variation, 2004

25 **S. V. Duzhin and B. D. Chebotarevsky,** Transformation groups for beginners, 2004

24 **Bruce M. Landman and Aaron Robertson,** Ramsey theory on the integers, 2004

23 **S. K. Lando,** Lectures on generating functions, 2003

22 **Andreas Arvanitoyeorgos,** An introduction to Lie groups and the geometry of homogeneous spaces, 2003

21 **W. J. Kaczor and M. T. Nowak,** Problems in mathematical analysis III: Integration, 2003

20 **Klaus Hulek,** Elementary algebraic geometry, 2003

19 **A. Shen and N. K. Vereshchagin,** Computable functions, 2003

18 **V. V. Yaschenko, Editor,** Cryptography: An introduction, 2002

17 **A. Shen and N. K. Vereshchagin,** Basic set theory, 2002

16 **Wolfgang Kühnel,** Differential geometry: curves – surfaces – manifolds, second edition, 2006

15 **Gerd Fischer,** Plane algebraic curves, 2001

14 **V. A. Vassiliev,** Introduction to topology, 2001

13 **Frederick J. Almgren, Jr.,** Plateau's problem: An invitation to varifold geometry, 2001

TITLES IN THIS SERIES